THE KEY

STUDENT STUDY GUIDE

Chemistry 20

THE KEY student study guide is designed to help students achieve success in school. The content in each study guide is 100% curriculum aligned and serves as an excellent source of material for review and practice. To create this book, teachers, curriculum specialists, and assessment experts have worked closely to develop the instructional pieces that explain each of the key concepts for the course. The practice questions and sample tests have detailed solutions that show problem-solving methods, highlight concepts that are likely to be tested, and point out potential sources of errors. **THE KEY** is a complete guide to be used by students throughout the school year for reviewing and understanding course content, and to prepare for assessments.

Rao,Gautam,1961 –
THE KEY – Chemistry 20 Alberta

1. Chemistry – Juvenile Literature. I. Title

ISBN: 978-1-77044-418-8
Castle Rock Research Corp.
2410 Manulife Place
10180 – 101 Street
Edmonton, AB T5J 3S4

10 9 8 7 6 5 4 3 2

Publisher
Gautam Rao

Contributors
Chris Dambrowitz
Alison Donner
Rob Schultz
Sanjay K. Sharma
John Yule

Reviewers
Debra Hay

Dedicated to the memory of Dr. V. S. Rao

THE KEY—Chemistry 20

THE KEY consists of the following sections:

KEY Tips for Being Successful at School gives examples of study and review strategies. It includes information about learning styles, study schedules, and note taking for test preparation.

Class Focus includes a unit on each area of the curriculum. Units are divided into sections, each focusing on one of the specific expectations, or main ideas, that students must learn about in that unit. Examples, definitions, and visuals help to explain each main idea. Practice questions on the main ideas are also included. At the end of each unit is a test on the important ideas covered. The practice questions and unit tests help students identify areas they know and those they need to study more. They can also be used as preparation for tests and quizzes. Most questions are of average difficulty, though some are easy and some are hard. Each unit is prefaced by a *Table of Correlations*, which correlates questions in the unit to the specific curriculum expectations. Answers and solutions are found at the end of each unit.

KEY Strategies for Success on Tests helps students get ready for tests. It shows students different types of questions they might see, word clues to look for when reading them, and hints for answering them.

Practice Tests includes one to three tests based on the entire course. They are very similar to the format and level of difficulty that students may encounter on final tests. In some regions, these tests may be reprinted versions of official tests, or reflect the same difficulty levels and formats as official versions. This gives students the chance to practice using real-world examples. Answers and complete solutions are provided at the end of the section.

For the complete curriculum document (including specific expectations along with examples and sample problems), visit http://education.alberta.ca/media/654849/chem2030_07.pdf.

THE KEY Study Guides are available for many courses. Check www.castlerockresearch.com for a complete listing of books available for your area.

For information about any of our resources or services, please call Castle Rock Research at 780.448.9619 or visit our website at http://www.castlerockresearch.com.

At Castle Rock Research, we strive to produce an error-free resource. If you should find an error, please contact us so that future editions can be corrected.

CONTENTS

KEY Tips for Being Successful at School

KEY TIPS FOR BEING SUCCESSFUL AT SCHOOL

KEY FACTORS CONTRIBUTING TO SCHOOL SUCCESS

In addition to learning the content of your courses, there are some other things that you can do to help you do your best at school. Some of these strategies are listed below.

- **Keep a positive attitude:** Always reflect on what you can already do and what you already know.

- **Be prepared to learn**: Have ready the necessary pencils, pens, notebooks, and other required materials for participating in class.

- **Complete all of your assignments:** Do your best to finish all of your assignments. Even if you know the material well, practice will reinforce your knowledge. If an assignment or question is difficult for you, work through it as far as you can so that your teacher can see exactly where you are having difficulty.

- **Set small goals for yourself when you are learning new material:** For example, when learning the parts of speech, do not try to learn everything in one night. Work on only one part or section each study session. When you have memorized one particular part of speech and understand it, then move on to another one, continue this process until you have memorized and learned all the parts of speech.

- **Review your classroom work regularly at home:** Review to be sure that you understand the material that you learned in class.

- **Ask your teacher for help**: Your teacher will help you if you do not understand something or if you are having a difficult time completing your assignments.

- **Get plenty of rest and exercise:** Concentrating in class is hard work. It is important to be well-rested and have time to relax and socialize with your friends. This helps you to keep your positive attitude about your school work.

- **Eat healthy meals:** A balanced diet keeps you healthy and gives you the energy that you need for studying at school and at home.

HOW TO FIND YOUR LEARNING STYLE

Every student learns differently. The manner in which you learn best is called your learning style. By knowing your learning style, you can increase your success at school. Most students use a combination of learning styles. Do you know what type of learner you are? Read the following descriptions. Which of these common learning styles do you use most often?

- **Linguistic Learner**: You may learn best by saying, hearing, and seeing words. You are probably really good at memorizing things such as dates, places, names, and facts. You may need **to write and then say out loud** the steps in a process, a formula, or the actions that lead up to a significant event.

- **Spatial Learner**: You may learn best by looking at and working with pictures. You are probably really good at puzzles, imagining things, and reading maps and charts. You may need to use strategies like **mind mapping and webbing** to organize your information and study notes.

- **Kinaesthetic Learner**: You may learn best by touching, moving, and figuring things out using manipulative. You are probably really good at physical activities and learning through movement. You may need to **draw your finger over a diagram** to remember it, **"tap out" the steps** needed to solve a problem, or **"feel" yourself writing or typing** a formula.

SCHEDULING STUDY TIME

You should review your class notes regularly to ensure that you have a clear understanding of all the new material you learned. Reviewing your lessons on a regular basis helps you to learn and remember ideas and concepts. It also reduces the quantity of material that you need to study prior to a test. Establishing a study schedule will help you to make the best use of your time.

Regardless of the type of study schedule you use, you may want to consider the following suggestions to maximize your study time and effort:

- Organize your work so that you begin with the most challenging material first.
- Divide the subject's content into small, manageable chunks.
- Alternate regularly between your different subjects and types of study activities in order to maintain your interest and motivation.
- Make a daily list with headings like "Must Do," "Should Do," and "Could Do."
- Begin each study session by quickly reviewing what you studied the day before.
- Maintain your usual routine of eating, sleeping, and exercising to help you concentrate better for extended periods of time.

CREATING STUDY NOTES

MIND-MAPPING OR WEBBING

Use the key words, ideas, or concepts from your reading or class notes to create a *mind map* or *web* (a diagram or visual representation of the given information). A mind map or web is sometimes referred to as a knowledge map.

- Write the key word, concept, theory, or formula in the centre of your page.

- Write down related facts, ideas, events, and information and then link them to the central concept with lines.

- Use coloured markers, underlining, or other symbols to emphasize things such as relationships, time lines, and important information.

- The following examples of a Frayer Model illustrate how this technique can be used to study scientific vocabulary.

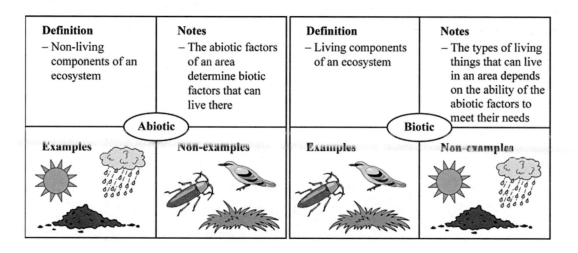

INDEX CARDS

To use index cards while studying, follow these steps:

• Write a key word or question on one side of an index card.

• On the reverse side, write the definition of the word, answer to the question, or any other important information that you want to remember.

> What is the difference between
> heat and thermal energy?

> What is the difference between
> heat and thermal energy?
>
> Thermal energy is the total energy of the
> particles in a solid, liquid, or gas.
> Heat is the amount of thermal energy
> transferred between objects.

SYMBOLS AND STICKY NOTES—IDENTIFYING IMPORTANT INFORMATION

• Use symbols to mark your class notes. For example, an exclamation mark (!) might be used to point out something that must be learned well because it is a very important idea. A question mark (?) may highlight something that you are not certain about, and a diamond (◊) or asterisk (*) could highlight interesting information that you want to remember.

• Use sticky notes when you are not allowed to put marks in books.

• Use sticky notes to mark a page in a book that contains an important diagram, formula, explanation, etc.

• Use sticky notes to mark important facts in research books.

MEMORIZATION TECHNIQUES

- **Association** relates new learning to something you already know. For example, to remember the spelling difference between *dessert* and *desert*, recall that the word *sand* has only one *s*. So, because there is sand in a desert, the word *desert* only has on *s*.

- **Mnemonic** devices are sentences that you create to remember a list or group of items. For example, the first letter of each word in the phrase "**E**very **G**ood **B**oy **D**eserves **F**udge" helps you to remember the names of the lines on the treble clef staff (E, G, B, D, and F) in music.

- **Acronyms** are words that are formed from the first letters or parts of the words in a group. For example, **RADAR** is actually an acronym for **Ra**dio **D**etecting **A**nd **R**anging, and **MASH** is an acronym for **M**obile **A**rmy **S**urgical **H**ospital. **HOMES** helps you to remember the names of the five Great Lakes (**H**uron, **O**ntario, **M**ichigan, **E**rie, and **S**uperior).

- **Visualizing** requires you to use your mind's eye to "see" a chart, list, map, diagram, or sentence as it is in your textbook or notes, on the chalk board or computer screen, or in a display.

- **Initialisms** are abbreviations that are formed from the first letters or parts of the words in a group. Unlike acronyms, initialisms cannot be pronounced as a word themselves. For example, **BEDMAS** is an initialism for the order of operations in math (**B**rackets, **E**xponents, **D**ivide, **M**ultiply, **A**dd, **S**ubtract).

KEY STRATEGIES FOR REVIEWING

Reviewing textbook material, class notes, and handouts should be an ongoing activity. Spending time reviewing becomes more critical when you are preparing for tests. You may find some of the following review strategies useful when studying during your scheduled study time.

- Before reading a selection, preview it by noting the headings, charts, graphs, and chapter questions.
- Before reviewing a unit, note the headings, charts, graphs and chapter questions.
- Highlight key concepts, vocabulary, definitions and formulas.
- Skim the paragraph and note the key words, phrases, and information.
- Carefully read over each step in a procedure.
- Draw a picture or diagram to help make the concept clearer.

KEY STRATEGIES FOR SUCCESS: A CHECKLIST

Review, review, review: review is a huge part of doing well at school and preparing for tests. Here is a checklist for you to keep track of how many suggested strategies for success you are using. Read each question and then put a check mark (✓) in the correct column. Look at the questions where you have checked the "No" column. Think about how you might try using some of these strategies to help you do your best at school.

KEY Strategies for Success	Yes	No
Do you attend school regularly?		
Do you know your personal learning style—how you learn best?		
Do you spend 15 to 30 minutes a day reviewing your notes?		
Do you study in a quiet place at home?		
Do you clearly mark the most important ideas in your study notes?		
Do you use sticky notes to mark texts and research books?		
Do you practise answering multiple-choice and written-response questions?		
Do you ask your teacher for help when you need it?		
Are you maintaining a healthy diet and sleep routine?		
Are you participating in regular physical activity?		

Chemical Bonding

THE DIVERSITY OF MATTER AND CHEMICAL BONDING

Table of Correlations				
Outcome	**Practice Questions**	**Unit Test Questions**	**Practice Test 1**	**Practice Test 2**
1 Describe the role of modelling, evidence and theory in explaining and understanding the structure, chemical bonding and properties of ionic compounds				
20-A1.1k *recall principles for assigning names to ionic compounds*	1	1		
20-A1.2k *explain why formulas for ionic compounds refer to the simplest whole-number ratio of ions that result in a net charge of zero*	2, 3	2, 3		
20-A1.3k *define valence electron, electronegativity, ionic bond and intramolecular force*	4, 5, 6, 7, 8	4, 5		
20-A1.4k *use the periodic table and electron dot diagrams to support and explain ionic bonding theory*	9			
20-A1.5k *explain how an ionic bond results from the simultaneous attraction of oppositely charged ions*	10	6		32
20-A1.6k *explain that ionic compounds form lattices and that these structures relate to the compounds' properties.*	11, 12, 13	7	8	
2 Describe the role of modelling, evidence and theory in explaining and understanding the structure, chemical bonding and properties of molecular substances				
20-A2.1k *recall principles for assigning names to molecular substances*	14, 15	8		
20-A2.2k *explain why formulas for molecular substances refer to the number of atoms of each constituent element*	16			
20-A2.3k *relate electron pairing to multiple and covalent bonds*	17, 18	9		
20-A2.4k *draw electron dot diagrams of atoms and molecules, writing structural formulas for molecular substances and using Lewis structures to predict bonding in simple molecules*	19		4a, 4b	
20-A2.5k *apply VSEPR theory to predict molecular shapes for linear, angular (V-shaped, bent), tetrahedral, trigonal pyramidal and trigonal planar molecules*	20, 21	15		
20-A2.6k *illustrate, by drawing or by building models, the structure of simple molecular substances*	22			
20-A2.7k *explain intermolecular forces, London (dispersion) forces, dipole-dipole forces and hydrogen bonding*	23, 24, 25, 26, 27, 28, 29, 30, 31	10, 11	1, 2	
20-A2.8k *relate properties of substances to the predicted intermolecular bonding in the substances*	32	12, 13	3	19, 20, 21, 26a, 26b
20-A2.9k *determine the polarity of a molecule based on simple structural shapes and unequal charge distribution*	33	14		25
20-A2.10k *describe bonding as a continuum ranging from complete electron transfer to equal sharing of electrons.*	34, 35, 36		24	22, 23, 24

20-A1.1k recall principles for assigning names to ionic compounds

Naming Ionic Compounds

To name an ionic compound, look at the formula and pick out the cation (positive ion) and anion (negative ion) present. The compound name is the name of the cation followed by the name of the anion. The name of the cation will be its elemental name. The elemental name of the anion will end in *-ide*. For example, the compound derived from beryllium and fluorine is beryllium fluor*ide*.

Of the compound cations, the most common is ammonium NH_4^+. Some compound anions are sulfate (SO_4^{2-}), sulfite (SO_3^{2-}), carbonate (CO_3^{2-}), and phosphate (PO_4^{3-}).

When naming a compound with a polyatomic ion, the ion keeps its name; for example, ammonium carbonate, $(NH_4)_2CO_3$.

This table provides examples for how these compound ions are used and named.

Formula	Cation	Anion	Compound Name
MgCl$_2$	Mg^{2+}	Cl$^-$	magnesium chloride
	magnesium	chloride (monatomic ions always have an -ide ending)	
ZnS	Zn^{2+}	S^{2-}	zinc sulfide
	zinc	sulfide	
(NH$_4$)$_2$SO$_4$	NH$_4^+$	SO$_4^{2-}$	ammonium sulfate
	ammonium	sulfate	
Cr$_2$(CO$_3$)$_3$	Cr^{3+}	CO$_3^{2-}$	chromium(III) carbonate
	chromium(III)	carbonate	

For elements such as chromium that can have more than one ion charge (or oxidation state), it is necessary to first determine the cation charge by working backward from the balanced formula. The name of the cation is then stated and followed by a roman numeral to indicate the charge. Therefore, chromium(III) indicates that the charge on the chromium ion is 3+.

1. The formula for zinc oxide is
   A. Zn_2O_3 B. Zn_2O
   C. ZnO_2 D. ZnO

20-A1.2k explain why formulas for ionic compounds refer to the simplest whole-number ratio of ions that result in a net charge of zero

Writing Ionic Formulas

When writing formulas for ionic compounds, it is necessary to balance the ion charges so that the total charge of the anions and cations adds to zero. In many cases, it will be necessary to multiply each ion charge by a balancing coefficient. It is this balancing coefficient that appears in the formula and indicates how many of each ion is present.

Example

Sodium chloride is composed of two ions: Na^+ and Cl^-. The total charge of these ions is 1 sodium ion + 1 chloride ion.
$$1 \times (+1) + 1 \times (-1) = 0$$

The balanced formula is NaCl.

Example

Nickel(II) bromide has two ions: Ni^{2+} (the (II) in the written name indicates what the charge on the ion will be) and Br^-. To make the total ionic charge equal to zero, $1 \times (+2) + 2 \times (-1) = 0$.

From this, there is one nickel ion with a charge of 2+, so two bromide ions with a total negative charge of 2− will be required to make the total charge zero. The formula is $NiBr_2$, and the subscripts show that there are two bromide ions and one nickel ion.

Example

Magnesium nitrate has two ions: Mg^{2+} and NO_3^-. In the case of ions such as nitrate that are composed of two or more elements, the ion is treated as a single unit. To balance this equation, two nitrate ions, each with a charge of -1, are required to balance out the $+2$ charge on each magnesium ion.

$1 \times (+2) + 2 \times (-1) = 0$

The balanced formula $Mg(NO_3)_2$ shows one magnesium ion and two nitrate ions. For ions such as nitrate, brackets are placed around the entire ion and the subscript. Then, the total number of that ion is placed outside the brackets as indicated.

Example

Aluminum sulfide has two ions: Al^{3+} and S^{2-}. The total charge of these ions must equal zero. An integral number must be multiplied by each charge so that the sum will add to zero. This can be done by multiplying the charge on Al by 2 (the balancing coefficient) and the charge on the sulfide by 3 (the balancing coefficient).

$2 \times (+3) + 3 \times (-2) = 0$

The balanced formula is Al_2S_3, which indicates that there are two aluminum ions for every three sulfide ions in a single molecule of aluminum sulfide.

Use the following information to answer the next question.

A metal with three valence electrons forms a compound with oxygen, which has a valence of -2.

2. Which of the following statements **best** describes the exchange of electrons that occurs during this chemical reaction?

A. Each metallic atom donates one electron to each oxygen atom.

B. Each metallic atom donates six electrons to each oxygen atom.

C. A pair of metallic atoms donates six electrons to three oxygen atoms.

D. Three metallic atoms donate three electrons to a pair of oxygen atoms.

Written Response

3. Write the ionic formula for zinc chlorate, and identify the number of zinc ions and chlorate ions in the formula. Explain why the net charge of the compound is zero.

_____

_____

20-A1.3k define valence electron, electronegativity, ionic bond and intramolecular force

INTRAMOLECULAR BONDING IN IONIC COMPOUNDS

Electronegativity is a value that describes the relative ability of an element to attract electrons to itself. When two elements form a bond, the electronegativity values for each will determine how ionic or covalent the bond will be. The larger the difference between the individual elements' electronegativity values, the more ionic the intramolecular bond will be.

Valence electrons are electrons in the highest, or outermost, energy level of the atom. These electrons are the ones involved in chemical reactions and bonding. Looking at the position of the Group A elements in the periodic table (this discussion will be limited to these elements), it is important to remember that the noble gases have the most stable electron configurations of all the elements. The outer valence shells of the noble gases are full (complete). When elements gain or lose electrons, they do so in a way that the number of electrons gained or lost gives the resulting ion the same number of electrons as the nearest noble gas.

Ionic bonding is characteristically found between metals and non-metals. Metals, in general, have low electronegativity values, while non-metals have high electronegativity values. When forming an ionic bond, metals lose one or more of their valence electrons. The resulting positively charged ion (cation) will now have the same electron configuration as the nearest noble gas, a very stable configuration for the ion formed. For example, $Na - e^- \rightarrow Na^+$. Na^+ has the same number of valence electrons as neon (10). Similarly, non-metals gain one or more electrons to complete their outer valence shell. For example, $F + e^- \rightarrow F^-$. The negatively charged (anion) fluorine ion, F^-, now has the same electron configuration as the nearest noble gas: neon (10). The ionic bond that forms between a sodium ion and a fluorine ion is really an attraction between opposite charges.

The **intramolecular forces** within the crystal lattices of ionic solids are the electrostatic attractions between opposite charged ions.

4. The intramolecular bonding in $CH_2FCF_{3(g)}$ is called
   A. van der Waals bonding
   B. hydrogen bonding
   C. covalent bonding
   D. ionic bonding

Use the following information to answer the next question.

The Hindenburg airship made regular transatlantic flights during 1936 and 1937. The German-built Hindenburg, the largest aircraft ever flown, made its final flight in May 1937. During this fatal flight, the hydrogen gas–filled balloon burst into flames, killing 35 people onboard.

5. The bonding within a molecule of $H_{2(g)}$ could be described as
   A. intermolecular bonding
   B. hydrogen bonding
   C. covalent bonding
   D. ionic bonding

Use the following information to answer the next question.

Ethanethiol is a foul-smelling compound that utility companies use because pure natural gas is odorless, which makes gas leaks difficult to detect. Small amounts of ethanethiol are added to natural gas, butane, and propane so that they smell and any subsequent leaks are easily detected. The structural formula for ethanethiol is as shown.

$$CH_3 - \overset{\displaystyle H}{\underset{\displaystyle H}{\overset{|}{\underset{|}{C}}}} - SH$$

6. The bonding within an ethanethiol molecule involves
    A. valence orbital repulsion
    B. hydrogen bonding between hydrogen and sulfur
    C. sharing of electrons between the different atoms
    D. the continuous formation of instantaneous dipoles

7. Electronegativity is the tendency of an atom to attract pairs of electrons when combined in a compound. When arranged in order from lowest electronegativity to highest electronegativity, the atoms chlorine (Cl), magnesium (Mg), carbon (C), and sulfur (S) are
    A. $Mg < C < S < Cl$
    B. $C < S < Mg < Cl$
    C. $Mg < Cl < C < S$
    D. $C < Mg < Cl < S$

8. The elements in the periodic table with the highest electronegativity are the
    A. halogens
    B. alkali metals
    C. transition elements
    D. alkaline earth metals

20-A1.4k use the periodic table and electron dot diagrams to support and explain ionic bonding theory

IONIC BONDING THEORY

Since metals have small electronegativities, they have a weak attraction for their valence electrons. Likewise, non-metals have a strong attraction for their valence electrons because of their large electronegativities. Metallic and non-metallic elements do not share electrons to achieve stability when they react; instead electrons are transferred from metals to non-metals. This results in the formation of a metal cation and a non-metal anion. This transfer of electrons increases the stability of both the cation and the anion that are formed.

For example, when a K atom and an F atom collide, electrons will be transferred because F has a much higher electronegativity (4.0) than K (0.8).

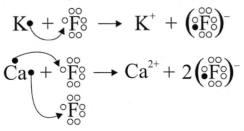

Another example is the result of calcium reacting with fluorine, as shown in the given diagram.

As these ions form, they cluster to form a crystal lattice of K^+ and F^- in the first case and Ca^{2+} and F^- in the second. These crystals will each contain an extremely large number of ions.

9. Which of the following statements correctly describes the bond that forms between an atom of aluminum and an atom of sulfur in a compound formed from these two elements?

    A. Electrons are transferred from the aluminum atom to the sulfur atom, resulting in an ionic bond.

    B. Electrons are transferred from the sulfur atom to the aluminum atom, resulting in an ionic bond.

    C. Electrons are shared between the aluminum atom and the sulfur atom, resulting in an ionic bond.

    D. Electrons are shared between the aluminum atom and the sulfur atom, resulting in a covalent bond.

20-A1.5k explain how an ionic bond results from the simultaneous attraction of oppositely charged ions

IONIC BOND FORMATION

Ionic bonds are formed between metals and non-metals. The metal atom transfers one or more electrons to the non-metal because of the non-metal's higher electronegativity. The number of electrons the metal transfers is related to the stability of the resulting metal cation. For example, for Group 1A and 2A metals, the number of electrons that will be transferred are 1 and 2, respectively. This leaves the resulting cation with a stable noble gas electron configuration, as shown in the given equations for the formation of the ions in NaF.

$$Na - e^- \rightarrow Na^+$$
$$F + e^- \rightarrow F^-$$

Na^+ and F^- have the same configuration as Ne, a noble gas, which makes them very stable.

These processes either require energy (the removal of an electron) or release energy (the uptake of an electron). The electrostatic attraction between oppositely charged ions makes the ionic bond. The amount of energy released because of this attraction determines the strength of the ionic bond. The release of energy makes ionic bond formation more energetically favourable than if the ions remained as free ions.

The relative sizes of the ions and the ratio of cations to anions (1:1 in NaF and 1:2 in CaF_2) help to determine the shape of the crystal lattice.

Use the following information to answer the next question.

Historically, oxidation was the term used to refer to the reaction of an element with oxygen. Today, such reactions are called reduction-oxidation (redox) reactions. The given reaction is one example.

$$2Mg_{(s)} + O_{2(g)} \rightarrow 2MgO_{(s)}$$

10. The bonding present in the product of the given reaction is

    A. a bond resulting from hydrogen bonding

    B. a bond resulting from a dipole-dipole attraction

    C. a covalent bond resulting from the sharing of electrons

    D. an ionic bond resulting from the attraction of oppositely charged ions

20-A1.6k explain that ionic compounds form lattices and that these structures relate to the compounds' properties.

THE STRUCTURE AND PROPERTIES OF IONIC COMPOUNDS

Ionic compounds consist of ions held together by strong ionic bonding forming a lattice structure. Considerable energy is required to split the lattice, so ionic compounds have high melting points. This means that ionic compounds will be solids at room temperature. Many ionic compounds will dissolve and dissociate into individual ions in a water solution. The dissociated cations and anions will be surrounded by water molecules. This is because water, even though it is a molecular compound, has one very positive end and one very negative end in its molecule. These charged ends will be attracted to either the cations or anions. Energy is required to break the bonds between ions in ionic compounds, and energy is released as the individual ions interact with the water molecules in solution. When the energy released is greater than the energy used to break apart an ionic solid into individual ions, the ionic solid will dissolve in water. Otherwise, the compound will be insoluble and not dissociate.

Ionic compounds tend to react as individual ions. In crystalline form, ionic compounds do not react easily. In the dissolved or aqueous state, the ionic compound exists as individual ions. Because of this, ionic compounds dissolved in water react much more easily than solid ionic compounds.

11. Which of the following statements about ionic compounds is **false**?

   A. Ionic compounds experience London dispersion forces.

   B. Ionic compounds exist in the form of a crystal lattice.

   C. Ionic compound bond formation involves electron sharing.

   D. Ionic compound bond formation involves metals and non-metals.

Use the following information to answer the next question.

> The dissolving of an ionic substance in water involves two processes:
>
> i. Ionic bonds within the solid break.
> ii. New bonds form between the ions and the water molecules.

Written Response

12. Use these processes to explain why the dissolving of some ionic compounds is endothermic.

_____
_____
_____
_____
_____
_____
_____

Use the following information to answer the next question.

> A student is given an unknown white, solid substance.

Written Response

13. What physical characteristics of the substance could be tested to determine if the substance is ionic or molecular?

_____
_____
_____
_____
_____
_____
_____

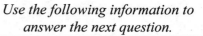

20-A2.1k recall principles for assigning names to molecular substances

NAMING MOLECULAR SUBSTANCES

Binary molecular compounds (containing two elements) are named using a system of prefixes. Prefixes are inserted in front of the element to indicate the number of atoms in each molecule. The second atom in the formula gets an *-ide* ending. The prefix *mono* is only used on the second atom in the formula.

Number	Prefix	Number	Prefix
1	mono	6	hexa
2	di	7	hepta
3	tri	8	octa
4	tetra	9	nona
5	penta	10	deca

For example, CCl_4 is carbon <u>tetra</u>chloride, and As_2O_3 is <u>di</u>arsenic <u>tri</u>oxide.

Many binary molecular compounds have common names, and in these cases, the common names should be used. For example, H_2O is called water, not dihydrogen monoxide.

Most non-binary molecular compounds arc organic. They have a different system of nomenclature.

Use the following information to answer the next question.

For an assignment, Aden named three molecular compounds from chemical formulae that were given to her.

Compound	Formula Given	Aden's Answer
I	NF_3	Nitrogen trifluoride
II	N_2O	Dinitrogen dioxide
III	CCl_4	Carbon tetra-chloride

14. Which of the compounds did Aden name correctly?
    A. I and II
    B. I and III
    C. II and III
    D. I, II, and III

Use the following information to answer the next question.

One molecule of phosphorus pentachloride contains one phosphorus atom.

15. How many chlorine atoms are contained in one molecule of phosphorus pentachloride?
    A. 2
    B. 3
    C. 4
    D. 5

20-A2.2k explain why formulas for molecular substances refer to the number of atoms of each constituent element

FORMULAS FOR MOLECULAR COMPOUNDS

The bonds in ionic compounds result from the attractions between oppositely charged ions that exist in a particular 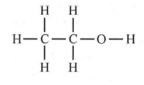 ratio. Ionic compounds are made up of ions of metals and non-metals. Molecular compounds are composed of non-metals. The atoms within each molecule are held together by covalent bonds where the atoms share electrons. Thus, the chemical formula for a molecular compound represents the actual number of atoms that make up the molecule. For example, a molecule of H_2O contains 2 atoms of hydrogen and 1 atom of oxygen. A molecule of ethanol (C_2H_5OH) contains 2 carbon atoms, 6 hydrogen atoms, and 1 oxygen atom as shown.

16. How many atoms does the molecule Al_2O_3 contain?
    A. 6
    B. 5
    C. 3
    D. 1

20-A2.3k relate electron pairing to multiple and covalent bonds

MOLECULAR COMPOUNDS

A **covalent bond** is the attraction of two nuclei for a pair (or pairs) of electrons that they share. Multiple covalent bonds are possible.

Number of Pairs Shared	Name of Bond
1	single covalent
2	double covalent
3	triple covalent

It is not possible to share more than three pairs of electrons.

Use the following information to answer the next question.

> An oxygen atom contains six electrons in its valence shell. As a result, an oxygen atom has the tendency to try to attain the stable electronic configuration of neon (2, 8). The last number gives the total valence electrons in neon. In this case, there are 8 valence electrons. Therefore, two oxygen atoms each contribute two electrons to form an oxygen molecule (O_2).

17. Which of the following types of chemical bonds exists between the oxygen atoms in an oxygen molecule?
   A. Ionic bond
   B. Hydrogen bond
   C. Triple covalent bond
   D. Double covalent bond

18. The bonding in molecular nitrogen can be described as the
   A. attraction of oppositely charged ions in an ionic bond
   B. sharing of three pairs of electrons in a covalent bond
   C. sharing of two pairs of electrons in a covalent bond
   D. sharing of one pair of electrons in a covalent bond

20-A2.4k draw electron dot diagrams of atoms and molecules, writing structural formulas for molecular substances and using Lewis structures to predict bonding in simple molecules

LEWIS DIAGRAMS

Electron pairing is important in understanding chemical bonds. Electrons occupy **orbitals**, which are areas of space where an electron of a given energy is most often found.

An orbital can hold a maximum of 2 electrons. Since electrons repel each other, electrons will occupy empty valence orbitals before pairing up. Paired electrons in an orbital are called **lone pairs**. Unpaired electrons in an orbital are called **bonding electrons**. The number of bonding electrons is called the **bonding capacity** of the atom. Atoms with a stable bonding condition will have 2 electrons in each of their 4 valence orbitals, a situation called a **stable octet**.

Lewis or electron-dot diagrams are a method of keeping track of the valence electrons of atoms. In these diagrams, the element symbol represents the nucleus and inner electrons of the atom. Each side of the symbol represents a valence orbital.

Example

$\cdot \overset{\displaystyle .}{\underset{\displaystyle .}{C}} \cdot$

Carbon: 4 valence electrons.
From the diagram, carbon has 4 bonding electrons and 0 lone pairs.

$\cdot \overset{\displaystyle .}{\underset{\displaystyle ..}{N}} \cdot$

Nitrogen: 5 valence electrons.
From the diagram, nitrogen has 3 bonding electrons and 1 lone pair.

It is unimportant which side has the lone pair.

To make Lewis diagrams of molecules, it is a matter of sharing electrons between atoms so that each atom (other than hydrogen) ends up with a stable octet.

Example

In the Lewis diagram of NH_3, nitrogen ends up with the stable octet, and each hydrogen has 2 electrons.

$$H \overset{\displaystyle ..}{\underset{\displaystyle H}{N}} H$$

For OF_2, each F and O have a stable octet.

$$\overset{\displaystyle ..}{\underset{\displaystyle ..}{F}} \overset{\displaystyle \circ\circ}{\underset{\displaystyle \circ\circ}{O}} \overset{\displaystyle ..}{\underset{\displaystyle ..}{F}}$$

In the case of HCN, it is necessary for C and N to share three pairs of electrons for each to achieve a stable octet.

$$H \overset{\displaystyle \times}{} C \overset{\displaystyle \circ\circ\circ}{} N \overset{\displaystyle \circ}{\underset{\displaystyle \circ}{}}$$

Written Response

19. Draw the Lewis dot diagram and structural diagram for ethene (C_2H_4).

_____

_____

_____

_____

_____

20-A2.5k apply VSEPR theory to predict molecular shapes for linear, angular (V-shaped, bent), tetrahedral, trigonal pyramidal and trigonal planar molecules

VALENCE SHELL ELECTRON PAIR REPULSION THEORY

The valence shell electron pair repulsion (VSEPR) theory is used to predict the shape that the other atoms form around the central atom of a molecule.

The theory consists of these main points:

• Lone pairs and bonding pairs around a central atom move as far apart as possible to minimize repulsion.
• Lone-pair electrons repel with greater force than bonding-pair electrons, creating wider angles around lone electron pairs.
• Multiple bonding pairs are treated as though they were single bonding pairs.

Key:

out of page   flat on page   behind page

PREDICTING MOLECULAR SHAPES USING VSEPR THEORY

The VSEPR theory can be used to explain the structures of many different molecular compounds.

With four separate hydrogen atoms bonded to a central carbon as is seen in methane (CH_4), the farthest apart that the hydrogen atoms can be from each other is if they adopt a tetrahedral shape.

Formula	CH$_4$
Lewis diagram	H $\overset{\bullet\circ}{\underset{\bullet\circ}{\text{H}}}$ C $\overset{}{\underset{}{}}$ H (H above and below)
Lone pairs	0
Bonding pairs	4
Shape name	Tetrahedral bond Angle = 109.5°
Shape diagram	

In ammonia (NH$_3$), the greater concentration of negative charge in the lone pair of electrons on the central nitrogen forces the remaining three hydrogen atoms to tilt downward slightly, forming a pyramidal shape.

Formula	NH$_3$
Lewis diagram	H $\overset{\bullet\bullet}{}$ N $\overset{}{\underset{\bullet\circ}{}}$ H (H below)
Lone pairs	1
Bonding pairs	3
Shape name	Trigonal pyramidal bond Angle = 107.3°
Shape diagram	

The oxygen atom in water (H$_2$O) has two lone pairs of electrons, forcing the two hydrogen atoms into a more V-shaped angular bond.

Formula	H$_2$O
Lewis diagram	H $\overset{\bullet\bullet}{\underset{\bullet\bullet}{\text{O}}}$ H
Lone pairs	2
Bonding pairs	2
Shape name	V-shaped bond Angle = 104.5°
Shape diagram	

In methanal (CH$_2$O), there is a double bond between the carbon and oxygen atoms. The molecule adopts a planar shape. VSEPR theory does predict that the molecule will adopt some sort of triangular shape, and this is what occurs.

Formula	CH$_2$O
Lewis diagram	H $\overset{}{\times}$ C $\overset{\circ\circ}{\underset{\bullet\times}{}}$ Ö (H below)
Lone pairs	0
Bonding pairs	3
Shape name	Trigonal planar bond Angle ≠ 120°
Shape diagram	

In hydrogen cyanide (HCN), a triple bond between the carbon and nitrogen concentrates much of the charge along this bond. From VSEPR theory, the farthest that the hydrogen could be from this dense charge would be by forming a linear molecule.

Formula	HCN
Lewis diagram	H $\overset{\bullet}{\underset{\circ}{}}$ C $\overset{\bullet\bullet\times}{\underset{\bullet\times}{}}$ N$^{\times}_{\times}$
Lone pairs	0
Bonding pairs	2
Shape name	Linear bond Angle = 180°
Shape diagram	H – C ≡ N

20. Hydrogen cyanide (HCN) is a highly poisonous compound. The shape of an HCN molecule is
    A. linear
    B. pyramidal
    C. tetrahedral
    D. trigonal planar

21. The shape of a CO_2 molecule is
    A. linear
    B. pyramidal
    C. tetrahedral
    D. trigonal planar

20-A2.6k illustrate, by drawing or by building models, the structure of simple molecular substances

USING VSEPR THEORY TO PREDICT MOLECULAR SHAPE

The principles of the valence shell electron pair repulsion (VSEPR) theory can be used to predict the shape of a molecule even when it has more than one central atom. This is done by examining the VSEPR arrangement around each central atom individually.

The given Lewis and shape diagrams illustrate the molecular shape of CH_3COOH.

Lewis Diagram of CH₃COOH

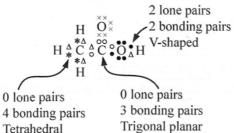

0 lone pairs
4 bonding pairs
Tetrahedral

0 lone pairs
3 bonding pairs
Trigonal planar

Shape Diagram of CH₃COOH

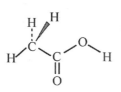

Making models of molecules is a good way to equate the diagrams with the three-dimensional shape of the molecules.

22. According to the VSEPR theory, what shape is a BF_3 molecule?
    A. Pyramidal
    B. Tetrahedral
    C. Square planar
    D. Trigonal planar

20-A2.7k explain intermolecular forces, London (dispersion) forces, dipole-dipole forces and hydrogen bonding

INTERMOLECULAR FORCES

Intermolecular forces are the forces between molecules that attract one molecule to another. If there were none, all molecular substances would be gases at all temperatures, even absolute zero. Some types of intermolecular forces are dipole-dipole forces, London forces, and hydrogen bonds.

VAN DER WAALS FORCES

Van der Waals forces describe the weak attractive interactions between molecules. There are two broad categories of van der Waals forces; London dispersion forces, and dipole-dipole forces.

London forces are temporary dipoles that are present in all molecular substances. Fritz London developed this theory in order to explain certain behaviours of non-polar molecules and atomic elements. Generally, electrons can be thought of as being evenly distributed around atoms and non-polar molecules. However, since these electrons are in constant motion, it is possible for them to concentrate temporarily in one location. When this occurs, a temporary dipole is established. This temporary dipole induces a complementary dipole in the adjacent atoms or molecules, setting up a weak intermolecular attraction, or a London dispersion force. The strength of this attraction depends primarily upon the number of electrons around the atom or molecule and the shape of the molecule.

For example, the boiling points of the noble gases increase as one goes from helium (boiling point of −269°C) to radon (boiling point of −62°C). Here the size of the electron cloud around each atom has increased with the number of electrons. The outer electrons in radon are less attracted to the nucleus, making them freer to redistribute themselves and form temporary dipoles. More dipoles strengthen the attraction between atoms reflected in higher boiling points. A similar argument can be made in explaining the increase in boiling point going from Cl_2 (−34°C) to Br_2 (59°C) to I_2 (184°C).

In non-polar molecular compounds such as hydrocarbons, it is the shape of the molecule that is important in determining the strength of the London forces. The molecule pentane (C_5H_{12}) can exist in several forms; one is linear, while the other can be considered spherical in shape. The boiling point of the linear pentane is 36°C, while that of the spherical pentane is 9.5°C. The linear shape allows for more interactions (stronger London force) along the length of the individual molecules, whereas the more spherical shape has a much smaller point of interaction (weaker London force) and thus a lower boiling point.

In dipole-dipole forces, the dipoles are permanent. The strength of a molecule's permanent dipole depends mainly upon the electronegativity of the atoms that make up the molecule and the geometry of the molecule. Any bond between two atoms in which one atom has a higher electronegativity relative to the other atom will be more negative on the more electronegative end and more positive on the less electronegative end, forming a dipole along that bond. For example, water (H_2O) has a very strong dipole because of the highly electronegative oxygen atom compared to hydrogen and the bent shape of the molecule. Carbon dioxide (CO_2) has no dipole even with the two oxygen atoms present because the molecule is linear and the individual C-O dipoles cancel each other.

These **dipole-dipole forces** are due to the attraction of the positive end or pole of one molecule to the negative end or pole of neighbouring molecules.

HYDROGEN BONDS

Hydrogen bonds are the attractive forces between a hydrogen atom covalently bonded to F, O, or N in one molecule and an F, O, or N of another molecule. The atoms F, O, and N have the highest electronegativities of all the elements and so any covalent bond between H and one of F, O, or N leaves H with a high positive charge; it is essentially electron-free while the F, O, or N has a high negative charge.

The strength of the hydrogen bond is greater than that of the van der Waals Forces but less than that of ionic and covalent bonds.

Hydrogen bonding can be intramolecular (within the same molecule) or intermolecular (between different molecules). Hydrogen bonding explains the high boiling point of H_2O versus the boiling points of H_2S, H_2Se, and H_2Te, It gives strength to various polymers through the hydrogen bonding between individual chains (nylon, Kevlar and cellulose are examples). Between complementary base pairs, it is critical in holding strands of DNA together. Intramolecular hydrogen bonding helps determine the shape of many proteins.

23. The molecule $NO_{(g)}$ has which of the following properties?
    A. It is polar and experiences dipole-dipole forces.
    B. It is non-polar and experiences London forces.
    C. It is isoelectronic with $O_{2(g)}$ molecules.
    D. It separates into ions in aqueous solution.

> Hydrogen bonds are weaker than ___*i*___ but are stronger than ___*ii*___.

24. This statement is completed by the information in which of the following tables?

A.

i	*ii*
covalent bonds	ionic bonds

B.

i	*ii*
London forces	covalent bonds

C.

i	*ii*
covalent bonds	dipole-dipole forces

D.

i	*ii*
ionic bonds	covalent bonds

25. The intermolecular bonding in $CHF_2CF_{3(l)}$ is **best** described as

A. covalent bonding and London forces

B. hydrogen bonding and London forces

C. London forces and dipole-dipole attraction

D. hydrogen bonding and dipole-dipole attraction

> The human body consumes glucose in order to fuel the production of adenosine triphosphate (ATP), the energy currency of many biochemical reactions. Glucose breakdown can be represented as follows:
> $C_6H_{12}O_6 + 6O_2 \rightarrow 6CO_2 + 6H_2O$

26. The strongest bonds made and broken during glucose consumption are

A. hydrogen bonds

B. intramolecular bonds

C. intermolecular bonds

D. London dispersion bonds

> Chemists at the University of Alberta often use infrared (IR) spectroscopy to obtain molecular information about nucleic acids. IR spectroscopy allows the chemists to gain insight into the structure of molecules by learning more about the types of bonds between their atoms. Different peaks, each pertaining to a different bond type, are shown on a graph. Hydrogen bonding, if present, causes a characteristic broadening in some of the peaks of the compound's infrared spectrum.

27. Which of the following molecules would **not** show evidence of hydrogen bonding on an infrared spectroscopy graph?

A. $H_2O_{(s)}$

B. $NH_{3(l)}$

C. $HF_{(aq)}$

D. $CH_{4(g)}$

> Water exists as a liquid at room temperature, whereas the isoelectronic, non-polar compound methane exists as a gas at room temperature.

28. Which of the following statements about the bonds between these molecules is **false**?

A. Both water and methane experience London forces.

B. Both water and methane experience hydrogen bonding.

C. Intermolecular bonds between water molecules help stabilize the liquid state.

D. The intermolecular forces of these molecules affect their melting and boiling points.

Use the following information to answer the next question.

The air in the vicinity of areas of geothermal activity, such as Yellowstone National Park, have a characteristic "rotten egg" aroma. The smell is caused by the toxic gas hydrogen sulfide (H_2S).

Water (H_2O) is a liquid at standard atmospheric temperature and pressure, but hydrogen sulfide, hydrogen selenide (H_2Se), and hydrogen telluride (H_2Te) are all gases under the same conditions.

29. Water has a higher boiling point than the other given compounds because of its

A. hydrogen bonds **B.** covalent bonds

C. London forces **D.** ionic bonds

Use the following information to answer the next question.

Four different types of bonds are given:

1. Ionic bonding
2. Covalent bonding
3. Hydrogen bonding
4. Van der Waal forces

Numerical Response

30. In general, when these bonding types are listed in order from strongest to weakest, the order is _____, _____, _____ and _____. (Record your answer as a four-digit number.)

Use the following information to answer the next question.

Use the following terms to complete the given statement.

1. Hydrogen bonds
2. London dispersion forces
3. Dipole
4. Protons
5. Electrons
6. Polar
7. Non-polar

The circulation of _____ within a molecule leads to the generation of a momentary _____ within that molecule, which induces dipoles in its near neighbours. The types of bonds that result are called _____. These kinds of intermolecular bonds are the only kind available to _____ molecules.

Numerical Response

31. In the correct order, the terms that complete the given statement are _____, _____, _____, and _____. (Record your answer as a four-digit number.)

20-A2.8k relate properties of substances to the predicted intermolecular bonding in the substances

INTERMOLECULAR BONDING AND THE PROPERTIES OF SUBSTANCES

Many of the properties of a substance are related to the intermolecular bonds within the substance. For example, the boiling point, melting point, and enthalpies of fusion and vaporization all increase as the strength of the intermolecular forces increases.

Some of the properties for a molecule can be used to predict the type and strength of the intermolecular bonds present. For example, compare the total number of electrons in order to predict the strength of the London forces, or determine if the molecule is polar in order to determine if dipole-dipole forces are present. Compounds that contain OH, NH, or FH bonds will reveal if hydrogen bonding is present.

Use the following information to answer the next question.

> The amount of energy required to split one mole of water into hydrogen and oxygen is seven times higher than the amount of energy required to vapourize one mole of water at its boiling point.

32. When compared to the energy required to split one mole of water, the energy required to boil one mole of water indicates that
   A. intermolecular bonds are stronger than intramolecular bonds
   B. intramolecular bonds are stronger than intermolecular bonds
   C. dipole-dipole bonds are stronger than covalent bonds
   D. hydrogen bonds are stronger than covalent bonds

20-A2.9k determine the polarity of a molecule based on simple structural shapes and unequal charge distribution

MOLECULAR SHAPE, ELECTRONEGATIVITY, AND POLARITY

When two atoms do not share electrons equally, the bond between them is called a **polar covalent bond**. The atom with higher electronegativity is partially negative, $\delta-$, while the one with lower electronegativity is partially positive, $\delta+$. For example, in the bond between carbon and hydrogen, carbon has the higher electronegativity and is $\delta-$, while hydrogen has the lower electronegativity and is $\delta+$. The given figure illustrates how to represent this bond.

$$\delta- \quad \delta+$$
$$\overleftarrow{\quad\;\;}\!\!+$$
$$C-H$$
$$2.6 \quad 2.2$$

A polar covalent bond

The arrow represents a bond dipole, where the arrowhead is the negative end and the tail is the positive end of the polar covalent bond.

Just as bonds can be polar or non-polar, so too can molecules. A molecule's polarity affects a number of its physical properties, including its solubility, melting point, and boiling point.

To determine whether or not a molecule will be polar, first determine if the molecule contains any polar bonds. Only one polar bond will give the molecule polarity. If there are two or more polar bonds, then it is necessary to consider the size or strength of the polar bonds present and to determine the shape of the molecule to see if the bond polarities cancel each other out or produce a net dipole.

Some examples of polar and non-polar molecules are shown in this table.

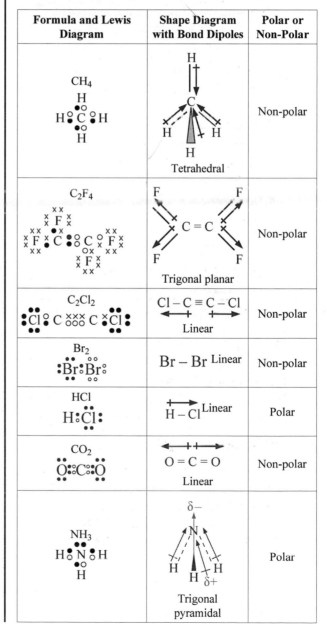

Formula and Lewis Diagram	Shape Diagram with Bond Dipoles	Polar or Non-Polar
CH_4	Tetrahedral	Non-polar
C_2F_4	Trigonal planar	Non-polar
C_2Cl_2	Linear	Non-polar
Br_2	Br – Br Linear	Non-polar
HCl	H – Cl Linear	Polar
CO_2	O = C = O Linear	Non-polar
NH_3	Trigonal pyramidal	Polar

Formula and Lewis Diagram	Shape Diagram with Bond Dipoles	Polar or Non-Polar
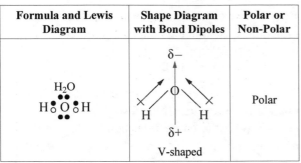 H_2O	V-shaped	Polar

Molecules that are symmetrical in shape (e.g., tetrahedral, linear, trigonal planar) can have polar bonds, but the molecule as a whole is not polar. The symmetrical shape of the molecule causes the dipoles to cancel each other out, making the molecule non-polar (e.g., CH_4, C_2F_4, and CO_2). If the dipoles are not equal, the molecule is polar, as can be seen in chloromethane.

Chloromethane

33. Use the VSEPR theory to draw the shape of each of the following molecules. Name their shape and determine if they are polar or non-polar.

Molecule	VSEPR 3-D Shape	Name of Shape	Polar? (Y/N)
HC_2F			
SCl_2			
$SiCl_4$			
N_2H_3F			

20-A2.10k describe bonding as a continuum ranging from complete electron transfer to equal sharing of electrons.

FORMATION OF IONIC AND COVALENT BONDS

When electrons are shared, they are not necessarily shared equally. It is conceivable that some atoms have a greater attraction for shared valence electrons than others. This relative attraction is known as **electronegativity**.

When two hydrogen atoms have the same electronegativity and share a pair of electrons equally between them, this is called a **non-polar covalent bond**.

The small difference in the electronegativity of sulfur (2.6) and hydrogen (2.2) means that the pair of electrons in a sulfur-hydrogen bond will not be shared equally. The higher electronegativity of sulfur means that the electrons will stay closer to it, making the covalent bond have one end that is partially negative, δ^-, and one end that is partially positive, δ^+. This is called a **polar covalent bond**.

In an extreme case, sodium with an electronegativity of 0.9 and fluorine with an electronegativity of 4.0 could react. In this case, sharing would not occur at all. When they react, sodium would simply transfer an electron to fluorine, forming a sodium ion (Na^+) and fluoride ion (F^-). The bond between Na^+ and F^- is an **ionic bond**.

There is not a sharp dividing line between ionic bonding and covalent bonding. Bonding becomes more ionic and less covalent the greater the electronegativity difference. In general, bonding between non-metals is referred to as covalent bonding, and bonding between metals and non-metals is referred to as ionic bonding.

Use the following information to answer the next question.

Compounds can be structurally simple like $NaCl_{(s)}$ or more complex like the molecular liquid chloroacetophenone. Chloroacetophenone has the structure shown in the given diagram.

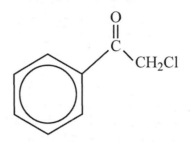

Chloroacetophenone (C_8H_7ClO) is the volatile liquid more commonly known as Mace or tear gas.

34. Which of the following statements **best** describes the main factor behind the bonding forces between the atoms in NaCl and chloroacetophenone?

    A. Bonding in both NaCl and chloroacetophenone occurs because of electron sharing.

    B. Bonding in both NaCl and chloroacetophenone occurs because of electron transfer.

    C. Bonding in NaCl occurs because of electron transfer, and bonding in chloroacetophenone occurs because of electron sharing.

    D. Bonding in NaCl occurs because of electron sharing, and bonding in chloroacetophenone occurs because of electron transfer.

35. The type of bonding interactions that occur in silicon dioxide ($SiO_{2(s)}$), the main ingredient in glass, would **most likely** involve

   A. electron transfer

   B. equal sharing of electrons

   C. unequal sharing of electrons

   D. attraction between individual electrons

Use the following information to answer the next question.

Rechargeable nickel-cadmium batteries rely on a cadmium metal anode and a cathode made from nickel(IV) oxide (this is a simplified description of the actual nickel compound used). These batteries are more costly than the traditional dry cell and alkaline batteries, but they are easily recharged and more economical in the long run.

36. The bonding in nickel(IV) oxide is a result of

   A. equal sharing of electrons

   B. unequal sharing of electrons

   C. complete transfer of electrons

   D. partial bond formation resulting from dipole formation

ANSWERS AND SOLUTIONS
THE DIVERSITY OF MATTER AND CHEMICAL BONDING

1. D	9. A	17. D	25. C	33. WR
2. C	10. D	18. D	26. B	34. C
3. WR	11. C	19. WR	27. D	35. C
4. C	12. WR	20. A	28. B	36. C
5. C	13. WR	21. A	29. A	
6. C	14. B	22. D	30. 2134	
7. A	15. D	23. A	31. 5327	
8. A	16. B	24. C	32. B	

1. D

Zinc has an oxidation number of 2^+, and oxygen has an oxidation number of 2^-. When these two elements are combined to form a compound, their charges cancel each other out, resulting in a net charge of zero. This is shown in the equation $Zn^{2+} + O^{2-} = ZnO$.

Therefore, the formula for zinc oxide is ZnO.

2. C

A metallic element with three valence electrons has a valence of +3. Metals with a +3 valence are expected to lose three electrons when reacting with a non-metal. For example, for aluminum,
$$Al \rightarrow Al^{3+} + 3e^-.$$

A valence of −2 means that the element will gain two electrons when reacting. For example, for oxygen,
$$O + 2e^- \rightarrow O^{2-}.$$

The electrons gained must equal the electrons lost. In this case, two aluminum atoms must lose three electrons each, for a total of six electrons. These electrons are gained by three oxygen atoms. Each oxygen atom gains two electrons, for a total of six.

Thus, a pair of metallic atoms donates a total of six electrons to three oxygen atoms.

3. WR

For the compound zinc chlorate, the cation is zinc, Zn^{2+}, and the anion is chlorate, ClO_3^-. In the compound, there is one Zn^{2+} ion and two ClO_3^- ions, so the ionic formula is $Zn(ClO_3)_2$. All compounds must have a net charge equal to zero, so the charges on the ions must balance out.
$1 \times (+2) + 2 \times (-1) = 0$, when combined in a ratio of 1 Zn^{2+}:2 ClO_3^-, the compound has a net charge of zero.

4. C

Intramolecular bonding is bonding between atoms within a molecule of a given compound. Intramolecular bonding in molecules such as CH_2FCF_3 consists of shared pairs of electrons between atoms. Bonds that form as a result of shared electrons are called covalent bonds. An easy way of determining if a compound has covalent intramolecular bonds is to check if the elements within a molecule are non-metals. Generally, covalent bonds hold non-metallic atoms together within a molecule. In this case, C, H, and F are all non-metals.

On the other hand, the complete transfer of a bonding pair of electrons to one of the bonded atoms creates what is called an ionic bond. A reaction of atoms when there is a large difference between their electronegativity values (generally metals with non-metals) tends to favour the formation of ionic bonds. This involves the metal losing electrons, which is called oxidation, and the non-metal gaining electrons, which is called reduction.

Intermolecular bonding is bonding between molecules of the same compound. Van der Waals and hydrogen bonding are types of intermolecular bonding.

5. C

Hydrogen is a molecular element composed of two hydrogen nuclei sharing a single pair of e^- in the bond that joins them. Since the electronegativity of each hydrogen atom is identical, the bond pair of e^- is shared equally by each nucleus. The strength of the covalent bond means that reactions that break apart a diatomic hydrogen molecule, such as combustion, tend to release a lot of bond energy exothermically.

6. C

Ethanethiol is a compound made up of non-metallic atoms. Its atoms are held together by covalent bonds, which are a result of the sharing of electrons between the different constituent atoms.

7. A

The electronegativity of each element can be found on the periodic table. When arranged in order of increasing electronegativity, the elements are $Mg < C < S < Cl$.

8. A

Electronegativity is the relative attraction of an atom to a shared pair of electrons. Electronegativity increases from left to right across the periodic table: alkali metals, alkaline earth metals, transition metals, and halogens. Of the four groups, the halogens have the highest electronegativity.

9. A

Aluminum is a metal, and sulfur is a non-metal. When bonding, metals tend to lose electrons and form positive ions, while non-metals tend to gain electrons and form negative ions. The attraction between positive and negative ions constitutes an ionic bond.

10. D

Magnesium oxide ($MgO_{(s)}$) is formed from two elements with a large difference in electronegativity. The ions Mg^{2+} and O^{2-} form a crystal lattice in which they are strongly attracted to their nearest oppositely charged neighbours. These strong attractions constitute ionic bonding, making $MgO_{(s)}$ an ionic compound.

11. C

Ionic compounds are formed by the complete transfer of electrons between two atoms. Atoms with large differences in electronegativity, such as metals and non-metals, tend to favour the formation of ionic bonds. All molecules and atomic chemical entities experience dispersion forces. They exist in the form of cations and anions in an array known as a crystal lattice. The sharing of electrons occurs in covalent bonds.

12. WR

When some ionic compounds dissolve in water, the energy required to break the bonds in the ionic crystal exceeds the energy released when new bonds form. The extra energy required is drawn from the surroundings, which is why a solution may feel cold as a compound dissolves.

13. WR

1. Test the hardness. Ionic substances tend to be harder than molecular substances.
2. Try to melt the substance. Ionic substances have extremely high melting points.
3. Dissolve some of the substance and test its conductivity. Ionic substances are good conductors in the liquid phase.
4. Test the brittleness. Ionic substances tend to be brittle, but molecular substances tend to be soft and waxy.

14. B

Step 1
Write out the symbols of the elements in the compound.
The element that appears first in the formula keeps its name. The second element ends with -*ide*.

Step 2
N^{3+}, F^- (The more common oxidation number for nitrogen is 3 + .)

N^+, O^{2-} (Notice that nitrogen has a different oxidation number. This is common for many elements. One oxidation number is usually more common.)

C^{4+}, F^-

Step 3

When there is more than one atom of an element in the formula, the name of the element usually contains a prefix that specifies the number of atoms present.

Examples of number prefixes include the following:

- 1: *mono*
- 2: *di*
- 3: *tri*
- 4: *tetra*
- 5: *penta*

In compound I, the three fluorines would be indicated with the prefix *tri* to give nitrogen trifluoride. In compound II the two nitrogens would have the prefix *di* for dinitrogen oxide. Finally, the four fluorines in compound III would be designated as *tetra*, giving a compound name of carbon tetrafluoride.

Often the single element is left with its name and no prefix; thus, compound II would not be dinitrogen monoxide but dinitrogen oxide.

Aden correctly named formula I (NF_3) and formula III (CCl_4), but made a mistake in naming formula II (N_2O). The correct name for N_2O is dinitrogen oxide, not dinitrogen dioxide.

15. D

Pentachloride has the prefix *penta*, which means five. One molecule of phosphorus pentachloride contains five chlorine atoms.

16. B

The number of atoms of each element is indicated by the subscript number immediately following the element's symbol. Since there are two Al atoms plus three O atoms, Al_2O_3 has a total of five atoms.

17. D

In an oxygen molecule, two oxygen atoms are held together by a double covalent bond. An oxygen molecule is often represented as O = O.

Ionic bonds exist between the positively and negatively charged ions of various elements. An oxygen molecule does not contain an ionic bond. There is no hydrogen atom in an oxygen molecule, so hydrogen bonding cannot occur. There is a double bond between the two oxygen atoms of an oxygen molecule, not a triple bond.

18. D

Nitrogen (N_2) is a molecular species composed of two nitrogen atoms that bond together by sharing three pairs of electrons, resulting in the formation of a triple bond. Since the bonding involves the sharing of electrons, it is a covalent bond.

19. WR

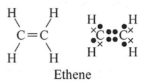

Ethene

20. A

In an HCN molecule, the central carbon atom has no lone pairs and two bonding pair sets of electrons. The only way both carbon (C) and nitrogen (N) can achieve stable octets is by sharing three pairs of electrons and forming a triple bond. Therefore, HCN has a linear shape: .

$$H - C \equiv N \bullet \bullet$$

21. A

The central carbon atom in carbon dioxide, CO_2, has two bonding pairs. The multiple bonding pair set counts as one bonding pair, and there are no lone pairs. These pairs can be up to 180° apart, leading to a linear structure.

$$O = C = O$$

22. D

In a BF_3 molecule, the central metal atom, boron, has three valence electrons that are shared equally by the three fluorine atoms. The bond angle FBF is 120°. According to the VSEPR theory, the shape of the BF_3 molecule is trigonal planar.

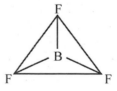

23. A

The electronegativity difference between N and O is too small to permit it to form ions, but it will make $NO_{(g)}$ a polar molecule. In addition, $NO_{(g)}$ is not an ideal gas. There are likely to be attractive forces between individual molecules if they are close enough. The most likely forces of attraction between $NO_{(g)}$ molecules, arranged from strongest to weakest, are dipole-dipole forces and dispersion forces.

24. C

Hydrogen bonds are the strongest of the available intermolecular bonds, but they are about 10% of the strength of typical covalent bonds. They are stronger than dipole-dipole forces but weaker than covalent bonds.

25. C

For any molecule, the type and extent of intermolecular bonding hinges on the nature of the molecules involved. All molecules experience London forces. Only polar molecules are affected by dipole-dipole forces. Only those molecules that contain O-H bonds, N-H bonds, or HF itself are capable of being affected by hydrogen bonding.

CHF_2CF_3 is a polar molecule.

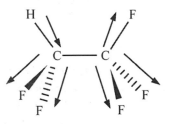

It will be affected only by London forces and by dipole-dipole forces. It will not be affected by hydrogen bonding since there is no F-H, O-H, or N-H bonds in the molecule.

26. B

The bonds that hold the atoms together within a glucose molecule are called intramolecular bonds. In this case, the intramolecular bonds are covalent. If the atoms in $C_6H_{12}O_6$ and O_2 are to be rearranged to give CO_2 and H_2O, then it is intramolecular bonds that must be broken and reformed. Relative bond strengths (bond energies) are illustrated in the following diagram.

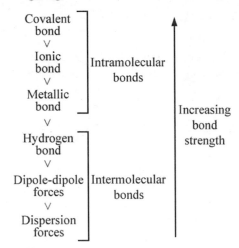

In general it can be said covalent bonds are stronger than ionic bonds but there is a lot of overlap in terms of strength between these two types of bonds.

27. D

Hydrogen bonds are the intermolecular attractions that form between molecules containing O-H and N-H bonds or in HF. $CH_{4(g)}$ does not have the necessary prerequisites for hydrogen bonding.

28. B

	Number of e⁻	Polarity	Types of Bonding Available
$H_2O_{(l)}$	10	Polar	London forces, dipole-dipole forces, and hydrogen bonds
$CH_{4(g)}$	10	Non-polar	London forces only

Water experiences intermolecular forces, primarily hydrogen bonding, as a result of its polar character. This is what generates its increased stability in the liquid state. Methane, CH_4, experiences no hydrogen bonding. The only intermolecular bonding that occurs in methane is due to London forces.

29. A

Intermolecular forces affect the melting and boiling points of molecular compounds. There are three types of intermolecular forces:

1. London forces
2. Dipole-dipole forces
3. Hydrogen bonds

Hydrogen bonds are the strongest intermolecular forces (followed by dipole-dipole, then London), but they are present only in molecules with O–H, N–H, or H–F bonds.

The given table summarizes the attractive forces affecting H_2O, H_2S, H_2Se, and H_2Te. Water has hydrogen bonds in addition to the other two types of intermolecular forces. It therefore takes more energy to vaporize water, which means that water has a higher boiling point than the other substances.

Substance	London Forces	Dipole-Dipole Interactions	Hydrogen Bonds
$H_2O_{(l)}$	✓	✓	✓
$H_2S_{(g)}$	✓	✓	✗
$H_2Se_{(g)}$	✓	✗	✗
$H_2Te_{(g)}$	✓	✗	✗

30. 2134

In general, the strengths of bonds can be ordered as follows:
covalent bond > ionic bond > metallic bond> hydrogen bond > Van der Waal forces

Listed from strongest to weakest, the bonds are covalent bonding (2), ionic bonding (1), hydrogen bonding (3), and Van der Waal forces (4).

31. 5327

The circulation of electrons within a molecule leads to the generation of a momentary dipole within that molecule, which induces dipoles in its near neighbours. The types of bonds that result are called London dispersion forces. These kinds of intermolecular bonds are the only kind available to non-polar molecules.

The answer is 5, 3, 2, and 7.

32. B

Since the energy required to split one mole of water far exceeds the energy required to vapourize the same quantity of water, stronger bonds must be broken in chemical reactions than must be broken in physical transformations. Splitting water involves breaking intramolecular bonds, while vapourizing water breaks intermolecular bonds. Thus, intramolecular bonds are the stronger of the two.

33. WR

Molecule	VSEPR 3-D Shape	Name of Shape	Polar? (Y/N)
HC_2F	H – C ≡ C – F	Linear	Y
SCl_2	Cl $\overset{103°}{\frown}$ Cl / S	V-shaped	Y
$SiCl_4$	Cl / Si ⫶ Cl / Cl Cl	Tetrahedral	N
N_2H_3F	H ⫶ N – N ⫶ H / F H	Trigonal pyramidal	Y

34. C

NaCl is an ionic compound; it is a compound of a metal and a non-metal. Therefore, NaCl has ionic bonds. In ionic bonds, electrons are transferred.

Chloroacetophenone is a molecular compound. In molecular compounds, atoms are joined through covalent bonds. This means that electrons are shared between the atoms.

35. C

The elements that make up silicon dioxide are non-metals, and favour covalent over ionic bond formation. The electronegativity of oxygen is greater than that of silicon; oxygen is found both higher up and further to the right on the periodic table. The difference in their electronegativities is great enough to allow for unequal sharing of electrons, but not great enough to result in complete electron transfer.

36. **C**

Ionic compounds contain ions, which are entities formed from the complete transfer of electrons. In nickel(IV) oxide, the electrons lost by the nickel in forming Ni^{4+} have been gained by the oxygen to form O^{2-}.

UNIT TEST — THE DIVERSITY OF MATTER AND CHEMICAL BONDING

1. The chemical formula for ammonium phosphate is
   A. $NH_4PO_{4(s)}$
   B. $(NH_4)_3PO_{4(s)}$
   C. $NH_{43}(PO_4)_{4(s)}$
   D. $NH_4(I)PO_4(III)_{(s)}$

Use the following information to answer the next question.

> Calcium carbide is used in various metallurgical processes. It is also used in the preparation of acetylene and oxyacetylene, both of which are used in welding. Its preparation from calcium oxide involves the reaction
> $$CaO_{(s)} + 3C_{(s)} \rightarrow CaC_{2(s)} + CO_{(g)}$$

2. The type of bond found within calcium carbide is the result of
   A. a dipole-dipole force
   B. the sharing of electrons
   C. the attraction of oppositely charged ions
   D. the attraction between the nuclei and electrons

Use the following information to answer the next question.

> Barium carbonate is ___*i*___ compound held together by ___*ii*___ forces.

3. The statement is completed by the information in which of the following tables?

A.

i	*ii*
an ionic	intramolecular

B.

i	*ii*
an ionic	intermolecular

C.

i	*ii*
a covalent	intramolecular

D.

i	*ii*
a covalent	intermolecular

4. The elements in the periodic table with the lowest electronegativity are the
   A. halogens
   B. alkali metals
   C. transition elements
   D. alkaline-earth metals

Use the following information to answer the next question.

> Chloral hydrate is a sedative with the following chemical structure:
>
>   Cl OH
> | |
> Cl—C—C—OH
> | |
>   Cl OH

5. The bonding that occurs within the chloral hydrate molecule involves
   A. a complete transfer of electrons
   B. unequal sharing of electrons
   C. unequal sharing of protons
   D. equal sharing of electrons

Use the following information to answer the next question.

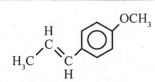

Anethole ($C_{10}H_{12}O$), as shown in the given structure, is the molecular substance responsible for the odour of licorice.

6. The chemical bonds that occur within a molecule of anethole are the result of

A. dipole-dipole interactions

B. complete electron transfer

C. non-valence electron interactions

D. simultaneous attraction of electrons by adjacent nuclei

Use the following information to answer the next question.

Chlorine ($Cl_2(g)$) is used in great quantity as a bleach for the pulp and paper industry and as a disinfectant for municipal water supplies. Iodine is another chemical commonly used for water disinfection on a smaller scale. The boiling point of chlorine is −34.6°C, while the boiling point of iodine is 184°C.

7. The difference in boiling points between chlorine and iodine can be attributed to

A. ionic bonds

B. covalent bonds

C. intramolecular bonds

D. London dispersion forces

Use the following information to answer the next question.

An iron ion can have a charge of 3+, and an oxygen ion has a charge of 2−. Iron and oxygen readily combine to form a compound commonly known as rust.

8. Which of the following tables identifies the correct formula and IUPAC name for rust?

A.
Chemical Formula	IUPAC Name
Fe_3O_2	Iron(III) oxide

B.
Chemical Formula	IUPAC Name
Fe_3O_2	Iron(II) oxide

C.
Chemical Formula	IUPAC Name
Fe_2O_3	Iron(III) oxide

D.
Chemical Formula	IUPAC Name
Fe_2O_3	Iron(II) oxide

Use the following information to answer the next question.

The two types of intermolecular forces that are demonstrated by H_2S are _____ *i* _____ and _____ *ii* _____.

9. The information in which of the following tables completes the given statement?

A.
i	*ii*
London forces	hydrogen bonding

B.
i	*ii*
dipole-dipole forces	London forces

C.
i	*ii*
hydrogen bonding	dipole-dipole forces

D.
i	*ii*
dipole-dipole forces	ionic bonds

Use the following information to answer the next question.

Researchers at the University of Alberta are using state-of-the-art technology and innovative experiments to study van der Waals forces in certain substances. These experiments will expand understanding of what happens in a substance at a microscopic level.

10. The subject of their research is **most likely**

   A. interactions between atoms of Ne

   B. bonding of atoms in molecules of O_2

   C. interactions between molecules of H_2O

   D. bonding of atoms in molecules of NaCl

Use the following information to answer the next question.

The boiling point of a molecular compound is a measure of the type and extent of bonding between the molecules of that compound. In an experiment, a chemist heated four unidentified organic samples to their boiling point. The given table provides the data gathered from the experiment.

Sample	Boiling Point (°C)	Identity
1	47.9	
2	−2.5	
3	97.2	
4	−42.1	

Written Response

11. The chemist knows that each of the samples is either $CH_3CH_2CH_3$, CH_3CH_2F, $CH_3CH_2NH_2$, or CH_3CH_2OH. Using the experimental data, determine the identity of each sample and explain your answer.

_____
_____
_____
_____
_____

12. A substance is regarded as a liquid when its intermolecular force of attraction is

   A. negligible

   B. very strong

   C. greater than the intermolecular force of attraction of a solid but less than the intermolecular force of attraction of a gas

   D. less than the intermolecular force of attraction of a solid but greater than the intermolecular force of attraction of a gas

Use the following information to answer the next question.

The amount of energy required to split one mole of water into hydrogen and oxygen is seven times higher than the amount of energy required to vapourize one mole of water at its boiling point.

13. The reason more energy is needed to split water into hydrogen and oxygen gases is that the

   A. intramolecular ionic bonds have to be broken

   B. intramolecular covalent bonds have to be broken

   C. intermolecular hydrogen bonds have to be broken

   D. intermolecular dipole-dipole bonds have to be broken

Use the following information to answer the next question.

```
   H              F             S              
   |              |             ||             
F--C--F       F--C--F          C          H--P--H
   |              |             ||             |
   H              F             S              H

   I              II           III            IV
```

14. Which of the given molecules is polar?

   A. I   **B.** II

   C. III   **D.** IV

15. Which of the following tables indicates the shape of SO_2 and its number of lone pairs?

A.

Shape	Lone pairs
linear	none

B.

Shape	Lone pairs
linear	two

C.

Shape	Lone pairs
v-shaped	one

D.

Shape	Lone pairs
v-shaped	two

ANSWERS AND SOLUTIONS — UNIT TEST

1.	B	5.	B	9.	B	13.	B
2.	C	6.	D	10.	A	14.	A
3.	A	7.	D	11.	WR	15.	C
4.	B	8.	C	12.	D		

1. B

Ammonium (NH_4^+) is a polyatomic ion that has a charge of $+1$. Phosphate (PO_4^{3-}) is a polyatomic ion that has a charge of -3. Three ammonium ions are required (total charge of $+3$) to balance one phosphate ion. To indicate that the 3 refers to both the nitrogen and the hydrogens of the ammonium, the ammonium must be in brackets; therefore, $(NH_4)_3PO_{4(s)}$.

The roman numerals in the formula $NH_4(I)PO_4(III)_{(s)}$ are from the Stock system. They are used in the names of some transition metals, but never in a formula.

2. C

Calcium carbide (CaC_2) consists of calcium (Ca^{2+}) and carbide (C_2^{2-}) ions. CaC_2 is formed by the complete transference of electrons from calcium to carbon forming an ionic bond. These ions are arranged in a crystal lattice and are held together because of the attraction of oppositely charged ions.

3. A

Barium carbonate contains barium (Ba^{2+}) and carbonate (CO_3^{2-}) ions. Therefore, barium carbonate is an ionic compound.

Ionic bonds are the result of intramolecular forces within the compound.

4. B

Electronegativity is the relative attraction of an atom for a shared pair of electrons in chemical bonding. It increases from left to right across the periodic table. The order in which electronegativity increases is alkali metals, alkaline-earth metals, transition metals, and halogens. Of the four groups, the alkali metals have the lowest electronegativity.

5. B

Chloral hydrate is a molecular substance. The molecules are held together by covalent bonds. In addition, virtually all the bonds in chloral hydrate are polar. Polar bonds involve one or more shared electron pairs between two atoms in which the higher electronegativity atom has the greater share. The bonding within chloral hydrate molecules involves unequal sharing of electrons.

6. D

The bonds that hold individual atoms together within an organic molecule like anethole are covalent bonds, which result from the simultaneous attraction of valence electrons between adjacent nuclei. Dipole-dipole interactions occur primarily between two individual molecules that have polar covalent bonds, and complete electron transfers result in the formation of ionic bonds.

7. D

The strength of London dispersion forces, the only intermolecular attractions available to non-polar Cl_2 and I_2 molecules, is proportional to the total numbers of electrons within their molecules. With over three times as many electrons per molecule as chlorine, iodine molecules experience dispersion forces of greater strength than chlorine. This, in part, explains iodine's much higher boiling point than the boiling point of chlorine.

8. C

Fe_2O_3 is the correct chemical formula for the combination of these two ions. The balance of the charges is zero—two iron ions with a $3+$ charge is a total of $6+$, and three oxygen ions with a $2-$ charge is a total of $6-$.

The correct IUPAC name has to show the charge on the positive ion using an indicator in parentheses. Iron ions can commonly have two charges. A $2+$ charge indicates an Fe^{2+} ion, and the IUPAC name would include iron(II). A $3+$ charge would be written as iron(III). In this case, the charge is $3+$, and the correct name for this compound is iron(III) oxide.

9. B

All molecular and atomic chemical entities are subject to London forces, H_2S included. H_2S is a polar covalent compound, so its atoms are also subject to dipole-dipole forces.

The covalent bond also indicates that the valence electrons of the atoms are being shared. In an ionic bond, electrons are lost and gained by constituent atoms, such that they become positive and negative ions that are attracted to one another by virtue of their charge. H_2S does not have any ionic bonds in its structure. Ionic bonds are considered intramolecular and not intermolecular bonds.

H_2S does not contain hydrogen bonds because at least one of the three most electronegative elements —nitrogen, oxygen, and fluorine—must be present for hydrogen bonds to form.

10. A

Neon is a noble gas and is monatomic.
Since Ne atoms do not bond to each other to form molecules, interactions between atoms of neon involve intermolecular or, more particularly, van der Waals forces. Van der Waals forces are types of relatively weak intermolecular attractions.

The bonding of atoms in molecules of O_2 and NaCl concern intramolecular bonds. The attractive force between water molecules is known as hydrogen bonding.

11. WR

Sample	Boiling Point (°C)	Identity
1	47.9	$CH_3CH_2NH_2$
2	−2.5	CH_3CH_2F
3	97.2	CH_3CH_2OH
4	−42.1	$CH_3CH_2CH_3$

Propane, $CH_3CH_2CH_3$, has the fewest intermolecular bonds (only London forces), so it has the lowest boiling point compared with the other compounds. Fluoroethane, CH_3CH_2F, has both London forces and dipole-dipole intermolecular forces; it has the second-lowest boiling point of the given compounds. The boiling point of ethanol, CH_3CH_2OH, exceeds that of ethanamine, $CH_3CH_2NH_2$, because –OH functional groups tend to have stronger hydrogen bonds than N–H functional groups: the –OH bond is more polar. Both ethanol and ethanamine have boiling points higher than fluoroethane because hydrogen bonds are stronger than London forces and dipole-dipole forces.

12. D

The intermolecular force of attraction of a liquid is not as great as it is in a solid, nor as low as it is in a gas. The range of intermolecular attraction lies between that of a solid and that of a gas.

13. B

Changing a liquid molecular substance like water into its elements involves breaking the intramolecular covalent bonds within each molecule to generate oxygen and hydrogen as gases. The intermolecular bonds are broken in both the splitting of water into its elements and the vapourization of water.

14. A

Only molecules that contain polar bonds can be polar, and then only if the bond dipoles do not cancel each other out as a result of molecular geometry. Therefore, to predict a molecule's polarity, the shape of a molecule must be determined using the VSEPR theory.

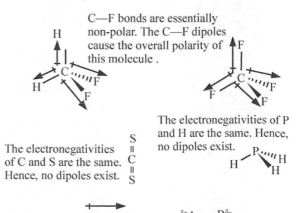

15. C

SO$_2$ has a bent V-shape (it is really a resonance structure). It has two bonding pairs of electrons and one lone pair.

$$O=S\diagdown O$$

NOTES

Gases

STATES OF MATTER: GASES

Table of Correlations				
Outcome	**Practice Questions**	**Unit Test Questions**	**Practice Test 1**	**Practice Test 2**
1 Explain molecular behaviour, using models of the gaseous state of matter				
20-B1.1k *describe and compare the behaviour of real and ideal gases in terms of kinetic molecular theory*	1, 2	1, 2, 3		
20-B1.2k *convert between the Celsius and Kelvin temperature scales*	3, 4	8, 9		1
20-B1.3k *explain the law of combining volumes*	5	10		28
20-B1.4k *illustrate how Boyle's and Charles's laws, individually and combined, are related to the ideal gas law (PV = nRT)*	6, 7, 8, 9, 10, 11, 12	4, 5, 6, 7	5, 6, 10	4, 18

20-B1.1k describe and compare the behaviour of real and ideal gases in terms of kinetic molecular theory

REAL VERSUS IDEAL GASES

An ideal gas is a gas that obeys all the gas laws perfectly:

1. Pressure and volume are inversely proportional to each other.
2. Volume is directly proportional to absolute temperature (measured in kelvins, K).
3. Volume is directly proportional to the number of moles of gas.

An ideal gas will never condense no matter how low the temperature or how high the pressure is. According to kinetic molecular theory (KMT), the following differences exist:

Real Gas	Ideal Gas
Molecules have a distinct size.	Molecules are point masses (have no size).
Forces of attraction between molecules cause them to condense into a liquid if the temperature gets low enough.	Molecules do not have forces of attraction among them, so there is no cause for them to condense into liquid.
Molecules move about randomly, but because of the attraction between them, they do not travel in straight lines—they are influenced by each other.	Molecules of gas move about randomly; only collisions with container walls and other molecules cause them to change direction.
Collisions between molecules are inelastic—kinetic energy is not conserved.	Collisions between molecules are elastic—kinetic energy is conserved.

1. If gas in a closed rigid steel container is heated from 0°C to 300°C, which of the following properties would not change?
   A. pressure
   B. gas density
   C. thermal energy
   D. average kinetic energy

2. Carbon monoxide (CO) is a real gas rather than an ideal gas because
   A. carbon monoxide molecules have measurable molecular volume
   B. carbon monoxide molecules cannot form intermolecular bonds
   C. the product of pressure and volume for one mole is constant at a given temperature
   D. the kinetic energy of carbon monoxide molecules does not increase with temperature

20-B1.2k convert between the Celsius and Kelvin temperature scales

TEMPERATURE SCALE CONVERSIONS

The reference point for the Kelvin scale is absolute zero. This is the point at which there is no longer any thermal energy present in a system. This temperature is zero kelvin (0 K) on the absolute or Kelvin temperature scale. The relation between the temperature in kelvins and degrees Celsius is −273.15°C = 0 K.

There is no degree symbol for Kelvin temperatures.

Celsius (°C)	Subtract 273.15 ⇌ Add 273.15	Kelvin (K)
−273.15		0

Use the following information to answer the next question.

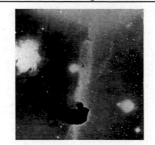

In 1960, scientists discovered interstellar dust clouds containing carbon chains, and they measured the internal temperatures of the clouds to be approximately 42.0 K.

3. When expressed in degrees Celsius, the temperature of these interstellar dust clouds is approximately

    A. − 195°C   **B.** − 231°C

    C. − 279°C   **D.** − 315°C

Use the following information to answer the next question.

Venus is roughly the same size as Earth but is approximately 26% closer to the sun. The atmosphere of Venus experiences a tremendous greenhouse effect due to the high percentage of carbon dioxide (95%), and a surface temperature that is much higher than Earth's.

Venus

Numerical Response

4. What is the equivalent temperature in degrees Celsius if the temperature on the surface of Venus is 750 K? _____ °C (Record your three-digit answer.)

20-B1.3k explain the law of combining volumes

LAW OF COMBINING VOLUMES

The law of combining volumes loosely states that in reactions of gases, volumes of gaseous reactants and products, measured at the same temperature and pressure, will always be related by simple whole number ratios. This law is explained by Avogadro's theory (also known as Avogadro's hypothesis and Avogadro's law). It states that equal volumes of gases at the same temperature and pressure contain equal numbers of particles (atoms or molecules).

Today, it is believed that molecules are made up of a fixed number of atoms. For example, in a water molecule, there are two hydrogen atoms for every one oxygen atom. If water is decomposed by electrolysis, there will be two times as many hydrogen molecules (H_2) as oxygen molecules (O_2), and the volume of hydrogen will be double that of oxygen.

5. Which of the following statements **best** illustrates Avogadro's hypothesis?

   A. $CH_{4(g)}$ and $O_{2(g)}$ react together in a simple ratio.

   B. The rates of diffusion of $CH_{4(g)}$ and $O_{2(g)}$ are inversely proportional to the square root of their densities.

   C. An equal volume of $O_{2(g)}$ and $CH_{4(g)}$ under the same conditions of temperature and pressure contain an equal number of atoms.

   D. An equal volume of $O_{2(g)}$ and $CH_{4(g)}$ under the same conditions of temperature and pressure contain an equal number of molecules.

20-B1.4k illustrate how Boyle's and Charles's laws, individually and combined, are related to the ideal gas law (PV = nRT)

THE GAS LAWS

Some relationships exist between Boyle's law, Charles's law, Avogadro's theory, and the ideal gas law.

BOYLE'S LAW

Boyle's law states that the pressure and volume of a gas at constant temperature in a closed system are inversely proportional to one another. Boyle's law can be stated as $PV = k$, where k is a constant, or $P_1V_1 = P_2V_2$.

For questions dealing with Boyle's law, any pressure unit can be used as long as it is used consistently throughout. Some of the more common pressure units are kilopascals (kPa), atmospheres (atm), and millimetres of mercury (mmHg). For example, standard air pressure is 101.325 kPa. In atmospheres, standard air pressure is 1 atm (760 mm Hg).

Example

A closed cylinder of gas initially at a pressure of 200 kPa has a volume of 45 L.

If the pressure is decreased to 25 kPa and the temperature is constant, what will be the final volume of the gas?

Solution

Step 1

Using Boyle's law $P_1V_1 = P_2V_2$, determine the known values.

$P_1 = 200$ kPa

$V_1 = 45$ L

$P_2 = 25$ kPa

Step 2

Substitute the known values.

$200 \text{ kPa} \times 45 \text{ L} = 25 \text{ kPa} \times V_2$

$200 \text{ kPa} \times \dfrac{45 \text{ L}}{25 \text{ kPa}} = V_2$

$360 \text{ L} = V_2$

The final volume of the gas will be 360 L.

CHARLES'S LAW

Charles's law describes the relationship between the volume and temperature of a gas in a closed system at constant pressure. Charles's law can be stated as $\dfrac{V}{T} = k$, where k is a constant and temperature is in kelvins (K). As with Boyle's law, the changing conditions in a closed system can then be stated as $\dfrac{V_1}{T_1} = \dfrac{V_2}{T_2}$.

Example

A piston contains 30 L of gas at 298 K.

If the temperature is increased to 350 K, what will be the final volume of the gas assuming constant pressure?

Solution

Step 1

Using Charles's law $\dfrac{V_1}{T_1} = \dfrac{V_2}{T_2}$, determine the known values.

$V_1 = 30$ L

$T_1 = 298$ K

$T_2 = 350$ K

Step 2

Substitute the known values.

$$\frac{30 \text{ L}}{298 \text{ K}} = \frac{V_2}{350 \text{ K}}$$

$$\frac{30 \text{ L}}{298 \text{ K}} \times 350 \text{ K} = V_2$$

$$35 \text{ L} = V_2$$

The final volume of the gas will be 35 L.

COMBINED GAS LAW

Since Boyle's law and Charles's law both equal a constant, they can be combined and restated as the combined gas law, $\frac{PV}{T} = k$, where k is a constant. For the changing conditions of a particular sample of gas, then $\frac{P_1V_1}{T_1} = \frac{P_2V_2}{T_2}$, where temperature is in kelvins (K).

Example

A sample of gas in a closed system at 45 psi has a volume of 38 L and a temperature of 30°C. When the temperature is increased to 65°C, the volume of the gas was found to be 50 L.

Calculate the final pressure of the gas.

Solution

Step 1

Using the combined gas law $\frac{P_1V_1}{T_1} = \frac{P_2V_2}{T_2}$, determine the known values.

$P_1 = 45$ psi
$V_1 = 38$ L
$T_1 = 30$°C
$V_2 = 50$ L
$T_2 = 65$°C

Step 2

Convert the temperatures into kelvin by adding 273.15 to the Celsius temperatures.
30°C = 303.15 K
65°C = 338.15 K

Step 3

Substitute the known values into the equation, and solve.

$$\frac{45 \text{ psi} \times 38 \text{ L}}{303.15 \text{ K}} = \frac{P_2 \times 50 \text{ L}}{338.15 \text{ K}}$$

$$\frac{45 \text{ psi} \times 38 \text{ L} \times 338.15 \text{ K}}{303.15 \text{ K} \times 50 \text{ L}} = P_2$$

$$38 \text{ psi} = P_2$$

The final pressure of the gas is 38 psi.

IDEAL GAS LAW

Using Avogadro's theory and the combined gas law, it is possible to derive the ideal gas law. Avogadro's theory states that equal volumes of gases at the same temperature and pressure contain equal numbers of molecules. In other words, the volume of a gas is directly proportional to the number of moles (n) of the gas.

The combined gas law can now be restated as $\frac{PV}{T} = k \cdot n$. Replacing the constant k with the universal gas constant R gives $\frac{PV}{T} = R \cdot n$, which finally becomes the ideal gas law equation $PV = nRT$.

The universal gas law constant is
$$R = 8.314 \frac{\text{kPa} \cdot \text{L}}{\text{mol} \cdot \text{K}}.$$

Example

What pressure is exerted by 25.5 g of $N_{2(g)}$ in a 25.0 L container at 20.0°C?

Solution

Step 1

Find the number of moles of nitrogen. Nitrogen gas is diatomic ($N_{2(g)}$), so the molar mass is 28.02 g/mol, not 14.01 g/mol.

$$n = \frac{m}{M}$$

$$n = \frac{25.5 \text{ g}}{28.02 \text{ g/mol}}$$

$$n = 0.910 \text{ mol}$$

Step 2

Change degrees Celsius to kelvin.
20.0°C + 273.15 = 293.15 K

Step 3

Use the ideal gas law to calculate pressure.

$$PV = nRT$$

$$P = \frac{nRT}{V}$$

$$P = \frac{(0.910 \text{ mol})\left(8.314\frac{\text{L·kPa}}{\text{mol·K}}\right)(293.15 \text{ K})}{25.0 \text{ L}}$$

$$P = 88.7 \text{ kPa}$$

The pressure exerted is 88.7 kPa.

For a closed system question where one variable is changed, it is possible to use either Boyle's law $(PV = k)$ or Charles's law $\left(\frac{V}{T} = k\right)$, but it is easier to use the combined gas law $\left(\frac{PV}{T} = k\right)$. This will cover most situations and may reduce down to Boyle's or Charles's law depending on what, if anything, is constant.

Example

A syringe is filled with air to a volume of 20 cm^3 at an air pressure of 93.5 kPa.

If the end is sealed off and is squeezed down to a new volume of 12 cm^3, what will be the new pressure in the syringe (assuming constant temperature)?

Solution

Since $T_1 = T_2$, the only variables are pressure and volume.

Step 1

Using Boyle's law $P_1V_1 = P_2V_2$, determine the known values.

$P_1 = 93.5 \text{ kPa}$

$V_1 = 20 \text{ cm}^3$

$V_2 = 12 \text{ cm}^3$

Step 2

Substitute the known values, and solve.

$$93.5 \text{ kPa} \times 20 \text{ cm}^3 = P_2 \times 12 \text{ cm}^3$$

$$P_2 = \frac{93.5 \text{ kPa} \times 20 \text{ cm}^3}{12 \text{ cm}^3}$$

$$= 1.6 \times 10^2 \text{ kPa}$$

The new pressure in the syringe will be 1.6×10^2 kPa.

Example

If a sample of gas at 120 kPa occupies a volume of 40.0 L at 20.0°C, how many moles of gas are present?

Solution

Use the ideal gas law.

$$PV = nRT$$

$$n = \frac{PV}{RT}$$

$$= \frac{120 \text{ kPa} \times 40.0 \text{ L}}{8.314\frac{\text{kPa·L}}{\text{mol·K}} \times 293.15 \text{ K}}$$

$$= 1.97 \text{ mol}$$

In the sample of gas, there are 1.97 mol of gas present.

Example

A sample of chlorine gas ($Cl_{2(g)}$) at 120 kPa and 20.0°C occupies a volume of 40.0 L.

What will be the mass of chlorine gas present under these conditions?

Solution

Step 1

Convert the temperature to kelvins.

$20.0°C + 273.15 = 293.15 \text{ K}$

Step 2

Use the ideal gas law equation to obtain the number of moles of chlorine gas.

$$PV = nRT$$

$$n = \frac{PV}{RT}$$

$$= \frac{(120 \text{ kPa})(40.0 \text{ L})}{\left(8.314\frac{\text{L·kPa}}{\text{mol·K}}\right)(293.15 \text{ K})}$$

$$= 1.97 \text{ mol}$$

Step 3

Convert the moles of chlorine gas into mass of chlorine gas. Remember chlorine gas is diatomic, so the molar mass is 70.90 g/mol.

$$n = \frac{m}{M}$$
$$m = nM$$
$$m = 1.97 \text{ mol} \times 70.90 \text{ g/mol}$$
$$m = 140 \text{ g}$$

There will be 140 g of chlorine gas present under the conditions described.

Numerical Response

6. If a 5.00 g sample of gaseous ethyl mercaptan (MW = 62.14 g/mol) is allowed to fill a 3.50 L rigid sealed container, the theoretical pressure, exerted at 25.0°C will be _____ kPa. (Record your three-digit answer.)

Use the following information to answer the next question.

The advent of the steam engine was one of the major breakthroughs of the Industrial Revolution. In a typical steam engine, water vapour forms in the boiler and expands into the cylinder. The vapour then forces the piston up to do work. The steam then condenses and collects in order to repeat the cycle.

Numerical Response

7. Assuming steam is an ideal gas, if a 15.0 L cylinder filled with steam has a temperature of 100 °C and a pressure of 500 kPa, the number of moles of water in the cylinder is _____ mol. (Record your three-digit answer.)

Use the following information to answer the next question.

After the First World War, Fritz Haber perfected the industrial production of large quantities of ammonia from the catalyzed reaction of nitrogen and hydrogen, as represented in the given equation.

$$N_{2(g)} + 3H_{2(g)} \rightarrow 2NH_{3(g)}$$

This is done at high temperatures and pressure.

Numerical Response

8. The volume occupied by 1.00 mol of ammonia in reaction conditions of 400 °C and 250 atm is $a.bc \times 10^{-d}$ L. The values of a, b, c, and d are _____, _____, _____, and _____. (Record your four-digit answer.)

Use the following information to answer the next question.

It is important to maintain an appropriate air pressure in car tires to assure optimum performance and safety. Small pressure gauges available to consumers often measure air pressure in units known as pounds per square inch (psi). Before a long journey, the air in an automobile's tire was measured to have a pressure of 35 psi and a temperature of 10°C. The temperature of the air in the tire at the end of the journey was 56°C.

9. Assuming that there was no change in tire volume, what was the final pressure of the air in the tire?

A. 30 psi B. 35 psi

C. 38 psi D. 41 psi

Use the following information to answer the next question.

Researchers have been able to convert carbon into diamond at 2 000°C and at 1.00×10^5 atm.

10. The IUPAC equivalent of this temperature and pressure in kelvins and kilopascals is

A. 1 727 K and 987 kPa

B. 2 273 K and 987 kPa

C. 1 727 K and 1.01×10^7 kPa

D. 2 273 K and 1.01×10^7 kPa

Use the following information to answer the next question.

Low-density polyethylene (LDPE) is a thermoplastic made from petroleum. It is used for packaging and as protective coating on paper, textiles, and other plastics. In the absence of catalysts, the synthesis of LDPE requires pressures as high as 3.00×10^5 atm and temperatures of 500°C.

11. The approximate pressure in kilopascals and temperature in kelvins required for the synthesis of LDPE are

A. 3.04×10^3 kPa and 227 K

B. 3.04×10^3 kPa and 773 K

C. 3.04×10^7 kPa and 227 K

D. 3.04×10^7 kPa and 773 K

Use the following information to answer the next question.

Researchers at the University of Alberta use a helium liquefier to change helium gas into liquid helium. Liquid helium is used to cool substances to very low temperatures in order to study the properties of superconductivity. The boiling point of helium is approximately 4.0 K.

12. Assuming constant pressure, how many litres of helium gas at 20°C are required make 1.0 L of helium gas at 5.0 K?

A. 4 L   B. 59 L

C. 100 L   D. 1 465 L

ANSWERS AND SOLUTIONS
STATES OF MATTER: GASES

1. B	4. 477	7. 2.42	10. D
2. A	5. D	8. 2211	11. D
3. B	6. 57.0	9. D	12. B

1. B

The gas cannot enter or leave the cylinder, and the cylinder is made of rigid steel and will not expand in volume, so both the volume and the mass of the gas heated within the container remain constant. Therefore, the density of the gas will also remain unchanged. The pressure, thermal energy, and average kinetic energy (temperature) of a gas heated in a container with a fixed volume will all increase.

2. A

Carbon monoxide, like all real gases, consists of molecules with an actual measurable volume and some degree of intermolecular attraction.

An ideal gas is a hypothetical gas consisting of particles with zero volume moving randomly and exerting no force on one another. Although no real gases are completely ideal, the ideal gas concept is useful because most real gases have behaviours that are very close to those predicted for an ideal gas at normal temperatures and pressures.

One mole of an ideal gas at a constant temperature would behave exactly as predicted by Boyle's law: $PV = k$, where P is the pressure, V is the volume, and k is a constant.

Real gases such as CO do not conform to this law exactly, especially at low temperatures and high pressures, where the molecular volume and intermolecular attractive forces result in non-ideal behaviour.

The kinetic energy and the inherent temperature that a gas possesses do not contribute to a gas being defined as ideal or real.

3. B

To convert degrees Celsius to Kelvin, add 273.15. To convert back, subtract 273.15.
$$T = (42.0 - 273.15)$$
$$= -231.15°C$$

Therefore, the temperature of the interstellar dust clouds is approximately − 231°C.

4. 477

To convert degrees Celsius to Kelvin, add 273.15. To convert back, subtract 273.15.
$$T(°C) = (750 - 273.15)°C = 477°C$$

The surface temperature of Venus is 477°C.

5. D

Avogadro's hypothesis states that equal volumes of all gases under the same conditions of temperature and pressure contain an equal number of molecules. In the case of

$CH_{4(g)}$ and $O_{2(g)}$ the number of molecules will be equal but the number of atoms will not be equal.

6. 57.0

The pressure of a known mass of gas at a fixed volume and temperature is calculated using the ideal gas law.
$$P = \frac{nRT}{V}$$

Determine the number of moles of ethyl mercaptan present.
$$n = \frac{m}{M}$$
$$= \frac{5.00 \text{ g}}{62.14 \text{ g/mol}}$$
$$= 0.0805 \text{ g/mol}$$

When converting 25°C to an absolute temperature, simply add 273.15.
$$P = \frac{(0.0805 \text{ mol})(8.314 \text{ L·kPa / mol·K})(298.15 \text{ K})}{(3.50 \text{ L})}$$
$$= 57.0 \text{ kPa}$$

7. 2.42

Since steam is assumed to be an ideal gas, use the ideal gas law,

$n = \dfrac{PV}{RT}$, in which the following applies:

- n is the number of moles
- P is the pressure (500 kPa)
- V is the volume (15.0 L)
- R is the universal gas constant $\left(8.314\dfrac{\text{kPa} \cdot \text{L}}{\text{mol} \cdot \text{K}}\right)$
- T is the temperature $100°C = 373.15$ K

$$n = \dfrac{PV}{RT}$$

$$= \dfrac{500 \text{ kPa} \times 15.0 \text{ L}}{8.314\dfrac{\text{kPa} \cdot \text{L}}{\text{mol} \cdot \text{K}} \times 373.15 \text{ K}}$$

$$= 2.42 \text{ mol}$$

The cylinder contains 2.42 mol of steam under the given conditions.

8. 2211

At these pressures and temperatures, the ideal gas law may not apply, but it is a reasonable approximation.

$PV = nRT$, where P = pressure (kPa), V = volume (L), n = number of mols (mol), $R = 8.314 \dfrac{\text{L} \cdot \text{kPa}}{\text{mol} \cdot \text{K}}$, and T = temperature (K)

To find volume, we must isolate for V.

First convert units given into ideal gas law units.

- Temperature: $400°C + 273.15 = 673.15$ K
- Pressure:

$$250 \text{ atm} \times \dfrac{101.325\text{kPa}}{\text{atm}} = 25\,331.25 \text{ kPa}$$

$$V = \dfrac{nRT}{P}$$

$$= \dfrac{1 \text{ mol} \times 8.314 \dfrac{\text{L} \cdot \text{kPa}}{\text{mol} \cdot \text{K}} \times 673.15 \text{ K}}{25\,331.25 \text{ kPa}}$$

$$= 0.221 \text{ L or } 2.21 \times 10^{-1} \text{ L}$$

Therefore, the values of a, b, c, or d are 2, 2, 1, and 1, respectively.

9. D

Gay-Lussac's law describes the relationship between the pressure and temperature of a fixed quantity of gas. This relationship can be summarized by the equation $\dfrac{P_1}{T_1} = \dfrac{P_2}{T_2}$.

Step 1

Define the variables of the equation $\dfrac{P_1}{T_1} = \dfrac{P_2}{T_2}$.

P_1 and P_2 represent the initial and final pressures, respectively, of a fixed quantity of gas. T_1 and T_2 represent the initial and final temperatures in Kelvin, respectively, of the same fixed quantity of gas.

Step 2

Convert the temperatures in degrees Celsius to Kelvin.

$T_1 = 10°C + 273.15 = 283.15$ K
$T_2 = 56°C + 273.15 = 329.15$ K

Step 3

Determine the final pressure of air in the tire.

$$\dfrac{P_1}{T_1} = \dfrac{P_2}{T_2}$$

$$P_2 = \dfrac{P_1 \times T_2}{T_1}$$

$$= \dfrac{35 \text{ psi} \times 329 \text{ K}}{283 \text{ K}}$$

$$= 41 \text{ psi}$$

When using any of the gas law equations, except for the ideal gas equation, it is possible to use a wide variety of pressure and volume units with the condition that all units are consistent. Temperatures, however, must always be in Kelvin.

10. D

Add 273.15 to convert °C to K.
$T(\text{K}) = (2\,000°C + 273.15) \text{ K}$
$= 2\,273.15$ K

The conversion of pressure is as follows:
1 atm = 101.325 kPa = 760 mm Hg.

Thus,

$$P_1(\text{kPa}) = 1.00 \times 10^5 \text{ atm} \times \dfrac{101.325 \text{ kPa}}{1 \text{ atm}}$$

$$= 1.01 \times 10^7 \text{ kPa}$$

11. D

Remember, add 273.15 to convert degrees Celsius to Kelvin.
$T = 500°C + 273.15\text{K} = 773.15$ K

The conversion of pressure is
1 atm = 101.325 kPa = 760 mm Hg.

$$P = 3.00 \times 10^5 \text{ atm} \times \dfrac{101.325 \text{ kPa}}{1 \text{ atm}}$$

$$= 3.04 \times 10^7 \text{ kPa}$$

12. B

At constant pressure, Charles's law can be used to find the volume of helium gas required:

$$\frac{V_1}{T_1} = \frac{V_2}{T_2}$$

Step 1

Identify the variables.

Let V_1 be the initial volume before cooling and T_1 be the initial temperature before cooling. Convert T_1 from degrees Celsius to Kelvin.

$$T_1 = 20°C$$
$$= (20 + 273.15) \text{ K}$$
$$= 293.15 \text{ K}$$

Let V_2 be the final volume after cooling and T_2 be the final temperature after cooling.

Step 2

Reorder Charles's law to solve for the initial volume, V_1.

$$\frac{V_1}{T_1} = \frac{V_2}{T_2}$$

$$V_1 = \frac{T_1}{T_2} V_2$$

Step 3

Substitute the known values and solve for the initial volume.

$$V_1 = \frac{T_1}{T_2} V_2$$

$$= \frac{293.15 \text{ K}}{5.0 \text{ K}} \times 1.0 \text{ L}$$

$$= 59 \text{ L}$$

To the nearest litre, the volume of 20°C helium gas needed to make 1.0 L of helium gas at 5.0 K is 59 L.

UNIT TEST — STATES OF MATTER: GASES

Use the following information to answer the next question.

Neon glows when subjected to a high voltage at low pressure and is often used in lights to make signs. It is an extremely inert (unreactive) gas, but it is not an ideal gas.

1. Which of the following statements describes how neon and all other real gases differ from an ideal gas?

    A. Real gas molecules do not exert pressure on the walls of a container, but ideal gas molecules do.

    B. Real gas molecules are attracted to each other, but ideal gas molecules are not.

    C. Real gas molecules are not in constant motion, but ideal gas molecules are.

    D. Real gas molecules have no volume, but ideal gas molecules do.

2. The ideal gas law holds **best** at which conditions?

    A. High pressure and high temperature

    B. Low pressure and high temperature

    C. High pressure and low temperature

    D. Low pressure and low temperature

Use the following information to answer the next question.

The molar volume of a gas at STP is 22.4 L/mol. The ideal gas law is a useful equation when predicting the molar volume of a gas at near ambient conditions. At higher pressures, the ideal gas law fails to predict gas molar volumes accurately.

3. Which of the following statements **best** explains why the ideal gas law cannot predict molar volumes accurately at high pressures?

    A. At high pressures, gas particles are closer to each other and the interactions between them are no longer negligible.

    B. At high pressures, the gas particles may no longer be assumed to be volumeless.

    C. As pressure goes to very high values, the temperature drops dramatically.

    D. As pressure increases, measuring instruments become less accurate.

Use the following information to answer the next question.

The ideal gas law equation is $PV = nRT$. This equation can be rearranged to show that pressure and volume are inversely proportional for a fixed amount of gas at a constant temperature.

$$V = \frac{nRT}{P} \text{ or } V \propto \frac{1}{P}$$

4. The law that summarizes the relationship between the volume and pressure of a fixed quantity of gas at constant temperature is

    A. Boyle's law   B. Henry's law

    C. Charles's law   D. Avogadro's law

Use the following information to answer the next question.

 The student council rented a tank of compressed helium gas to inflate balloons with helium for their high school's graduation ceremony. The full tank held a volume of 25.3 L of $He_{(g)}$ at a pressure of 1 793 kPa at room temperature. (Assume the temperature within the tank is the same as the room.)

Numerical Response

5. If the balloons were filled in a room where the pressure was 1.00 atm, the total volume of $He_{(g)}$ that could be released from the tank would be _____ L. (Record your three-digit answer.)

Numerical Response

6. By what factor is the final volume of an ideal gas changed if the pressure is doubled and the temperature is increased by a factor of 6? (Record your one-digit answer.)

Numerical Response

7. If the temperature inside a 16 L freezer is −20.0 °C and the pressure is 1.00 atm, the amount of air in the freezer is $a.b \times 10^{-c}$ mol. The values of a, b, and c are _____, _____, and _____. Assume air behaves as an ideal gas. (Record your three-digit answer.)

Numerical Response

8. If a sealed container of nitrogen has a temperature of 295.0 K, the temperature of the gas in degrees Celsius is _____. (Record your three-digit answer.)

Use the following information to answer the next question.

Celsius, Fahrenheit, and Kelvin are three different scales used to measure temperature. For example, absolute 0 is the theoretical temperature where all molecular motion stops. This temperature can be represented as 0 K or − 273.15°C.

9. What is 50°C in kelvins?
    A. 323.15 K   B. 268.15 K
    C. 223.15 K   D. − 223.15 K

Use the following information to answer the next question.

1.0 L of $O_{2(g)}$ has the same number of molecules as 1.0 L of $H_{2(g)}$ at the same temperature and pressure.

10. The statement can be explained by
    A. Boyle's law   B. Charles' law
    C. Avogadro's law   D. Ideal Gas law

ANSWERS AND SOLUTIONS — UNIT TEST

1. B	4. A	7. 771	10. C
2. B	5. 423	8. 21.9	
3. A	6. 3	9. A	

1. B

Except at low temperatures and high pressures, real gases behave like ideal gases. The given table lists the differences between ideal gas molecules and real gas molecules.

Ideal Gas Molecules	Real Gas Molecules
experience no intermolecular forces	can and do experience intermolecular forces
always travel in straight lines	curve when they pass by other molecules
collide elastically (no energy lost)	collide inelastically (energy lost as heat when molecules "stick")
obey all the gas laws perfectly	do not obey the gas laws well at high pressures
have mass but zero volume	have mass and a finite volume
do not condense at any temperature	condense at low temperatures

2. B

The ideal gas equation is based on the assumptions that molecules of a gas have no intermolecular force of attraction and that the volume occupied by the molecules of that gas is negligible. When the pressure is high and the temperature is low, the volume of the gas decreases. Therefore, the molecules come closer to each other and experience an intermolecular force of attraction. Under the given conditions, the volume occupied by gaseous molecules cannot be completely ignored. Therefore, the ideal gas law gives the best results at low pressure and at a temperature that is relatively high compared with the boiling point of a gas.

In all conditions that have either high pressure, low temperature, or both, molecules come closer to each other. Therefore, the intermolecular forces of attraction between the molecules, as well as the volume occupied by gaseous molecules, cannot be neglected. The ideal gas law will not give the best results under these conditions.

The conditions of low pressure and high temperature result in an increase in the volume of the gas. The individual gas molecules will have greater separation and a reduction in intermolecular forces between molecules.

3. A

At very high pressures, gas particles are very close to each other. As a result, the interactions between gas particles become more significant. At very high pressures, the assumption of neglecting interactions between gas particles the ideal gas law makes is no longer valid. This is the main cause why the ideal gas law cannot predict molar volumes accurately at these pressures.

4. A

The ideal gas law combines three laws:

1. Boyle's law: $V \propto \dfrac{1}{P}$

2. Charles's law: $V \propto T$

3. Avogadro's law: $V \propto n$

This combination gives $V \propto \dfrac{nT}{P}$.

The constant of proportionality R, when included, gives $V = \dfrac{nRT}{P}$, which is usually written as $PV = nRT$.

The value R is known as the universal gas constant of which the most commonly used values are

$8.3145 \dfrac{L \cdot kPa}{mol \cdot K}$ or $0.082\,06 \dfrac{L \cdot atm}{mol \cdot K}$.

The gas law that summarizes the relationship between gas volume and pressure is Boyle's law, which states that the volume of a fixed quantity of gas at a constant temperature is inversely proportional to its pressure.

5. 423

Assume that the temperature within the tank is the same as the temperature of the room it is in (SATP). Therefore, Boyle's law can be used to find the final volume of the gas. Boyle's law states that at a constant temperature, the pressure of a fixed amount of gas is inversely proportional to its volume.

$P_1 V_1 = P_2 V_2$

Step 1

Define the known terms in the equation for Boyle's law.

- P_1 = Pressure of helium gas in the tank = 1 793 kPa
- V_1 = Volume of helium gas in the tank = 25.3 L
- P_2 = Pressure of helium gas in the room = 1.00 atm = 101.325 kPa
- V_2 = Volume of helium gas in the room

Step 2

Solve the equation for V_2.

$$P_2V_2 = P_1V_1$$
$$V_2 = \frac{P_1V_1}{P_2}$$
$$= \frac{1\ 793\ \text{kPa} \times 25.3\ \text{L}}{101.325\ \text{kPa}}$$
$$= 448\ \text{L}$$

Step 3

The helium gas in the tank occupies 448 L at room pressure. However, once the pressures outside and inside the tank become equal, the tank will stop releasing helium gas. As a result, 25.3 L of helium gas will remain in the tank. Subtract this volume from the total volume of helium gas.

448 L – 25.3 L = 422.7 L = 423 L

Therefore, 423 L of helium gas will be released from the tank.

6. 3

Doubling the pressure would decrease the volume of the gas by half, but increasing the temperature of the gas by a factor of 6 would increase the volume by that factor as well. So the overall increase would be by a factor of 3.

$P_2 = 2 \times P_1$ and $T_2 = 6 \times T_1$

Also:

$$\frac{P_1V_1}{T_1} = \frac{P_2V_2}{T_2}$$

Substituting gives:

$$\frac{P_1V_1}{T_1} = \frac{2P_1V_2}{6T_1}$$
$$3V_1 = V_2$$

Under the described conditions the final volume will be three times the initial volume.

7. 771

The ideal gas law equation can be used to solve this problem.

Step 1

Convert pressure into kPa and temperature into K.

1 atm = 101.325 kPa

K = –20°C + 273.15
= 253.15 K

Step 2

Rearrange the ideal gas law to solve for n and solve the equation.

$$PV = nRT$$
$$n = \frac{PV}{RT}$$
$$= \frac{101.325\ \text{kPa} \times 16\ \text{L}}{\dfrac{8.314\ \text{L} \cdot \text{kPa}}{\text{K} \cdot \text{mol}} \times 253.15\ \text{K}}$$
$$= \frac{1\ 621.2\ \text{kPa} \cdot \text{L}}{2\ 104.8\ \text{L} \cdot \text{kPa}}$$
$$= 0.77\ \text{mol or } 7.71 \times 10^{-1}\ \text{mol}$$

Therefore, the values of a, b, and c are 7, 7, and 1, respectively.

8. 21.9

0 K = –273.15°C
°C = –273.15°C + 295.0
= 21.9°C

Therefore 295.0 K is equal to 21.9°C.

9. A

There is a partial variation between degreesCelsius (C) and kelvin (K).

0°C = 273.15 K
0 K = –273.15°C

For every change in degreesCelsius, there is an equal change in kelvin.

0°C = 273.15 K
50°C = 273.15 + 50
= 323.15 K

Therefore, 50°C is equal to 323.15 K.

10. C

The law of combining volumes states that equal volumes of gases at the same temperature and pressure contain the same number of molecules (or particles). This law is explained by Avogadro's Law (also known as Avogadro's hypothesis or theory).

Matter as Solutions: Acids and Bases

MATTER AS SOLUTIONS: ACIDS AND BASES

Table of Correlations

Outcome		Practice Questions	Unit Test Questions	Practice Test 1	Practice Test 2
1	Investigate solutions, describing their physical and chemical properties				
20-C1.1k	*recall the categories of pure substances and mixtures and explain the nature of homogeneous mixtures*	1			
20-C1.2k	*provide examples from living and nonliving systems that illustrate how dissolving substances in water is often a prerequisite for chemical change*	2			
20-C1.3k	*explain dissolving as an endothermic or exothermic process with respect to the breaking and forming of bonds*	3	1		
20-C1.4k	*differentiate between electrolytes and nonelectrolytes*	4, 5, 6	2		
20-C1.5k	*express concentration in various ways; i.e., moles per litre of solution, percent by mass and parts per million*	7, 8, 9, 10, 11, 12		7a, 7b, 7c, 22	13a, 13b, 14, 15
20-C1.6k	*calculate, from empirical data, the concentration of solutions in moles per litre of solution and determine mass or volume from such concentrations*	13, 14	3a, 3b, 3c	9a, 9b	
20-C1.7k	*calculate the concentrations and/or volumes of diluted solutions and the quantities of a solution and water to use when diluting*	15	4		
20-C1.8k	*use data and ionization/dissociation equations to calculate the concentration of ions in a solution*	16, 17	5		
20-C1.9k	*define solubility and identify related factors; i.e., temperature, pressure and miscibility*	18, 19, 20, 21, 22, 23		26	
20-C1.10k	*explain a saturated solution in terms of equilibrium; i.e., equal rates of dissolving and crystallization*	24, 25, 26, 27a, 27b	6	11	3
20-C1.11k	*describe the procedures and calculations required for preparing and diluting solutions.*	28, 29	7		16
2	Describe acidic and basic solutions qualitatively and quantitatively				
20-C2.1k	*recall International Union of Pure and Applied Chemistry (IUPAC) nomenclature of acids and bases*	30			
20-C2.2k	*recall the empirical definitions of acidic, basic and neutral solutions determined by using indicators, pH and electrical conductivity*	31, 32, 33, 34, 35, 36	8, 9, 10		12
20-C2.3k	*calculate $H_3O^+_{(aq)}$ and $OH^-_{(aq)}$ concentrations and the pH and pOH of acidic and basic solutions based on logarithmic expressions; i.e., $pH = -log\left[H_3O^+\right]$ and $pOH = -log\left[OH^-\right]$*	37, 38, 39	11, 12, 13	12, 19	27
20-C2.4k	*use appropriate SI units to communicate the concentration of solutions and express pH and concentration answers to the correct number of significant digits; i.e., use the number of decimal places in the pH to determine the number of significant digits of the concentration*	40			
20-C2.5k	*compare magnitude changes in pH and pOH with changes in concentration for acids and bases*	41, 42, 43			
20-C2.6k	*Explain how the use of indicators, pH paper or pH meters can be used to measure $H_3O^+_{(aq)}$*	44, 45, 46	14	21	
20-C2.7k	*define Arrhenius (modified) acids as substances that produce $H_3O^+_{(aq)}$ in aqueous solutions and recognize that the definition is limited*	47, 48, 49, 50, 51	15		

20-C2.8k	define Arrhenius (modified) bases as substances that produce OH⁻$_{(aq)}$ in aqueous solutions and recognize that the definition is limited		16		
20-C2.9k	define neutralization as a reaction between hydronium and hydroxide ions	52, 53	17	23	
20-C2.10k	differentiate, qualitatively, between strong and weak acids and between strong and weak bases on the basis of ionization and dissociation; i.e., pH, reaction rate and electrical conductivity	54, 55, 56, 57, 58, 59	18, 19	18	5, 17a, 17b, 30
20-C2.11k	identify monoprotic and polyprotic acids and bases and compare their ionization/dissociation.	60, 61	20		

20-C1.1k recall the categories of pure substances and mixtures and explain the nature of homogeneous mixtures

SOLUTION TERMINOLOGY

Pure substances are substances that cannot be separated by physical processes. Elements and compounds are pure substances.

Any mixture of pure substances that is the same throughout is a solution or **homogeneous mixture**. This includes solutions of solids dissolved in liquids, liquids dissolved in liquids, gases dissolved in liquids, gases dissolved in gases, and even solids dissolved in solids.

Heterogeneous mixtures are not the same throughout. Often, you can see different components of the mixture within a heterogeneous mixture.

1. When sugar dissolves in water, the type of mixture formed is classified as

    A. heterogeneous **B.** homogeneous

    C. heterolytic   **D.** homolytic

20-C1.2k provide examples from living and nonliving systems that illustrate how dissolving substances in water is often a prerequisite for chemical change

SOLUTIONS AND CHEMICAL CHANGE

Many ionic compounds in solution react readily with each other in double-replacement reactions to form precipitates. If the same compounds are simply placed side by side, in the solid state in a beaker, nothing happens. Even if you stir them together, nothing happens. In some cases, if you grind a pair of ionic substances together with a mortar and pestle, you may see evidence of a reaction, but it does not readily happen as it does in solution.

Ionic compounds are most soluble in polar solvents. Polar solvents bind more strongly to the individual solute ions overcoming the intramolecular bonding of the solute ions. The solute is effectively pulled apart into individual ions increasing the surface area between reacting particles. These solute ions are now free to react with other ions in the solution. In the case of double-replacement reactions the evidence of a chemical change is seen with the formation of precipitates.

More heterogeneous systems such as the human digestive system are much more complex. Saliva is needed to moisten the food before chemical digestion can begin. Enzymes in the saliva begin the digestion process in the mouth beginning the breakdown of sugars and complex starches. Chewing breaks down large pieces increasing the surface area of the food permitting faster reaction time with the enzymes.

2. When two aqueous solutions are mixed, and two of the solutes can make an insoluble substance, what is **most likely** to form?

    A. a precipitate

    B. conjugate acid

    C. conjugate base

    D. a nonpolar substance

20-C1.3k explain dissolving as an endothermic or exothermic process with respect to the breaking and forming of bonds

REACTION THERMODYNAMICS

Breaking bonds is always endothermic, while forming bonds is always exothermic.

The dissolution of a solute in water can be considered as a two-step process:

1. When an ionic solid dissolves in water, energy is first required (absorbed) to break apart the individual ions that formed the crystal lattice within that ionic solid. This is an endothermic process because energy is being added to the system.
2. Energy is then released from the system as the individual ions now are surrounded by water molecules. (This surrounding of the individual ions by water is called hydrolysis or solvation). This new attraction between the individual ions and the water molecules releases energy. This release of energy to the surroundings is an exothermic process.

The overall dissolving process can be represented by this equation:
final system energy = energy to break apart solute +energy to bind solute ions to water

If the energy absorbed to break apart the solute is less than the energy released as the ions bind to water, then the overall process of dissolving is exothermic. If the energy absorbed is greater than the energy released, then the overall process of dissolving will be endothermic.

Since intermolecular bonds between water molecules also break, this is also endothermic. For example, a sample of ammonium chloride was dissolved in water. Careful measurements found that the energy to break apart the ammonium chloride was 345 kJ while 283 kJ are released as the ions are hydrolyzed. Representing the energy absorbed by the system as +345 kJ and that released to the surroundings as −283 kJ, then the overall energy change is 345 kJ + (−283 kJ) = +62 kJ. Since the overall energy change is positive (more energy absorbed than released), the dissolving of ammonium chloride is endothermic.

When a molecular solute dissolves, the process is similar except that there is no separation into ions. Molecules are separated from other molecules as intermolecular bonds are broken. This is endothermic. Energy is released as new intermolecular bonds form between water and the solute molecules.

Whether or not the dissolving process for a substance will be endothermic or exothermic must be tested individually as there is no way to predict what will occur.

Use the following information to answer the next question.

Household bleach can be a dangerous substance. A significant hazard may result from the mixing of bleach with ammonia cleansers. The initial product of this reaction is the toxic gas chloramine $(NH_2Cl_{(g)})$. Its formation is represented by this equation:
$$NH_{3(aq)} + ClO^-_{(aq)} \rightarrow NH_2Cl_{(g)} + OH^-_{(aq)}$$

3. If this reaction is exothermic, then the **best** definition of this process is that the energy
   A. needed to break bonds in the reactants is greater than the energy released from bond formation in the products
   B. released in breaking bonds in the reactants is greater than the energy needed in bond formation in the products
   C. needed to break bonds in the reactants is less than the energy released from bond formation in the products
   D. released in breaking bonds in the reactants is less than the energy needed in bond formation in the products

20-C1.4k differentiate between electrolytes and nonelectrolytes

ELECTROLYTIC SOLUTIONS

Electrolytes are substances that conduct electricity when dissolved in water. Electricity flows from one location to another through a conductive substance that acts as a medium through which electrons can travel. Metals are often good conductors because they tend to form lattice structures that make it very easy for electrons to bounce from atom to atom in a current. The conductivity of solutions is determined by the concentration of ions dissolved in the solution. The more positively and negatively charged particles there are in the solution, the greater the ease with which electrons can move from one point of electric potential to another.

Non-electrolytes do not conduct electricity when dissolved in water, since they are electrically neutral molecules. Ionic compounds are electrolytes. Most molecular compounds are non-electrolytes, but there are a few exceptions, such as organic acids and some dissolved gases, like carbon dioxide in an aqueous solution.

Use the following information to answer the next question.

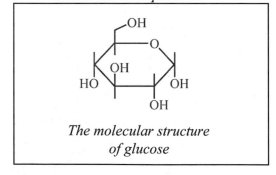

The molecular structure of glucose

4. Glucose, $C_6H_{12}O_6$, is **best** described as
   A. an insoluble electrolyte
   B. a water-soluble electrolyte
   C. an insoluble non-electrolyte
   D. a water-soluble non-electrolyte

Use the following information to answer the next question.

Phosphoric acid $(H_3PO_{4(aq)})$ is a component of many soft drinks. Phosphoric acid is a molecular substance that only partially ionizes in aqueous solution because it is a weak acid.

5. An aqueous solution of phosphoric acid can **best** be described as a
   A. strong electrolyte and a good conductor of electricity
   B. strong electrolyte and a poor conductor of electricity
   C. weak electrolyte and a good conductor of electricity
   D. weak electrolyte and a poor conductor of electricity

Use the following information to answer the next question.

$NaOCl_{(aq)}$ is a _____*i*_____ conductor of electricity in water because it is a(n) _____*ii*_____.

6. This statement is completed by the information in which of the following tables?

A.

i	*ii*
poor	non-electrolyte

B.

i	*ii*
good	non-electrolyte

C.

i	*ii*
poor	electrolyte

D.

i	*ii*
good	electrolyte

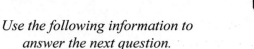

MOLARITY OR MOLAR CONCENTRATION

Molarity or molar concentration is the number of moles of solute per liter of solution.

Molar concentration can then be calculated as

$c = \dfrac{n}{V}$, in which c represents molarity, n represents number of moles, and V represents volume in liters.

Molarity, or molar concentration, is the most common way of expressing the concentration of a solution in the study of chemistry. However, solution concentrations are so commonly used in other situations that other units are often used to express them.

Note: All of these units, including molarity, are with respect to the volume of a solution, not the volume of a solvent. This will affect how solutions are prepared.

- **Parts per million (ppm):** The number of milligrams (mg) of solute per litre (L) of solution, or the number of grams (g) of solute per 1 000 litres of solution. The unit ppm is used for very small concentrations, such as the concentrations of pollutants in a river.
- **Mass-volume percentage (% w/v):** The number of grams of solute per 100 mL of solution. Consumer hydrogen peroxide is 3% w/v.
- **Mass percentage:** The number of grams of solute per 100 g of solution.
- **Volume-volume percentage (% v/v):** The number of millilitres of solute per 100 mL of solution. The concentration of propan-2-ol (isopropyl alcohol) in rubbing alcohol is 70% v/v.

Use the following information to answer the next question.

In a 125 mL cup of strong English Breakfast tea, there is approximately 110 mg of caffeine.

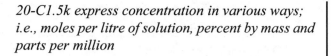

7. The concentration of caffeine in this tea, expressed as a percentage of weight for this volume, is

   A. 0.0880%   **B.** 0.138%

   C. 1.14%   **D.** 1.25%

8. By mass, the percentage composition of potassium permanganate is

         24.74% K
   A. 34.76% Mn
         40.50% O

         49.24% K
   B. 30.61% Mn
         20.15% O

         35.53% K
   C. 49.93% Mn
         14.54% O

         30.69% K
   D. 19.08% Mn
         50.23% O

Use the following information to answer the next question.

Although not used that widely in chemistry anymore, the concentrations of some products present as part of a mixture are still reported as a percentage by mass (often referred to as percentage by weight). The percentage by mass of a solute in a mixture is determined by the expression $\dfrac{\text{mass of solute (g)}}{\text{mass of mixture (g)}} \times 100\%$. The unit used for percentage by mass is % (m/m), or more commonly,% (w/w).

9. If 3.00 kg of liquid CO_2 dissolves 43.2 g of grease in the presence of 200 g of surfactant, the percentage by mass of grease in this mixture is
   A. 0.133% (w/w)   B. 1.33% (w/w)
   C. 2.12% (w/w)   D. 6.17% (w/w)

Use the following information to answer the next question.

Hydrogen peroxide, $H_2O_{2(aq)}$, is a strong oxidizing agent that was once used as rocket fuel. Today, it is commercially sold as a disinfectant. Hydrogen peroxide decomposes over time to form water and oxygen.

10. A 1.0 L bottle of liquid labeled "30% hydrogen peroxide by weight" is analyzed three years after production, and its concentration is determined to be 6.0 mol/L. Assuming the density of the entire solution is 1.10 g/mL, the percentage, by mass, of hydrogen peroxide in the bottle is
    A. 0.016%   B. 0.018%
    C. 16%   D. 18%

Use the following information to answer the next question.

Despite the key role it plays in the transport of oxygen in blood, the abundance of iron in the body is only 0.004% by weight.

11. Based on this information, the mass of iron in a person with a body mass of 68 kg is
    A. 3 g   B. 0.3 kg
    C. 0.06 g   D. 0.0006 kg

12. What mass of pure, solid sodium chloride is required to make 200 mL of a 2.3% w/v solution?
    A. 1.2 g   B. 2.3 g
    C. 4.6 g   D. 9.2 g

20-C1.6k calculate, from empirical data, the concentration of solutions in moles per litre of solution and determine mass or volume from such concentrations

CALCULATING CONCENTRATIONS

FINDING MOLAR CONCENTRATION GIVEN MOLES AND VOLUME

The concentration of a solution is an expression of the amount of substance per unit of volume. Molar concentration is usually expressed in mol/L, or M. When you are given the number of moles and a volume, divide the former by the latter, then resolve the units to get the correct answer.

Example

What is the molarity, or molar concentration, of a solution containing 1.50 mol of solute in 500 mL of solution?

Solution

The formula for determining molar concentration is $c = \dfrac{n}{V}$, where c is molar concentration (measured in moles per litre), n is the number of moles of solute, and V is the volume of solution.

The solution is the same whether you use a formula or do a unit analysis.

$$c = \dfrac{n}{V}$$
$$= \dfrac{1.50 \text{ mol}}{0.500 \text{ L}}$$
$$= 3.00 \text{ mol/L}$$

FINDING MASS GIVEN VOLUME AND MOLAR CONCENTRATION

This stoichiometric operation requires two steps, rather than just a formula application. In this case, the number of moles of a substance can be determined by multiplying the volume by the molar concentration. To find the amount of mass that corresponds to the number of moles of a substance, the amount in moles must be multiplied by the molar mass of the substance to yield a mass, usually expressed in grams.

Example

What is the mass of solid necessary to prepare 500 mL of 0.100 mol/L $Na_2CO_{3(aq)}$?

Solution

Step 1
Calculate the number of moles of sodium carbonate in the given solution

$$c = \dfrac{n}{V} \rightarrow n = c \times V$$
$$n = 0.100 \text{ mol/L} \times 0.500 \text{ L}$$
$$n = 0.0500 \text{ mol}$$

Step 2
Calculate the mass of sodium carbonate from the moles given

$$n = \dfrac{m}{M} \rightarrow m = n \times M$$
$$m = 0.0500 \text{ mol} \times 105.99 \text{ g/mol}$$
$$m = 5.30 \text{ g}$$

FINDING VOLUME GIVEN MASS AND MOLAR CONCENTRATION

This is another two-step process of computation. The mass must be converted to moles first, then divided by the molar concentration in order to find volume.

Example

If a student has 4.50 g of $KOH_{(s)}$, what volume of 0.250 mol/L $KOH_{(aq)}$ solution can he or she prepare?

Solution

Step 1
Because the question indicates the molarity of the final solution, it is necessary to convert the given mass of KOH into moles.

$$n = \dfrac{m}{M}$$
$$n = \dfrac{4.50 \text{ g}}{56.11 \text{ g/mol}}$$
$$= 0.0802 \text{ mol}$$

Step 2
Use the moles of KOH and the desired final concentration of the solution to calculate the final volume.

$$c = \dfrac{n}{V}$$
$$V = \dfrac{n}{c}$$
$$= \dfrac{0.0802 \text{ mol}}{0.250 \text{ mol/L}}$$
$$= 0.321 \text{ L or } 321 \text{ mL}$$

Use the following information to answer the next question.

Although aqueous formaldehyde ($HCHO_{(aq)}$), or formalin, is gradually being phased out for health reasons, concentrated solutions of it are sometimes used to preserve biological specimens.

Numerical Response

13. To three digits, the mass of formaldehyde in 3.00 L of 11.6 mol/L formalin is _____ kg. (Record your three-digit answer.)

Use the following information to answer the next question.

In an experiment, a student weighed 0.40 g of $NaOH_{(s)}$ in a flask and then added water to make a 50 mL solution.

14. What is the molarity of the prepared $NaOH_{(aq)}$ solution?

   A. 0.10 M   **B.** 0.20 M

   C. 0.30 M   **D.** 0.50 M

20-C1.7k calculate the concentrations and/or volumes of diluted solutions and the quantities of a solution and water to use when diluting

DILUTION

When an aqueous solution is diluted, the number of moles of solute does not change. Water is added to make the concentration smaller.

The concentration of a solution is related to the number of moles of solute and the volume of the solution by the formula $c = \dfrac{n}{V}$. Rearranging to solve for the number of moles gives $n = cV$. Since the number of moles of solute does not change, $n_i = n_f$, where n_i stands for the initial number of moles of solute and n_f stands for the final number of moles of solute. Substituting gives $c_iV_i = c_fV_f$.

Example

If concentrated $HCl_{(aq)}$ has a concentration of 11.6 mol/L, what volume of concentrated $HCl_{(aq)}$ will be required to prepare 500 mL of 0.100 mol/L diluted $HCl_{(aq)}$?

Solution

Step 1
To keep all of the volume units the same, convert 500 mL to litres.

$$500 \text{ mL} \times \frac{1.00 \text{ L}}{1\,000 \text{ mL}} = 0.500 \text{ L}$$

Step 2
Calculate the volume of concentrated $HCl_{(aq)}$.

$$c_iV_i = c_fV_f$$
$$V_i = \frac{c_fV_f}{c_i}$$
$$= \frac{0.100 \text{ mol/L} \times 0.500 \text{ L}}{11.6 \text{ mol/L}}$$
$$= 4.31 \times 10^{-3} \text{ L}$$
$$= 4.31 \text{ mL}$$

Example

If 200 mL of water are added to 500 mL of a 0.250 mol/L $CuSO_{4(aq)}$ solution, what is the new concentration?

Solution

Step 1
Calculate the total volume of the final solution.

$$500 \text{ mL} + 200 \text{ mL} = 700 \text{ mL}$$

Step 2
Keep all the volume units the same by converting to litres.

$$0.500 \text{ L} + 0.200 \text{ L} = 0.700 \text{ L}$$

Step 3
Calculate the new concentration.

$$c_iV_i = c_fV_f$$
$$c_f = \frac{c_iV_i}{V_f}$$
$$= \frac{0.250 \text{ mol/L} \times 0.500 \text{ L}}{0.700 \text{ L}}$$
$$= 0.179 \text{ mol/L}$$

Use the following information to answer the next question.

> A solution of a given concentration is diluted by adding a volume of water.

15. Which of the following sets of information is **not** sufficient for calculating the concentration of the solution after dilution?
    A. The number of moles of solute before dilution and the volume of water added
    B. The number of moles of solute before dilution and the volume of solution after dilution
    C. The volume of solution after dilution, the concentration of solution before dilution, and the volume of water added
    D. The volume of solution before dilution, the concentration of solution before dilution, and the volume of water added

20-C1.8k use data and ionization/dissociation equations to calculate the concentration of ions in a solution

CONCENTRATION OF IONIC SOLUTIONS

Ionic compounds are created by the mutual attraction of positively charged ions (cations) and negatively charged ions (anions). Structurally, ions differ from atoms as a result of having more or fewer electrons than protons in the orbitals about the nucleus. Having more electrons than protons results in a negative net ionic charge, and a positive net ionic charge is generated when protons outnumber electrons.

Ionic compounds are electrically conductive as a result of these electron imbalances. Positive and negative ionic charges cause ions to form structures through which a current of electrons can flow across all of the positive and negative pathways between ions, particularly when in a molten state or in solution.

DISSOCIATION

When ionic compounds dissolve in water, they dissociate, or separate, into the individual ions already present in the original compound. In a dissociation equation, the solute is indicated as solid on the left side and the ions are indicated as aqueous ions on the right side. The equation shows what happens to the solid solute as it dissolves.

These two equations show the dissociation of sodium chloride and aluminum sulfate.

$$NaCl_{(s)} \rightarrow Na^+_{(aq)} + Cl^-_{(aq)}$$
$$Al_2(SO_4)_{3(s)} \rightarrow 2Al^{3+}_{(aq)} + 3SO_4^{2-}_{(aq)}$$

IONIZATION

The term ionization has another definition when applied to aqueous ions in solution. When a molecular solute ionizes in solution the molecular solute reacts with the solvent, in this case water, to form ions not present in the original molecule. Strong acids will ionize completely; weak acids will ionize only partially.

The ionization of hydrochloric acid in water producing chloride ions and hydrogen ions that react with water to form $H_3O^+_{(aq)}$ is illustrated by the equation

$$HCl_{(aq)} + H_2O_{(l)} \rightarrow H_3O^+_{(aq)} + Cl^-_{(aq)}$$

The ionization of ammonia gas in water producing ammonium ions and hydroxide ions is illustrated by the equation

$$NH_{3(g)} + H_2O_{(l)} \rightleftarrows NH_4^+_{(aq)} + OH^-_{(aq)}$$

In both examples, none of the ions formed existed in the original solute (HCl or NH_3).

CONCENTRATION OF IONS

Dissociation and ionization equations can be used to calculate the concentration of individual ions in solution. When looking at the balanced equation, the coefficients of the ions produced in solution will give you ratios of concentration relative to the concentration of the solute.

Example

What are the concentrations of $Na^+_{(aq)}$ and $PO^{3-}_{4(aq)}$ in a solution of $0.500\ mol/L\ Na_3PO_{4(aq)}$?

Solution

Step 1

Write a balanced dissociation equation.

$Na_3PO_{4(s)} \rightarrow 3Na^+_{(aq)} + PO^{3-}_{4(aq)}$

The balanced equation indicates that there will be three times as many moles of sodium ions as there are of solid sodium phosphate.

Step 2

Find the concentrations of $Na^+_{(aq)}$ and $PO^{3-}_{4(aq)}$.

Use square brackets to represent concentration.

$\left[Na^+_{(aq)}\right] = \dfrac{3}{1} \times 0.500\ mol/L$

$\qquad = 1.50\ mol/L$

$\left[PO^{3-}_{4(aq)}\right] = \dfrac{1}{1} \times 0.500\ mol/L$

$\qquad\quad = 0.500\ mol/L$

---

16. If the concentration of a lead(II) nitrate solution is 0.16 mol/L, what is the concentration of nitrate ions in the solution?

    A. 0.040 mol/L   **B.** 0.16 mol/L

    C. 0.32 mol/L   **D.** 0.64 mol/L

Use the following information to answer the next question.

An aqueous solution of lead(IV) nitrate has a nitrate ion concentration of 0.32 mol/L.

17. What is the concentration of the lead(IV) nitrate solution?

    A. 0.080 mol/L   **B.** 0.16 mol/L

    C. 0.32 mol/L   **D.** 1.3 mol/L

20-C1.9k define solubility and identify related factors; i.e., temperature, pressure and miscibility

SOLUBILITY

Solubility is the amount or mass of a solute that dissolves in a given volume of solvent. It is often recorded in units of g/100 mL. A large solubility means the substance dissolves well.

Solubility is affected by temperature:

- Solubility of solids in liquids increases with temperature.
- Solubility of liquids in liquids is unaffected by temperature.
- Solubility of gases in liquids decreases with temperature.

Solubility is also affected by pressure:

- Solubility of gases in liquids increases as the pressure of the particular gas above the solution increases.
- Solubility of solids in liquids is unaffected by changes in pressure.

Substances that mix completely with each other in all proportions are said to be **miscible**. Miscibility depends on the nature of the solute and solvent. In general, polar solutes dissolve well in polar solvents; non-polar solutes dissolve well in non-polar solvents. You can recall this with the phrase "Like dissolves like."

18. Which of the following compounds has the greatest solubility in water?

    A. $MgSO_4$ **B.** $CaSO_4$

    C. $BaSO_4$ **D.** $PbSO_4$

19. Which of the following pairs of compounds have high solubility in water?

    A. $AgCl, PbCl_2$

    B. $CaCO_3, FeCO_3$

    C. $BaSO_4, CaSO_4$

    D. $AgNO_3, Pb(NO_3)_2$

20. Which solid substance (precipitate) is formed when dilute HCl is added to a solution of $AgNO_3$?

    A. $AgCl$ **B.** Ag_2Cl

    C. $AgCl_2$ **D.** Ag_2Cl_2

21. Which solid substance is formed when $Pb(NO_3)_2$ and NaCl solutions are mixed together?

A. $PbCl_2$ **B.** $PbCl$

C. $NaNO_3$ **D.** Na_2NO_3

Use the following information to answer the next question.

Oven cleaner is a concentrated aqueous solution of sodium hydroxide.

22. The solute in oven cleaner is the

A. $Na^+_{(aq)}$ **B.** $OH^-_{(aq)}$

C. $H_2O_{(l)}$ **D.** $NaOH_{(s)}$

Written Response

23. Describe the factors that affect the solubility of gases, liquids, and solids in liquid solutions.

_____

_____

_____

_____

_____

_____

20-C1.10k explain a saturated solution in terms of equilibrium; i.e., equal rates of dissolving and crystallization

SATURATED SOLUTIONS

A saturated solution is a solution that contains both dissolved solute and undissolved solute. It is a solution said to have its maximum concentration of solute dissolved at a given temperature. Dissolving has not stopped in the solution because the solution is at equilibrium, which means the rate of dissolving is equal to the rate of crystallizing (the reverse of dissolving). The same amount of solute remains undissolved as solute continues to dissolve and crystallize out at the same rate. This is one type of **dynamic equilibrium**.

24. The solubility of a solute is **best** determined from which type of solution?

A. A saturated solution

B. Any solution at 25°C

C. An unsaturated solution

D. A supersaturated solution

Use the following information to answer the next question.

A sample of NaCl formed mainly of radioactive isotope sodium-22 and non-radioactive chlorine atoms has been synthesized. The sample is present in aqueous solution as shown in the figure. The radioactive behaviour of the saturated solution is studied by extracting a sample of solid NaCl and testing for radioactivity. The same test is applied to a sample of the clear liquid present.

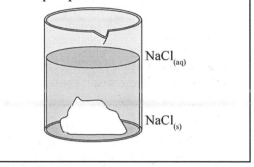

25. Which of the following statements correctly describes the most likely outcome of a test for radioactivity on the various components of the solution?

A. Only the $NaCl_{(s)}$ will register as radioactive.

B. Only the clear liquid will register as radioactive.

C. Both the $NaCl_{(s)}$ and the clear liquid will register as radioactive.

D. Neither the $NaCl_{(s)}$ nor the clear liquid will register as radioactive.

Use the following information to answer the next question.

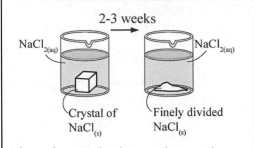

After a few weeks, large salt crystals immersed in a saturated salt solution tend to break up into many small powdery crystals.

26. The **best** explanation for the given observation is that

    A. the solid salt particles from the crystal continually dissolve, while the dissolved salt particles in the saturated solution continually precipitate at the same rate

    B. some of the water molecules and ions in the saturated solution constantly bombard the crystal, causing it to break down easily

    C. the water pressure above the salt crystals forces the Na^+ and Cl^- ions apart, causing the crystal to break up

    D. some of the salt in the crystal dissolves, making the salt crystal structurally so weak that it breaks apart

Use the following information to answer the next multipart question.

27. A saturated solution is one that has reached a point of maximum concentration. A saturation point of a substance is determined by temperature and can be observed when that substance begins to spontaneously precipitate upon further addition of the substance to the solution.

    Written Response

    a) Describe how to prepare a saturated solution at room temperature.

    ———————————————

    ———————————————

    b) Write a chemical equation to represent the equilibrium that exists in a saturated solution of $Be_3(PO_4)_2$.

    ———————————————

    ———————————————

20-C1.11k describe the procedures and calculations required for preparing and diluting solutions.

DILUTION IN THE LABORATORY

In order to prepare a solution of a specific concentration, the important variables are volume, mass, molar mass, and molarity.

Since concentration is simply expressed as the number of moles of solute divided by the net volume of the solution, a solution of any given concentration can be created by adding the correct amount of solute to an amount of solvent that is less than the net volume required and then diluting the solution with solvent until the desired volume is achieved.

CREATING SOLUTIONS GIVEN CONCENTRATION AND VOLUME

To demonstrate how to prepare a solution of a given concentration and volume, the following steps describe the proper method for preparing 100.0 mL of a 0.100 mol/L solution of ammonium chloride, $NH_4Cl_{(aq)}$.

1. Calculate the mass of $NH_4Cl_{(s)}$ required.

$$\frac{0.100 \text{ mol}}{1 \text{ L}} \times 0.1000 \text{ L} \times \frac{53.50 \text{ g}}{1 \text{ mol}}$$
$$= 0.535 \text{ g}$$

2. Using a balance, measure 0.535 g of $NH_4Cl_{(s)}$ into a 100 mL beaker.

3. Add approximately 40 mL of water to the $NH_4Cl_{(s)}$ in the beaker, and stir to dissolve. If the solute will not completely dissolve, you may add as much as 60 mL of water, but try not to exceed this limit. Do not remove the stirring rod from the beaker.

4. Pour the $NH_4Cl_{(aq)}$ solution through a funnel into a 100.0 mL volumetric flask. Use distilled water to rinse the beaker, stirring rod, and funnel, and pour the rinse water into the volumetric flask.

5. Add additional distilled water to make the water's meniscus sit on the 100.0 mL mark on the volumetric flask.

6. Stopper the flask, and invert to mix.

REDUCING CONCENTRATION

When reducing the known concentration of a solution by increasing the volume of solvent, the relationship between the initial and the final concentrations can be expressed by a direct equation. Since the number of moles of solute does not change, the initial concentration multiplied by the initial volume is equal to the final concentration multiplied by the final volume.

The following steps describe the proper method for diluting a commercially available 0.500 mol/L $Fe(NO_3)_{3(aq)}$ solution in order to prepare 100 mL of a 0.150 mol/L solution for an experiment.

1. Use the following formula to find the volume of concentrated solution needed to produce the desired volume of the diluted solution required. $c_i \times V_i = c_f \times V_f$, where c_i and V_i are the initial concentration and volume and c_f and V_f are the final concentration and volume.

$$c_i \times V_i = c_f \times V_f$$
$$0.500 \text{ mol/L} \times V_i = 0.150 \text{ mol/L} \times 100 \text{ mL}$$
$$V_i = \frac{0.150 \text{ mol/L} \times 100 \text{ mL}}{0.500 \text{ mol/L}}$$
$$V_i = 30.0 \text{ mL}$$

2. Rinse a graduated pipette (or a 30.0 mL pipette) with a small volume of the solution to be diluted, and then discard this solution. Fill the pipette using a rubber bulb beyond the 30.0 mL mark, and record this initial volume. Dispense 30 mL of this solution into a clean 100.0 mL volumetric flask.

3. Carefully add more distilled water into the volumetric flask until the water's meniscus reaches the 100.0 mL mark on the neck of the volumetric flask.

4. Stopper the flask, and invert to mix.

When diluting a concentrated acid, begin by adding slightly less than the required volume of water into the flask and then adding the concentrated acid. Once the acid is partially diluted, the remaining water can be added. It is also a good idea, particularly with sulfuric acid, not to invert and mix the solution until it has cooled down. You should notice that the solution volume will decrease as the temperature drops. Volumetric flasks are calibrated at 20°C.

Several students want to prepare 100 mL of 0.040 mol/L $HCl_{(aq)}$ from a standard 0.200 mol/L $HCl_{(aq)}$ solution.

28. Which of the following techniques would be the **best** way for them to accomplish this preparation?
    A. Use a pipette to transfer 20.0 mL of 0.200 mol/L $HCl_{(aq)}$ to a 100 mL volumetric flask. Then, top up the solution volume to the calibration mark with distilled water. Finally, put a stopper in the flask, and invert the flask several times to mix the contents thoroughly.

    B. Use a burette to transfer 40.0 mL of 0.200 mol/L $HCl_{(aq)}$ to a 100 mL Erlenmeyer flask. Then, top up the solution volume to the 100 mL line with distilled water. Finally, put a stopper in the flask, and invert the flask several times to mix the contents thoroughly.

    C. Measure 20 mL of 0.200 mol/L $HCl_{(aq)}$ in a graduated cylinder. Pour this into exactly 80 mL of distilled water in a beaker, and swirl the mixture to thoroughly mix the solution.

    D. Measure 40 mL of 0.200 mol/L $HCl_{(aq)}$ in a 100 mL volumetric cylinder. Then, top up the solution volume to 100 mL with distilled water.

29. Which of the following techniques is the **best** way to prepare 250 mL of 1.00 mol/L aqueous silver nitrate solution?
    A. Obtain 42.5 g of solid silver nitrate in a 100 mL beaker, dissolve it in about 80 mL of water, transfer the solution to a 250 mL volumetric flask with rinsing, and fill with water to the 250 mL graduation mark on the neck of the volumetric flask.

    B. Obtain 42.5 g of solid silver nitrate in a beaker, dissolve in a minimal volume of water, pipette into a 250 mL volumetric flask, and fill with water to the graduation mark on the neck of the flask.

    C. Obtain 42.5 g of solid silver nitrate in a 300 mL Erlenmeyer flask, dissolve in a minimal volume of water, and add water to the 250 mL graduation mark of the Erlenmeyer flask.

    D. Pour water into a 250 mL volumetric flask to just below the 250 mL graduation mark on the neck of the flask, add 42.5 g of solid silver nitrate, and swirl.

20-C2.1k recall International Union of Pure and Applied Chemistry (IUPAC) nomenclature of acids and bases

NAMING ACIDS AND BASES

Acids and bases are named using specific guidelines. The theoretical ionic name and traditional name for acids are the two that are used most frequently. The naming of bases follows the rules studied for naming ionic compounds.

NAMING ACIDS

There are two methods of naming acids.

To name acids traditionally, follow these steps:

1. Name the substance as if it were an ionic compound.
2. Using the suffix of the theoretical ionic name, determine the acid name.

This table shows how the suffixes of the theoretical ionic name determine the acid name.

Theoretical Ionic Name	Traditional Acid Name
hydrogen _____ -ide hydrogen chloride	hydro_____ -ic acid hydrochloric acid
hydrogen _____ -ate hydrogen sulfate	_____ -ic acid sulfuric acid
hydrogen _____ -ite hydrogen nitrite	_____ -ous acid nitrous acid

Recent IUPAC updates have allowed acids to be named simply by putting the word *aqueous* in front of the theoretical ionic name.

Example

Formula	Theoretical Ionic Name	IUPAC Name	Traditional Name
$HClO_4$	hydrogen perchlorate	aqueous hydrogen perchlorate	perchloric acid
$HClO_3$	hydrogen chlorate	aqueous hydrogen chlorate	chloric acid
$HClO_2$	hydrogen chlorite	aqueous hydrogen chlorite	chlorous acid
$HClO$	hydrogen hypochlorite	aqueous hydrogen hypochlorite	hypochlorous acid
HCl	hydrogen chloride	aqueous hydrogen chloride	hydrochloric acid

NAMING BASES

Bases are usually present in the form of alkali-metal or alkaline-earth hydroxides. They are named in a very similar way to ionic compounds. The names of the ions present in the base are stated, starting with the positive ion. In the case of alkaline bases, the name of the metal precedes the name of the hydroxide ion or ions that are ionically bonded to it.

Example

The following list includes the chemical formulas and names of some alkaline bases:

- $Ca(OH)_2$—calcium hydroxide
- $NaOH$—sodium hydroxide
- KOH—potassium hydroxide

In the case of a basic substance formed between hydroxide ions and transition metals, there are two systems of naming substances. The first, older system is not in common use anymore and is probably only found in older textbooks and industrial handbooks. In this system, transition metals named using Latin words use different suffixes to indicate their oxidation state (positive ionic charge). Since these specific metals only have two oxidation states each, the state with the lower number is given an *-ous* suffix, while the state with the greater number is given an *-ic* suffix. Transition metal elements that were incompatible with the suffix system were named in the same way as covalent compounds, using Greek prefixes to indicate the number of ions in the ionic compound.

The modern IUPAC system of naming and designating alkali-base compounds involves using a roman numeral in parentheses to represent the oxidation number of the metal, thus showing directly how many valence electrons each metal ion has shed. The system is also known as the Stock nomenclature system, after German chemist Alfred Stock. The system has undergone many changes since it was first developed, but it is still referred to using the original developer's name.

The following table shows the formulas and names of several transition-metal hydroxides, using both the older, classical system and the IUPAC or Stock system of nomenclature.

| Metal | Formula | Hydroxide | |
| | | Name | |
		Classic	IUPAC
Copper	CuOH	Cuprous hydrox-ide	Copper(I) hydroxide
	$Cu(OH)_2$	Cupric hydroxide	Copper(II) hydroxide
Iron	$Fe(OH)_2$	Ferrous hydroxide	Iron(II) hydroxide
	$Fe(OH)_3$	Ferric hydroxide	Iron(III) hydroxide
Ruthenium	$Ru(OH)_3$	Ruthenium trihydroxide	Ruthenium(III) hydroxide
	$Ru(OH)_4$	Ruthenium tetra-hydroxide	Ruthenium(IV) hydroxide
Tin	$Sn(OH)_2$	Stannous hydrox-ide	Tin(II) hydroxide
	$Sn(OH)_4$	Stannic hydroxide	Tin(IV) hydroxide

Non-alkaline bases do not donate hydroxide ions to a solution, but still lower the hydronium (H_3O^+) or hydrogen ion (H^+) concentration, increasing the pH. Sodium carbonate, for example, increases the pH of a solution using the following dissociation equation:

$$Na_2CO_{3(s)} + H_2O_{(l)} \rightarrow 2Na^+_{(aq)} + HCO^-_{3(aq)} + OH^-_{(aq)}$$

In the given instance, hydroxide ions are not donated, but hydrogen ions are taken from water molecules.

There are other bases with more complex names (e.g., organic bases). For example, ammonia (NH_3) is also a base.

30. The International Union of Pure and Applied Chemistry (IUPAC) has developed a specific set of rules for naming acids. The traditional and IUPAC names for the acid with the formula $HCN_{(aq)}$ are given in which of the following tables?

A.

Traditional Name	IUPAC Name
Cyanic acid	Aqueous hydrogen cyanide

B.

Traditional Name	IUPAC Name
Aqueous hydrogen cyanide	Cyanic acid

C.

Traditional Name	IUPAC Name
Aqueous hydrogen cyanide	Hydrocyanic acid

D.

Traditional Name	IUPAC Name
Hydrocyanic acid	Aqueous hydrogen cyanide

20-C2.2k recall the empirical definitions of acidic, basic and neutral solutions determined by using indicators, pH and electrical conductivity

EMPIRICAL DEFINITIONS OF ACIDS AND BASES

Empirical definitions are based on observations.

Acids, by observation, turn litmus paper red (or leave it red), and are electrolytes (although some are weak electrolytes). They also react with active metals (e.g., Zn and Mg) to produce hydrogen gas, and neutralize bases. Acids taste sour, but this should never be tested with laboratory acids.

Bases, by observation, turn litmus paper blue (or leave it blue), and are electrolytes (although some are weak electrolytes). They also feel slippery, and neutralize acids. Bases taste bitter, but this should never be tested with laboratory bases.

Neutral solutions have no effect on litmus paper, and may be electrolytes or non-electrolytes. They have no characteristic taste or feel.

31. Which of the following statements is true for an acidic solution at 30°C?

A. $\left[H_3O^+_{(aq)}\right] > \left[OH^-_{(aq)}\right]$

B. $\left[OH^-_{(aq)}\right] > \left[H_3O^+_{(aq)}\right]$

C. $\left[H^+_{(aq)}\right] < \left[OH^-_{(aq)}\right]$

D. $\left[OH^-_{(aq)}\right] = \left[H_3O^+_{(aq)}\right]$

32. Which of the following statements about a basic aqueous solution is **true**?

A. $\left[H_3O^+_{(aq)}\right] = 1.00 \times 10^{-7} mol/L$

B. $\left[H_3O^+_{(aq)}\right] = \left[OH^-_{(aq)}\right]$

C. $\left[H_3O^+_{(aq)}\right] > \left[OH^-_{(aq)}\right]$

D. $\left[H_3O^+_{(aq)}\right] < \left[OH^-_{(aq)}\right]$

33. Which of the following statements about a basic solution at 25°C is **true**?

A. $\left[OH^-_{(aq)}\right] = \left[H_3O^+_{(aq)}\right]$

B. $\left[OH^-_{(aq)}\right] > \left[H_3O^+_{(aq)}\right]$

C. pOH > 7.0

D. pH < 7.0

34. The type of solution is **incorrectly** matched with its ion concentration in which of the following tables?

A.
Solution	Ion Concentration
Strongly acidic	$\left[H_3O^+_{(aq)}\right] > \left[OH^-_{(aq)}\right]$

B.
Solution	Ion Concentration
Alkaline	$\left[H_3O^+_{(aq)}\right] < \left[OH^-_{(aq)}\right]$

C.
Solution	Ion Concentration
Strongly basic	$\left[H_3O^+_{(aq)}\right] < \left[OH^-_{(aq)}\right]$

D.
Solution	Ion Concentration
Slightly acidic	$\left[H_3O^+_{(aq)}\right] < \left[OH^-_{(aq)}\right]$

$\log 100 = 2$
$\log 10 = 1$
$\log 1 = 0$
$\log \frac{1}{10} = -1$
$\log \frac{1}{100} = -2$
$\log \frac{1}{1000} = -3$

35. Dish washing solutions feel slippery. A typical pH value for a dish washing solution might be

A. 2.0   **B.** 6.0

C. 10.0   **D.** 14.0

36. Solution X turns phenolphthalein (an indicator) solution pink when a few drops are added to it. What does solution X represent?

A. A base

B. An acid

C. A neutral salt

D. A non-electrolyte

20-C2.3k calculate $H_3O^+_{(aq)}$ and $OH^-_{(aq)}$ concentrations and the pH and pOH of acidic and basic solutions based on logarithmic expressions; i.e., pH = $-log\left[H_3O^+\right]$ and pOH = $-log\left[OH^-\right]$

THE pH SCALE

Not all acids and bases are equally strong. The tendency of an acid or a base to dissociate and affect the concentration of hydronium ions in solution is measured using a 14-point scale called the pH scale. The pH scale has no units because it is a negative logarithmic scale. A strong acid that completely dissociates to a concentration of 1.0 mol/L will yield a pH value of 0, which can be seen in the following computation:

$$pH = -\log\left[H_3O^+\right]$$
$$-pH = \log(1.0 \, mol/L)$$
$$-pH = \log(10^0 \, mol/L)$$
$$pH = 0$$

A pH measurement of 7 indicates a neutral compound at 25°C. A neutral compound is neither an acid nor a base. Distilled water is an example of a neutral compound.

A pH measurement of less than 7 indicates an acid. The lower the pH, the stronger the concentration of $H_3O^+_{(aq)}$ and therefore the more acidic the solution. For example, tomato juice has a pH of approximately 4, whereas stomach acid has a pH of 1. The solution of stomach acid is more acidic than the tomato juice.

A pH measurement greater than 7 indicates a basic compound. The higher the pH, the stronger the concentration of $OH^-_{(aq)}$ and the more basic the solution. A solution of baking soda, $NaHCO_{3(aq)}$, has a pH of around 9, whereas a solution of oven cleaner has a pH around 13. The oven cleaner solution is more basic (caustic) than the baking soda solution.

Use the following information to answer the next question.

The K_w at 25° C is 10^{-14}.

37. Which of the following equations is used to calculate $\left[OH^-_{(aq)}\right]$?

A. $\left[OH^-_{(aq)}\right] = \dfrac{1.00 \times 10^{-14}}{[H_3O^+_{(aq)}]}$

B. $\left[OH^-_{(aq)}\right] = \sqrt{\dfrac{1.00 \times 10^{-14}}{[H^+_{(aq)}]}}$

C. $\left[OH^-_{(aq)}\right] = 1.00 \times 10^{-14} + \left[H^+_{(aq)}\right]$

D. $\left[OH^-_{(aq)}\right] = 1.00 \times 10^{-14} \times \left[H_3O^+_{(aq)}\right]$

38. What is the value of $\left[OH^-_{(aq)}\right]$ if $\left[H_3O^+_{(aq)}\right]$ is 1.75×10^{-4} mol/L in a solution at 25°C?

A. 5.01×10^{-10} mol/L

B. 5.71×10^{-11} mol/L

C. 6.01×10^{-10} mol/L

D. 6.71×10^{-11} mol/L

Use the following information to answer the next question.

A tablet of acetylsalicylic acid (ASA) is dissolved in a glass of water and the pH of the solution is measured.

39. If the pH of the ASA solution is 3.0, then the $\left[H_3O^+_{(aq)}\right]$ is

A. 1×10^{-3} mol/L

B. 1×10^{-4} mol/L

C. 3 mol/L

D. 4 mol/L

20-C2.4k use appropriate SI units to communicate the concentration of solutions and express pH and concentration answers to the correct number of significant digits; i.e., use the number of decimal places in the pH to determine the number of significant digits of the concentration

CALCULATING pH AND pOH FROM $\left[H_3O^+_{(aq)}\right]$ AND $\left[OH^-_{(aq)}\right]$

The pH scale was developed as a convenient method for expressing the concentration of $\left[H^+_{(aq)}\right]$ in aqueous solutions. Generally, the range of the pH scale is 0 to 14. Since water dissociates into both hydronium and hydroxide ions, an analogous pOH scale expresses the $\left[OH^-_{(aq)}\right]$ in aqueous solutions. The relationships between the concentrations of both ions, pH, and pOH are shown in the given formulas, in which $\left[H^+_{(aq)}\right]$ and $\left[OH^-_{(aq)}\right]$ are in moles per litre (mol/L).

$$pH = -\log\left[H^+_{(aq)}\right]$$
$$\left[H^+_{(aq)}\right] = 10^{-pH}$$
$$pOH = -\log\left[OH^-_{(aq)}\right]$$
$$\left[OH^-_{(aq)}\right] = 10^{-pOH}$$
$$pH + pOH = 14.000 \text{ at } 25°C$$
$$\left[H^+\right] \times \left[OH^-\right] = 1.00 \times 10^{-14}(mol/L)^2$$

In these formulas, $\left[H^+_{(aq)}\right]$ can be replaced by $\left[H_3O^+_{(aq)}\right]$.

Example

What is the $\left[H_3O^+_{(aq)}\right]$ of 0.015 mol/L $NaOH_{(aq)}$?

Solution

$$\left[OH^-_{(aq)}\right] = \left[NaOH_{(aq)}\right] = 0.015 \text{ mol/L}$$
$$1.00 \times 10^{-14} = \left[H_3O^+_{(aq)}\right] \times \left[OH^-_{(aq)}\right]$$
$$\left[H_3O^+_{(aq)}\right] = \frac{1.00 \times 10^{-14}}{\left[OH^-_{(aq)}\right]}$$
$$\left[H_3O^+_{(aq)}\right] = \frac{1.00 \times 10^{-14}}{0.015 \text{ mol/L}}$$
$$= 6.7 \times 10^{-13} \text{ mol/L}$$

Example

What are the $\left[H_3O^+_{(aq)}\right]$ and $\left[OH^-_{(aq)}\right]$ in a solution of pH = 2.57?

Solution

Because the pH has two decimal places, the concentrations will have two significant digits.
$$\left[H_3O^+_{(aq)}\right] \text{ or } \left[H^+_{(aq)}\right] = 10^{-pH} = 10^{-2.57}$$
$$= 2.7 \times 10^{-3} \text{ mol/L}$$
$$\left[OH^-_{(aq)}\right] = \frac{1.00 \times 10^{-14}}{2.7 \times 10^{-3}}$$
$$= 3.7 \times 10^{-12} \text{ mol/L}$$

Sometimes, pH values can fall outside the range of 0 to 14. For example, a $\left[H^+_{(aq)}\right]$ of 1.0 M has a pH of 0. This concentration is considered to be very strongly acidic. At concentrations greater than this, the pH is negative.

Example

What is the pH of 1.6 mol/L $HCl_{(aq)}$?

Solution

$$pH = -\log\left[H^+_{(aq)}\right], \text{ and } \left[H^+_{(aq)}\right] = \left[HCl_{(aq)}\right].$$
$$pH = -\log(1.6 \text{ mol/L}) = -0.20$$

A 1.6 mol/L $HCl_{(aq)}$ solution has a pH of –0.20. The number of decimal places in a pH equals the number of significant digits in the $\left[H^+_{(aq)}\right]$. The same rule applies to pOH.

Strongly basic solutions can also have pH values greater than 14.

Example

What is the pH of 2.0 mol/L $NaOH_{(aq)}$?

Solution

$$pH = -\log\left[OH^-_{(aq)}\right] \text{ and } \left[OH^-_{(aq)}\right] = \left[NaOH_{(aq)}\right]$$
$$pOH = -\log(2.0 \text{ mo/L}) = -0.30$$
$$pH = 14.00 - pOH$$
$$= 14.00 - (-0.30) = 14.30$$

A 2.0 mol/L $NaOH_{(aq)}$ solution has a pH of 14.30.

> A 22.0 g sample of pure $NaOH_{(s)}$ is dissolved in water to make 10.0 L of solution.

40. What is the pH of the solution?

    A. 13.700   **B.** 12.740

    C. 11.300   **D.** 10.600

20-C2.5k compare magnitude changes in pH and pOH with changes in concentration for acids and bases

LOGARITHMS, pH, AND pOH

pH and pOH are numbers on logarithmic scales.

As pH increases, $[H_3O^+_{(aq)}]$ (or $[H^+_{(aq)}]$) decreases. An increase of 1 pH unit is a decrease in $[H_3O^+_{(aq)}]$ (or $[H^+_{(aq)}]$) by a factor of 10.

An increase of 2 pH units is a decrease in $[H_3O^+_{(aq)}]$ (or $[H^+_{(aq)}]$) by a factor of 100, and an increase of 3 pH units is a decrease in $[H_3O^+_{(aq)}]$ (or $[H^+_{(aq)}]$) by a factor of 1 000.

The same pattern applies to pOH; as pOH increases, $[OH^-_{(aq)}]$ decreases.

> Solution A has a pH of 2 and a concentration of $H^+_{(aq)}$ of C_A. Solution B has a pH of 12 and a concentration of $H^+_{(aq)}$ of C_B.

41. The relationship between the concentrations of solutions A and B can be expressed as

    A. $C_A = 6C_B$

    B. $C_A = 10C_B$

    C. $C_A = 2^6 C_B$

    D. $C_A = 10^{10} C_B$

42. If the pH of a solution rises from 10 to 11, the H^+ concentration has

    A. increased by 10%

    B. decreased by 10%

    C. increased by a factor of 10

    D. decreased by a factor of 10

43. When the pH of an acid solution increases,

    A. the number of H^+ and OH^- ions increase

    B. the number of H^+ and OH^- ions decrease

    C. the number of H^+ ions decreases and the number of OH^- ions increases

    D. the number of H^+ ions increases and the number of OH^- ions decreases

20-C2.6k Explain how the use of indicators, pH paper or pH meters can be used to measure H_3O^+ (aq)

pH INDICATORS

Acid-base indicators change color around a transition pH. Different indicators have different transition pH values. Bromothymol blue changes from yellow to blue as the pH of a solution goes from below 6.0 to above 7.6.

If bromothymol blue is yellow in a solution, you know that the pH is less than or equal to 6.0. If it is blue, you know that the pH is greater than or equal to 7.6.

Using several indicators allows you to narrow down the pH to a small range.

Example

Separate samples of a certain solution turn methyl orange yellow, thymolphthalein blue, and indigo carmine blue.

After consulting an indicator table, state a range for the possible values of the pH of this solution.

Solution

After consulting an indicator table, you can draw the following conclusions about this solution:

- Methyl orange test conclusion: $pH \geq 4.4$
- Thymolphthalein test conclusion: $pH \geq 10.6$
- Indigo carmine test conclusion: $pH \leq 11.4$

Thus, the pH of the solution is between 10.6 and 11.4.

pH paper is filter paper soaked in a solution of multiple indicators and then allowed to dry. pH paper will have different shades depending on how the test solution affects the indicators in the paper.

A pH meter determines pH electrochemically. The pH probe contains an internal solution that, together with the outside solution and the necessary attachments, produces a voltage that is affected by the solution pH.

Use the following information to answer the next question.

> Acidic solutions turn blue litmus paper ____*i*____ and ____*ii*____ with magnesium.

44. This statement in completed by the information in which of the following tables?

A.

i	ii
red	react

B.

i	ii
blue	react

C.

i	ii
red	do not react

D.

i	ii
blue	do not react

Use the following information to answer the next question.

> A few drops of phenolphthalein are added to two beakers. The first beaker contains an acid, and the second beaker contains a base.

45. The resultant colours of the two solutions are listed correctly in which of the following tables?

A.

Colour in Acid Solution	Colour in Base Solution
Colourless	Pink

B.

Colour in Acid Solution	Colour in Base Solution
Pink	Colourless

C.

Colour in Acid Solution	Colour in Base Solution
Red	Blue

D.

Colour in Acid Solution	Colour in Base Solution
Blue	Red

Use the following information to answer the next question.

> Three samples of a 5.7 pH solution are tested with different indicators: bromothymol blue, bromocresol green, and blue litmus paper.

46. Which of the following tables indicates the colour each indicator shows in the solution?

A.

Bromothymol Blue	Bromocresol Green	Blue Litmus Paper
blue	blue	blue

B.

Bromothymol Blue	Bromocresol Green	Blue Litmus Paper
blue	green	blue

C.

Bromothymol Blue	Bromocresol Green	Blue Litmus Paper
yellow	yellow	red

D.

Bromothymol Blue	Bromocresol Green	Blue Litmus Paper
yellow	blue	red

20-C2.7k define Arrhenius (modified) acids as substances that produce $H_3O^+_{(aq)}$ in aqueous solutions and recognize that the definition is limited

20-C2.8k define Arrhenius (modified) bases as substances that produce $OH^-_{(aq)}$ in aqueous solutions and recognize that the definition is limited

MODIFIED ARRHENIUS ACIDS

Modified Arrhenius acids react with water to produce $H_3O^+_{(aq)}$ and a familiar balancing species. Modified Arrhenius bases react with water to produce $OH^-_{(aq)}$ and a familiar balancing species.

A quick way to determine whether a substance will behave as a modified Arrhenius acid or base in aqueous solution is to write two equations: one in which a molecule of the substance forms hydronium ions $\left(H_3O^+_{(aq)}\right)$ in aqueous solution and another in which the molecule forms hydroxide ions $OH^-_{(aq)}$ in aqueous solution. The remaining product will generally produce a familiar or unfamiliar ionic species. Based upon the familiarity of that product, you can make a reasonable prediction as to how the substance will behave. Familiarity is usually based on remembering species from a table of common ions.

Example

Using $HNO_{3(aq)}$ as a reactant in an aqueous solution, predict the products and identify the familiar balancing species.

Solution

If $HNO_{3(aq)}$ produces $H_3O^+_{(aq)}$ ions in water, then the reaction will yield the following equation:

$$HNO_{3(aq)} + H_2O_{(l)} \rightarrow H_3O^+_{(aq)} + NO^-_{3(aq)}$$

$NO^-_{3(aq)}$ is familiar. Nitrate ions are commonly found in tables of ions. It is reasonable to predict that hydrogen nitrate will behave as an acid.

To confirm the prediction or to examine the possibility that hydrogen nitrate behaves as a base in aqueous solution, write an equation that represents the production of hydroxide ions in water.

$$HNO_{3(aq)} + H_2O_{(l)} \rightarrow OH^-_{(aq)} + H_2NO^+_{3(aq)}$$

$H_2NO^+_{3(aq)}$ is not familiar. It is very unlikely that $HNO_{3(aq)}$ will behave as a base in aqueous solution. It seems far more likely that hydrogen nitrate behaves as an acid in water.

Example

Using ammonia, $NH_{3(aq)}$, as a reactant in an aqueous solution, predict the products and identify the familiar balancing species.

Solution

The following equation describes the reaction of ammonia and water if $NH_{3(aq)}$ were to produce $H_3O^+_{(aq)}$ ions in water.

$$NH_{3(aq)} + H_2O_{(l)} \rightarrow H_3O^+_{(aq)} + NH^-_{2(aq)}$$

The molecule $NH^-_{2(aq)}$ is not familiar. Therefore, ammonia will not likely produce hydronium ions, and it would not act as an acid in aqueous solution.

To confirm whether or not ammonia acts as a modified Arrhenius base in water, write an equation that includes hydroxide ions as a product of the reaction.

$$NH_{3(aq)} + H_2O_{(l)} \rightarrow OH^-_{(aq)} + NH^+_{4(aq)}$$

The molecule $NH^+_{4(aq)}$ is a familiar species. Ammonium ions are often found in tables of common ions, so it is reasonable to predict that ammonia will behave as a base in aqueous solution.

Therefore, ammonia will acts as a modified Arrhenius base, producing hydroxide ions and the familiar balancing species ammonium.

Example

Using carbon dioxide, $CO_{2(aq)}$, as a reactant in an aqueous solution, predict the products and identify the familiar balancing species.

Solution

In order to determine whether or not carbon dioxide will behave as a modified Arrhenius acid or base in aqueous solution, write a reaction equation for carbon dioxide with hydronium ions as a product, and write another with hydroxide ions as a product.

In order for an aqueous solution of carbon dioxide to produce the hydronium ions, the carbon dioxide molecule would bond with hydroxide ions in solution, which causes the concentration of hydronium ions to increase and the pH of the solution to decrease. As a carbon dioxide molecule bonds with a hydroxide ion, a proton is released that will bond with another water molecule to form hydronium. Therefore, two water molecules are needed to produce hydronium ions in solution with carbon dioxide.

$$CO_{2(aq)} + 2H_2O_{(l)} \rightarrow H_3O^+_{(aq)} + HCO^-_{3(aq)}$$

The bicarbonate molecule, $HCO^-_{3(aq)}$, is familiar. Bicarbonate ions are often found on tables of common ions. Therefore, it is reasonable to predict that aqueous carbon dioxide will behave as an acid.

Now consider the situation in which the carbon dioxide will behave as a modified Arrhenius base. The balanced equation that shows carbon dioxide forming hydroxide ions in an aqueous solution is as follows:

$$CO_{2(aq)} + H_2O_{(l)} \rightarrow OH^-_{(aq)} + HCO^+_{2(aq)}$$

The molecule $HCO^+_{2(aq)}$ is not familiar. Therefore, it is reasonable to predict that carbon dioxide is a poor Arrhenius base.

Therefore, carbon dioxide will acts as a modified Arrhenius acid, producing hydronium ions and the familiar balancing species bicarbonate.

Equations can be written to explain either the acid or base behaviour of different substances, but in some cases the theory cannot be used to predict whether the substance is an acid or a base.

Example

Using $HSO_{4(aq)}^-$ as a reactant in an aqueous solution, predict the products and identify if $HSO_{4(aq)}^-$ behaves as modified Arrhenius acid or base, or is amphiprotic.

Solution

In order to determine whether or not bisulfate ions will behave as modified Arrhenius acids or bases in aqueous solution, two separate reaction equations must be written, one with hydronium ions as a product, the other with hydroxide ions as a product.

In the first case with hydronium ions as a product, the reaction equation is as follows:

$$HSO_{4(aq)}^- + H_2O_{(l)} \rightarrow H_3O_{(aq)}^+ + SO_{4(aq)}^{2-}$$

Sulfate ($SO_{4(aq)}^{2-}$) ions are commonly found in solutions. It is reasonable to predict that hydrogen sulfate will donate a proton to water. This will increase the hydronium concentration and lower the pH, which are actions attributable to an acid.

Now, consider the second case in which bisulfate is behaving as a base producing hydroxide ions. The balanced equation for that reaction is as follows:

$$HSO_{4(aq)}^- + H_2O_{(l)} \rightarrow OH_{(aq)}^- + H_2SO_{4(aq)}$$

The formation of sulfuric acid ($H_2SO_{4(aq)}$) should decrease the concentration of hydronium ions, raising the pH; thus, it is reasonable to predict that hydrogen sulfate can also behave as a base in aqueous solution.

Since both acid and base predictions seem viable, it can be concluded that the hydrogen sulfate ion is amphiprotic, meaning it can behave as either an acid or a base in solution.

47. Which of the following equations describes the ionization of hydrogen chloride in water?

A. $H_{(aq)}^+ + Cl_{(aq)}^- + H_{(aq)}^+ + OH_{(aq)}^-$
   $\rightleftharpoons HCl_{(aq)} + H_2O_{(l)}$

B. $HCl_{(g)} + H_2O_{(l)} \rightleftharpoons H_3O_{(aq)}^+ + Cl_{(aq)}^-$

C. $Cl_{(aq)}^- + H_2O_{(l)} \rightleftharpoons HCl_{(aq)} + OH_{(aq)}^-$

D. $H_{(aq)}^+ + Cl_{(aq)}^- \rightleftharpoons HCl_{(aq)}$

48. The ions obtained after the self-ionization of water are correctly paired in which of the following tables?

A.
I	II
$OH_{(aq)}^-$	$O_{2(aq)}^+$

B.
I	II
$H_3O_{(aq)}^+$	$OH_{(aq)}^-$

C.
I	II
$H_3O_{(aq)}^+$	$H_{(aq)}^+$

D.
I	II
$H_{(aq)}^+$	$O_{2(aq)}^-$

49. All acids contain hydrogen, but not all hydrogen-containing compounds are acids. Which of the following hydrogen-containing compounds is an acid?

A. NH_3 B. CH_4

C. PH_3 D. H_2SO_4

50. A modified Arrhenius acid can **best** be described as

A. substance that dissociates in water to produce hydroxide ions

B. substance that produces hydronium ions in water

C. proton acceptor

D. base donor

51. Which of the following balanced equations represents the predominant reaction of $NH_{3(g)}$ with $H_2O_{(l)}$?

A. $NH_{3(g)} + H_2O_{(l)} \rightleftharpoons NH_{2(aq)}^- + H_3O_{(aq)}^+$

B. $H_2O_{(l)} + NH_{3(g)} \rightleftharpoons NH_{4(aq)}^+ + OH_{(aq)}^-$

C. $2NH_{3(g)} \rightleftharpoons N_{2(g)} + 3H_{2(g)}$

D. $H_{(aq)}^+ + OH_{(aq)}^- \rightleftharpoons H_2O_{(l)}$

20-C2.9k define neutralization as a reaction between hydronium and hydroxide ions

NEUTRALIZATION

When acids (HA) dissociate in water, they produce $H_{(aq)}^+$ and $A_{(aq)}^-$ ions. The $H_{(aq)}^+$ ions further react with $H_2O_{(l)}$ to produce hydronium ions $(H_3O_{(aq)}^+)$. When strong bases such as sodium hydroxide dissociate in water, they release their hydroxide ions $(OH_{(aq)}^-)$ into solution.

In an acid-base neutralization, the hydronium ions and hydroxide ions react to form water as this net-ionic equation illustrates:

$H_3O_{(aq)}^+ + OH_{(aq)}^- \rightarrow 2H_2O_{(l)}$

52. According to the modified Arrhenius theory, neutralization reactions involve
A. hydronium ions and hydroxide ions
B. hydronium ions and hydrogen ions
C. hydroxide ions and water
D. hydrogen ions and water

Use the following information to answer the next question.

The Dow process for the production of magnesium metal exploits the high magnesium ion concentrations in seawater. By this process, magnesium is precipitated from seawater by adding calcium hydroxide. The magnesium hydroxide formed is then treated with hydrochloric acid to produce aqueous magnesium chloride, as represented by the following reaction.
$Mg(OH)_{2(s)} + 2HCl_{(aq)}$
$\rightarrow MgCl_{2(aq)} + 2H_2O_{(l)}$
The magnesium chloride solution is then evaporated, and the magnesium chloride undergoes electrolysis to produce the desired magnesium metal.

53. According to Arrhenius's definition, the formation of magnesium chloride as shown above is a neutralization reaction because the acid $HCl_{(aq)}$
A. receives hydrogen ions from the base $Mg(OH)_{2(aq)}$
B. donates hydrogen ions to the base $Mg(OH)_{2(aq)}$
C. is neutralized to form the base $Mg(OH)_{2(aq)}$
D. reacts with the base $Mg(OH)_{2(aq)}$

20-C2.10k differentiate, qualitatively, between strong and weak acids and between strong and weak bases on the basis of ionization and dissociation; i.e., pH, reaction rate and electrical conductivity

DISSOCIATION OF STRONG AND WEAK ACIDS AND BASES

Often confused with ionization, dissociation is the process by which a compound separates into its smaller component parts. Like ionization, dissociation often results in the formation of positively charged cations and negatively charged anions. In the case of Brønsted–Lowry acids and bases, dissociation within an aqueous solution results in a change in the hydrogen activity, altering the pH of that solution.

Strong acids dissociate completely (quantitatively) in water to form $H_3O^+_{(aq)}$ and a balancing anion. Weak acids dissociate only partially (sometimes only very slightly) to form $H_3O^+_{(aq)}$ and a balancing anion.

Strong bases dissociate completely (quantitatively) in water to form $OH^-_{(aq)}$ and a balancing cation. Weak bases react only partially (sometimes only very slightly) to form $OH^-_{(aq)}$ and a balancing cation.

Because of the greater ion concentration, strong acids have a lower pH, react faster, and have a greater conductivity than weak acids of the same concentration.

A similar statement can be made for bases.

54. Which of the following solutions would typically show the **least** electrical conductivity?
    A. 0.8 M weak acid
    B. 1.0 M weak base
    C. 0.5 M strong base
    D. 0.1 M strong acid

55. A strong acid is defined as
    A. any acid that only dissociates slightly in aqueous solution
    B. any metal hydroxide salt that completely dissociates into its ions in water
    C. an acid that dissociates 100 % to produce H^+ ions and the conjugate base
    D. a metal hydroxide salt that reacts with water to produce hydroxide ions to only a slight extent in aqueous solution

Use the following information to answer the next question.

White vinegar is composed of 5% acetic acid, a weak acid. Pure acetic acid is called glacial acetic acid, which is used by photographers to prepare a stop bath for photographic film during print development.

56. If a stop bath solution composed solely of acetic acid and water was tested for its electrical conductivity, the solution would
    A. be a poorer conductor of electrical current than water
    B. strongly conduct an electrical current
    C. poorly conduct an electrical current
    D. fail to conduct an electrical current

Nitric acid, which is used in the manufacture of fertilizers and explosives, is a good conductor of electricity.

57. Nitric acid has excellent electrical conductivity as a result of its
   A. inability to dissociate into ions
   B. partial dissociation in aqueous solution
   C. complete dissociation in aqueous solution
   D. maintenance of its molecular structure in solution

Use the following information to answer the next question.

When $CO_{2(g)}$ is bubbled through a sample of water, the resulting solution contains the weak acid $H_2CO_{3(aq)}$.

58. If an electrical current were applied to the $H_2CO_{3(aq)}$ solution, the current would **most likely**
   A. not be conducted
   B. be readily conducted
   C. conduct well if the concentration of CO_2 was high
   D. be weakly conduct because of the presence of ions

59. Which of the following resulting solutions will **not** be a good conductor of electricity?
   A. A mixture of two weak bases
   B. A mixture of two strong acids
   C. A mixture of a strong acid and a weak acid
   D. A mixture of a strong base and a weak base

20-C2.11k identify monoprotic and polyprotic acids and bases and compare their ionization/dissociation.

POLYPROTIC ACIDS AND BASES

Monoprotic acids like $HCl_{(aq)}$ have one hydrogen atom that can ionize and react with water to produce $H_3O^+_{(aq)}$. Polyprotic acids like $H_2SO_{4(aq)}$ and $H_3PO_{4(aq)}$ have more than one hydrogen atom that can ionize and react with water to produce $H_3O^+_{(aq)}$.

Monoprotic bases like $NO^-_{2(aq)}$ react with water to produce one mole of $OH^-_{(aq)}$ for every one mole of base. Polyprotic bases like $CO^{2-}_{3(aq)}$ react with water to produce more than one mole of $OH^-_{(aq)}$ for every one mole of base.

60. Which of the following compounds can act as a polyprotic base?
   A. $KOH_{(aq)}$
   B. $K_2CO_{3(aq)}$
   C. $NaOH_{(aq)}$
   D. $NaCH_3COO_{(aq)}$

61. An example of a polyprotic acid is
   A. $HCl_{(aq)}$ B. $H_2SO_{3(aq)}$
   C. $NH_4OH_{(aq)}$ D. $KHSO_{4(aq)}$

ANSWERS AND SOLUTIONS
MATTER AS SOLUTIONS: ACIDS AND BASES

1. B	14. B	27. a) WR	39. A	52. A
2. A	15. A	b) WR	40. B	53. D
3. C	16. C	28. A	41. D	54. A
4. D	17. A	29. A	42. D	55. C
5. D	18. A	30. D	43. C	56. C
6. D	19. D	31. A	44. A	57. C
7. A	20. A	32. D	45. A	58. D
8. A	21. A	33. B	46. D	59. A
9. B	22. D	34. D	47. B	60. B
10. D	23. WR	35. C	48. B	61. B
11. A	24. A	36. A	49. D	
12. C	25. C	37. A	50. B	
13. 1.05	26. A	38. B	51. B	

1. B

Sugar in water forms a homogeneous mixture, or solution. It is virtually impossible to detect any differences in one part of the solution from another part of the solution. The mixture is uniform (or even) throughout.

In a heterogenous mixture, it is possible to see distinct phases, or different substances, within the mixture. This mixture could be described as non-uniform. Stirring a fine, silty sand in water would produce a good example of a heterogenous mixture. Individual sand grains could still be distinguished as being separate from the water, and it may also be possible to note grain sizes that are slightly different sizes or colours.

2. A

When the product of a reaction in solution produces a substance that is insoluble, it is highly likely that the substance will take solid form and thus leave the solution as a precipitate. While it is possible that the insoluble product could remain in liquid suspension, these are not representative of the majority of chemical reactions. Precipitation may also occur when a solution becomes supersaturated.

3. C

An exothermic reaction results in the net release of heat. Energy is required to break bonds in the reactants, and bond formation releases energy. If the energy of bond formation in the products exceeds that of bonds breaking in the reactants, then the net result is a release of heat energy, producing an exothermic reaction.

4. D

The OH groups in sugar molecules such as glucose make them polar because of the unequal sharing of electrons between oxygen and hydrogen atoms. The fact that sugars are polar gives them high solubility in water, which is a polar solvent. (Remember that solutes dissolve well in solvents of similar polarity.) However, molecular compounds do not dissociate into ions in aqueous solution. This property makes glucose a non-electrolyte in solution.

5. D

Phosphoric acid is a weak acid in water because it dissociates or ionizes only partially. This equation represents its ionization:

$$H_3PO_{4(aq)} + H_2O_{(l)} \rightleftarrows H_3O^+_{(aq)} + H_2PO^-_{4(aq)}$$

All weak molecular acids are weak electrolytes. The low concentration of dissolved ions also makes them poor conductors of electricity.

6. D

NaOCl is an ionic compound with an alkali metal cation. In aqueous solution, NaOCl would dissociate completely to form $Na^+_{(aq)}$ and $OCl^-_{(aq)}$ ions. Therefore, an aqueous solution of this compound would be an electrolyte and a good conductor of electricity.

7. A

Percent weight for volume (%w/v) is a solution concentration that measures the mass of a solute, in grams, per 100 mL of solution. Simply divide the solute's mass, in grams, by the solution volume, in mL, and multiply by 100 %.

$$\% \text{ w/v} = \frac{0.110 \text{ g}}{125 \text{ mL}} \times 100\%$$
$$= 0.0880\%$$

8. A

The molar mass of potassium permanganate, $KMnO_{4(s)}$, is 158.04 g/mol.

$$\% \text{ K} = \left(\frac{39.10 \text{ g}}{158.04 \text{ g}}\right)(100\%)$$
$$= 24.74\% \text{ K}$$
$$\%\text{Mn} = \left(\frac{54.94 \text{ g}}{158.04 \text{ g}}\right)(100\%)$$
$$= 34.76\% \text{ Mn}$$
$$\% \text{ O} = 4\left(\frac{16.00 \text{ g}}{158.04 \text{ g}}\right)(100\%)$$
$$= 40.50\% \text{ O}$$

9. B

The mass of the solute (grease) in this case is 43.2 g. The total mass of the mixture is

3 000 g (CO_2)+ 43.2 g (grease)

+ 200 g (surfactant) = 3243.2 g.

Determine the percentage by mass percentage by mass

$$= \frac{\text{mass of solute}}{\text{mass of mixture}} \times 100\%$$
$$= \frac{43.2 \text{ g}}{3 \ 243.2 \text{ g}} \times 100\%$$
$$= 1.33\% \text{ (w/w)}$$

The percentage of grease by mass in this solution is 1.33% (w/w).

10. D

To determine the percentage mass of H_2O_2 in the bottle, first determine the mass of the entire solution and the mass of H_2O_2, $m_{H_2O_2}$, in the bottle.

$$\% \text{ } H_2O_2 = \frac{m_{H_2O_2}}{m_{sol}} \times 100\%$$

The remaining H_2O_2 in the 1 L bottle has a concentration of 6.0 mol/L.

$$m_{H_2O_2} = 6.0 \text{ mol} \times \frac{34.02 \text{ g}}{\text{mol}}$$
$$= 0.20 \text{ kg}$$

The density of the 1.0 L solution is 1.10 g/mL.

$$m_{sol} = \frac{1.10 \text{ g}}{\text{mL}} \times 1 \ 000 \text{ mL}$$
$$= 1.10 \text{ kg}$$

$$\% \text{ } H_2O_2 \text{ by mass} = \frac{m_{H_2O_2}}{m_{sol}} \times 100\%$$
$$= \frac{0.20 \text{ kg}}{1.10 \text{ kg}} \times 100\%$$
$$= 18\%$$

The percentage of H_2O_2 by mass in the bottle is 18%.

11. A

The amount of iron contained within a person (m_{Fe}) is 0.004% of the person's body mass.

$$m_{Fe} = \frac{0.004\%}{100\%} \times 68 \text{ kg}$$
$$= 3 \times 10^{-3} \text{ kg}$$
$$= 3 \text{ g}$$

The mass of iron is 3 g.

12. C

The weight by volume (w/v) percentage of a solution is defined as the mass in grams of solute per volume of solution in milliliters.

$$\% \text{ w/v} = \frac{\text{mass of solute in g}}{\text{volume of solution in mL}} \times 100$$

Therefore, 2.3% w/v ≡ 2.3 g/mL.

Substituting known data, the amount of solute needed can be calculated.

$$2.3 \text{ g/mL} = \frac{m}{200 \text{ mL}} \times 100$$
$$m = \frac{2.3 \text{ g/mL}}{100} \times 200 \text{ mL}$$
$$m = 4.6 \text{ g}$$

13. 1.05

Step 1

Calculate the number of moles of formaldehyde in solution.

$$n = cV$$
$$n_{HCHO} = \frac{11.6 \text{ mol}}{1 \text{ L}} \times 3.00 \text{ L}$$
$$= 34.8 \text{ mol}$$

Step 2

Use the number of moles and the molar mass of formaldehyde to calculate the mass.

$$m = nM$$

$$m_{HCHO} = 34.8 \text{ mol} \times \frac{30.03 \text{ g}}{1 \text{ mol}}$$

$$= 1.05 \times 10^3 \text{ g}$$
$$= 1.05 \text{ kg}$$

There is 1.05 kg of formaldehyde (also called methanal) in 3.00 L of 11.6 mol/L formalin.

14. B

Step 1

Calculate the molar mass of NaOH.

$$M_{NaOH} = \begin{pmatrix} 22.99 \text{ g/mol} \\ + 16.00 \text{ g/mol} \\ + 1.01 \text{g/mol} \end{pmatrix}$$
$$= 40.00 \text{ g/mol}$$

Step 2

Calculate the number of moles of NaOH in the 0.40 g sample.

$$n_{NaOH} = \frac{0.40 \text{ g}}{40.00 \text{ g/mol}}$$
$$= 0.010 \text{ mol}$$

Step 3

Calculate the molarity of the solution. Molarity is equal to the number moles of solute per litre of solution.

The molarity of the NaOH solution
$$= (0.010 \text{ mol})/(0.050 \text{ L})$$
$$= 0.20 \text{ mol/L or } 0.20 \text{ M}$$

15. A

To find the concentration of the solution after dilution, you need to know the number of moles in the solution after dilution and the volume of the solution after dilution:

$$M_{\text{after dilution}} = \frac{n_{\text{after dilution}}}{V_{\text{after dilution}}}$$

Since the number of moles of solute does not change during this process, the number of moles after dilution is known:

$$n_{\text{after dilution}} = n_{\text{before dilution}}$$

Also, the volume of the solution after dilution is known:

$$V_{\text{after dilution}} = V_{\text{before dilution}} + V_{\text{water added}}$$

The number of moles after dilution can then be calculated knowing the concentration and volume before dilution.

$$n_{\text{after dilution}} = n_{\text{before dilution}}$$
$$= M_{\text{before dilution}} \times V_{\text{before dilution}}$$

The volume of the water before dilution can be replaced:

$$n_{\text{after dilution}} = n_{\text{before dilution}}$$
$$= M_{\text{before dilution}} \times V_{\text{before dilution}}$$
$$= M_{\text{before dilution}} \times (V_{\text{after dilution}} - V_{\text{water added}}).$$

Therefore, the number of moles of solute before dilution and the volume of water added are not enough information to calculate the solution's concentration after the dilution.

16. C

The balanced dissociation equation for lead(II) nitrate is

$$Pb(NO_3)_{2(s)} \rightarrow Pb^{2+}_{(aq)} + 2NO^-_{3(aq)}$$

For every mole of $Pb(NO_3)_{2(s)}$ put into solution, two moles of nitrate ions will form.

Therefore,
$$\left[NO^-_{3(aq)} \right] = 2(0.16 \text{ mol/L})$$
$$= 0.32 \text{ mol/L}$$

17. A

Concentrations are expressed in terms of the dissolved compound, in this case, lead(IV) nitrate, $Pb(NO_3)_4$.

Write the balanced dissociation equation for $Pb(NO_3)_{4(aq)}$.

$$Pb(NO_3)_{4(aq)} \rightarrow Pb^{4+}_{(aq)} + 4NO^-_{3(aq)}$$

For every mole of $PB(NO_3)_{4(s)}$ in the solution, four moles of nitrate ions will form.

$$n_{Pb(NO_3)_4} = \frac{1}{4}\left(n_{NO^-_3} \right)$$

Simplify and solve the equation.

$$c = \frac{1}{4} c_{NO^-_3}$$
$$= \frac{1}{4}(0.32 \text{ mol/L})$$
$$= 0.080 \text{ mol/L}$$

18. A

According to the solubility table, $MgSO_4$ is the only compound having a solubility greater than or equal to 0.1 mol/L, which is the dividing line used in a solubility table. A compound with solubility ≥ 0.1 mol/L is described as "very soluble", while a compound with solubility < 0.1 mol/L is described as "slightly soluble."

19. **D**

The following information can be found on a solubility table:

- All nitrate salts are very soluble.
- All chloride salts are very soluble except those with Ag^+, Hg_2^{2+} (the mercury(I) cation), Pb^{2+}, Cu^+, and Tl^+.
- All carbonate salts are slightly soluble except those with Group 1 cations or NH_4^+.

Of the pairs given, only $AgNO_3$ and $Pb(NO_3)_2$ have high solubility in water.

20. **A**

When HCl reacts with $AgNO_3$ in a double-replacement reaction, the two products are HNO_3 and AgCl. According to a solubility table, HNO_3 is very soluble, whereas AgCl is only slightly soluble. The solid substance (precipitate) formed is AgCl.

21. **A**

The double-replacement reaction that takes place when aqueous $Pb(NO_3)_2$ is added to aqueous NaCl produces $PbCl_2$ and $NaNO_3$. According to a solubility table, $NaNO_3$ is very soluble and $PbCl_2$ is only slightly soluble. Therefore, the solid substance formed is $PbCl_2$.

The reaction is shown in the following balanced equation.

$$Pb(NO_3)_{2(aq)} + 2NaCl_{(aq)} \rightarrow PbCl_{2(s)} + 2NaNO_{3(aq)}$$

22. **D**

A solution is made up of two components: the solvent and the solute. Usually, the solvent is the major component of the solution, while the solute is the minor component. Since oven cleaner is an aqueous solution of sodium hydroxide, the sodium hydroxide is the solute, and water is the solvent.

23. **WR**

"Like dissolves like." Polar solutes are more soluble in polar solvents—e.g., alcohol in water; non-polar solutes are more soluble on non-polar solvents—e.g., bike chain grease in white gasoline.

Gases dissolve exothermically—this means that they tend to be more soluble at low temperatures and high pressure—e.g., the $CO_{2(g)}$ in pop is more soluble when it is kept in the refrigerator with the lid on.

Solids, which dissolve endothermically, tend to be more soluble at higher temperature—e.g., sugar is more soluble in hot coffee than it is in cold coffee.

Liquids soluble in each other, in all possible ratios, are said to be miscible—e.g., methanol in water.

Liquids that do not mix at all are said to be immiscible—e.g., oil and water.

24. **A**

The maximum possible concentration of a solute in a solution under normal circumstances defines the solubility of that solute. A solution containing the maximum concentration of solute normally soluble at a given temperature is a saturated solution.

25. **C**

The source of radioactivity is the sodium-22 atoms. Any sample containing these atoms will register as radioactive.

The sample of the NaCl precipitate contains sodium-22 atoms and will register as radioactive.

The sample of clear liquid is a homogeneous solution of dissociated radioactive sodium-22 ions and chloride ions, as shown in the dissociation equation:

$$NaCl_{(s)} \rightleftharpoons NaCl_{(aq)} \rightleftharpoons Na_{(aq)}^+ + Cl_{(aq)}^-$$

Thus, the clear liquid contains radioactive sodium-22 and will also register as radioactive.

The correct alternative is C.

26. **A**

The excess solid solute in a saturated solution is continually dissolving. At the same time, with the same reaction rate, dissolved solute in the saturated solution is continually precipitating (as small crystals). The result is that over time large crystals are replaced by much smaller crystals.

27. **a) WR**

Add the solute to the solvent until undissolved solute is present in the solution. At this time the solution is said to be saturated because no additional solute will dissolve.

b) WR

$$Be_3(PO_4)_{2(s)} \rightleftharpoons 3Be_{(aq)}^{2+} + 2PO_{4(aq)}^{3-}$$

The double arrows ($\rightleftharpoons$) represent an equilibrium reaction showing that both the forward and reverse reaction are occurring.

28. A

Use the formula $c_1V_1 = c_2V_2$ to calculate the initial volume of $HCl_{(aq)}$ required.

$$V_1 = \frac{c_2V_2}{c_1}$$

$$= \frac{100 \text{ mL} \times \dfrac{0.0400 \text{ mol}}{L}}{0.200 \text{ mol/L}}$$

$$= 20.0 \text{ mL}$$

Therefore, 20.0 mL of 0.040 mol/L are required to prepare the desired solution. Standard solutions are prepared in volumetric flasks of the appropriate volume, which in this case is 100 mL. To ensure a high level of precision, it is important to use quality glassware such as pipettes and volumetric flasks.

29. A

First, calculate the required mass of $AgNO_{3(s)}$ for a 250 mL, 1 mol/L solution.

$$n_{AgNO_3} = 0.250 \text{ L} \times 1.00 \text{ mol/L}$$
$$= 0.250 \text{ mol}$$

$$n_{AgNO_3} = 0.250 \text{ mol} \times 169.88 \text{ g/mol}$$
$$= 42.5 \text{ g}$$

Whenever a standard solution is prepared, it is best to dissolve the solute (if it is solid and crystalline) in roughly half the final solvent volume with the aid of a glass stirring rod. This solution is then transferred with rinsing to a volumetric flask. Add water to bring the level of liquid to the graduation mark on the neck of the volumetric flask.

30. D

In the traditional naming system, acids that do not contain oxyanions (anions with oxygen in them) are given the prefix *hydro* followed by the anion name modified to end in the letters *-ic* and then the word *acid*. Therefore, the traditional name for $HCN_{(aq)}$ is hydrocyanic acid.

According to recent IUPAC rules, acids are allowed to be named by putting the word *aqueous* in front of the name formed by writing hydrogen before the anion name. Since the anion CN^- is called cyanide, the IUPAC name for the acid $HCN_{(aq)}$ is aqueous hydrogen cyanide.

31. A

An acidic solution has $\left[H_3O^+_{(aq)}\right] > \left[OH^-_{(aq)}\right]$ at any temperature where water is liquid.

32. D

In bases, $\left[OH^-_{(aq)}\right] > \left[H_3O^+_{(aq)}\right]$, so $\left[H_3O^+_{(aq)}\right] < \left[OH^-_{(aq)}\right]$.

In acids, $\left[H_3O^+_{(aq)}\right] > \left[OH^-_{(aq)}\right]$.

For neutral solutions,
$$\left[H_3O^+_{(aq)}\right] = \left[OH^-_{(aq)}\right]$$
$$= 1.00 \times 10^{-7} \text{mol/L}$$

33. B

A basic solution will have $\left[OH^-_{(aq)}\right] > \left[H_3O^+_{(aq)}\right]$, pH > 7.0, and pOH < 7.0.

34. D

For any acidic solution, $\left[H_3O^+_{(aq)}\right] > \left[OH^-_{(aq)}\right]$.
For neutral solutions, $\left[H_3O^+_{(aq)}\right] = \left[OH^-_{(aq)}\right]$. For any basic or alkaline solution, $\left[H_3O^+_{(aq)}\right] < \left[OH^-_{(aq)}\right]$.
The type of solution is incorrectly matched with its ion concentration in the following table:

Solution	Ion Concentration
Slightly acidic	$\left[H_3O^+_{(aq)}\right] < \left[OH^-_{(aq)}\right]$

35. C

All soap solutions are basic and have a somewhat high pH, which is why they have a slippery feel. Soaps are generally made by reacting fatty acids with strong alkaline solutions to create long molecules with both a hydrophilic end and hydrophobic end, allowing water to dissolve normally insoluble materials like dirt and oils.

However, a pH of 14.0 is excessively high and would be considered caustic and potentially damaging to any substance being cleaned. The pH for a soapy solution is most likely to be close to 10.0.

Solutions with pH < 7 are acidic.

36. A

The colour of phenolphthalein in a basic solution is pink. Phenolphthalein solution remains colourless in an acid solution.

A neutral salt is produced by the neutralization reaction i.e., the reaction of acids with bases. Therefore, at the point of neutralization (ph = 7), phenolphthalein is colourless.

Acids and bases are electrolytes because they dissociate in solution. A non-electrolyte solution would not be basic, so it would not change the colour of phenolphthalein.

37. A

Since $1.00 \times 10^{-14} = \left[H_3O^+_{(aq)}\right]\left[OH^-_{(aq)}\right]$, the concentration of hydroxide ions can be solved by manipulating this formula.

Therefore, the equation used to calculate $\left[OH^-_{(aq)}\right]$ is

$$\left[OH^-_{(aq)}\right] = \frac{1.00 \times 10^{-14}}{[H_3O^+_{(aq)}]}.$$

38. B

Use the ionic product constant or equilibrium constant for water: $K_w = \left[H_3O^+_{(aq)}\right]\left[OH^-_{(aq)}\right]$ to solve this question.

By definition: K_w at 25°C = 1.00×10^{-14}.

Using this information and the given hydronium ion concentration, substitute to get

$$1.00 \times 10^{-14} = \left(1.75 \times 10^{-4}\right)\left[OH^-_{(aq)}\right]$$

$$\frac{1.00 \times 10^{-14}}{1.75 \times 10^{-4}} = \left[OH^-_{(aq)}\right]$$

$$5.71 \times 10^{-11} \text{ mol/L} = \left[OH^-_{(aq)}\right]$$

39. A

For a given pH, $\left[H_3O^+_{(aq)}\right] = 10^{-pH}$.

In this case, the pH of the ASA solution is 3.0.

Therefore, $\left[H_3O^+_{(aq)}\right] = 1 \times 10^{-3}$ mol/L.

40. B

Calculate the molar mass of NaOH.
23.0 + 16.0 + 1.01 = 40.01 g/mol

Calculate the number of mol of NaOH.
$$\frac{22.0 \text{ g}}{40.01 \text{ g/mol}} = 0.550 \text{ mol}$$

Calculate the concentration of NaOH.
$$\frac{0.550 \text{ mol}}{10.0 \text{ L}} = 0.0550 \text{ mol/L}$$

Calculate pOH and then pH.
$$pOH = -\log\left[OH^-_{(aq)}\right]$$
$$pOH = -\log\left[0.0550\right]$$
$$= 1.260$$
$$pH = 14.000 - 1.260$$
$$= 12.740$$

41. D

Step 1
Convert the pH of solution A into moles per litre (mol/L).
The pH of solution A is 2.
$$C_A = \left[H^+_{(aq)}\right]_A$$
$$= 10^{-pH_A}$$
$$= 10^{-2} \text{ mol/L}$$

Step 2
Convert the pH of solution B into moles per litre (mol/L).
The pH of solution B is 12.
$$C_B = \left[H^+_{(aq)}\right]_B$$
$$= 10^{-pH_B}$$
$$= 10^{-12} \text{ mol/L}$$

Step 3
Calculate the ratio of $\left[H^+_{(aq)}\right]$ of solution A to that of solution B.
$$\frac{C_A}{C_B} = \frac{10^{-2} \text{ mol/L}}{10^{-12} \text{ mol/L}} = 10^{10}$$
$$C_A = 10^{10} C_B$$

The concentration of $H^+_{(aq)}$ in solution A is 10^{10} times greater than the concentration of $H^+_{(aq)}$ in solution B.

42. D

$\left[H^+_{(aq)}\right] = 10^{-10}$ when pH = 10
$\left[H^+_{(aq)}\right] = 10^{-11}$ when pH = 11

Thus:
$$\frac{[H^+_{initial\ (aq)}]}{[H^+_{final\ (aq)}]} = \frac{10^{-10}}{10^{-11}} = 10$$

If pH of a solution increases from 10 to 11 then $\left[H^+_{(aq)}\right]$ decreases by a factor of 10.

43. C

When the pH of an acid solution increases, $\left[H^+_{(aq)}\right]$ decreases and $\left[OH^-_{(aq)}\right]$ increases.

44. A

Acids turn blue litmus paper red and display some degree of reaction with active metals like magnesium.

45. A

Phenolphthalein turns colourless in acidic solutions and remains pink in basic solutions.

Blue litmus turns red in acidic solutions and remains blue in basic solutions. Red litmus remains red in acidic solutions and turns blue in basic solutions.

46. D

Bromothymol blue is yellow below a pH of 6.0. Bromocresol green is blue above a pH of 5.4. Blue litmus is red below a pH of 6.0. Therefore, the table that shows the correct reaction for each indicator is

Bromothymol Blue	Bromocresol Green	Blue Litmus Paper
yellow	blue	red

47. B

Ionization occurs when a molecular compound reacts with water to produce a solution of ions not present in the original solute.

$$HCl_{(g)} + H_2O_{(l)} \rightleftharpoons H_3O^+_{(aq)} + Cl^-_{(aq)}$$

48. B

The self-ionization of water gives the ions $H_3O^+_{(aq)}$ and $OH^-_{(aq)}$.

$$2H_2O_{(l)} \rightleftharpoons H_3O^+_{(aq)} + OH^-_{(aq)}$$

49. D

Using the Arrhenius definition of acids, H_2SO_4 (sulfuric acid) is the only acidic entity listed because it produces $H_3O^+_{(aq)}$ ions upon hydrolysis in an aqueous solution.

Alternatively, a compound that contains one or more hydrogen atoms in its molecule is labelled as an acid only when these atoms are replaced by either a metal or a group of elements behaving like a metal in a spontaneous reaction at SATP, producing salt. For example, $Zn_{(s)} + H_2SO_{4(aq)}$

$$\rightarrow ZnSO_{4(aq)} + H_{2(g)}.$$

50. B

A modified Arrhenius acid is a substance that produces hydronium ions $\left(H_3O^+_{(aq)}\right)$ in water. This is illustrated by the dissociation equation of hydrogen chloride gas, $HCl_{(g)} + H_2O_{(l)} \rightarrow H_3O^+_{(aq)} + Cl^-_{(aq)}$.

51. B

Ammonia, $NH_{3(g)}$, acts predominantly as a base with water. It has a much greater tendency to remove a proton from water than to donate a proton to water. When $NH_{3(g)}$ removes a proton, $H^+_{(aq)}$, from water, it forms an ammonium ion, $NH^+_{4(aq)}$, and a hydroxide ion, $OH^-_{(aq)}$.

52. A

In terms of the modified Arrhenius theory, neutralization reactions involve the combination of positively charged hydronium ions and negatively charged hydroxide ions. As the ions combine to form water, the excess of hydronium and hydroxide is reduced, and the pH of the solution approaches 7. Other theories, such as the Brønsted-Lowry and Lewis theories involve the movement and activity of protons and electron pairs respectively, and can describe changes in pH where no direct interactions between hydronium ions and hydroxide ions occur.

53. D

The neutralization reactions of strong Arrhenius acids and bases produce water and a salt. The reaction of $Mg(OH)_{2(s)}$ and $HCl_{(aq)}$ is one such reaction.

54. A

The solutions with the least ion concentration will have the least electrical conductivity. It must be either a weak acid or a weak base, since strong acids and strong bases dissociate completely. Their solutions have large ion concentrations. Since the weak acid concentration in a 0.8 M solution of weak acid is lower than the weak base concentration in a 1.0 M solution of weak base, a 0.8 M solution of weak acid will likely have the least ion concentration and the least electrical conductivity.

55. C

Strong acids completely dissociate in water. For example, $HCl_{(aq)} \rightarrow H^+_{(aq)} + Cl^-_{(aq)}$. Notice that there is a unidirectional reaction arrow, and not a bidirectional equilibrium arrow.

56. C

Since acetic acid is a weak acid that dissociates, or partially ionizes, at most normal concentrations, it will be a weak electrolyte. Weak electrolytes will conduct electricity, but poorly.

57. C

Nitric acid, like all strong acids, dissociates completely in aqueous solution.

Thus, with two moles of dissolved ions per mole of acid, nitric acid is a good conductor of electricity.

58. D

The presence of the weak acid $H_2CO_{3(aq)}$ will cause the current to be weakly conducted. The $H_2CO_{3(aq)}$ will partially ionize in water to produce $H_3O^+_{(aq)}$ and $HCO^-_{3(aq)}$.

$$H_2CO_{3(aq)} + H_2O_{(l)} \rightleftharpoons H_3O^+_{(aq)} + HCO^-_{3(aq)}$$

59. A

Strong acids and bases are good conductors of electricity, whereas weak acids and bases are not. Therefore, a mixture of two weak bases will not be a good conductor of electricity.

60. B

A polyprotic base can accept two or more H^+ ions. $K_2CO_{3(aq)}$ is capable of doing this.

$K_2CO_{3(aq)}$ undergoes these reactions.

$$CO^{2-}_{3(aq)} + H_2O_{(l)} \rightarrow HCO^-_{3(aq)} + OH^-_{(aq)}$$
$$HCO^-_{3(aq)} + H_2O_{(aq)} \rightarrow H_2CO_{3(aq)} + OH^-_{(aq)}$$

61. B

A polyprotic acid can donate two or more H^+ ions.

Sulfurous acid, $H_2SO_{3(aq)}$, has two H^+ ions to donate; therefore, $H_2SO_{3(aq)}$ is a polyprotic acid.

The following chemical equations illustrate how sulfurous acid can donate two protons, forming hydronium ions in aqueous solution.

$$H_2SO_{3(aq)} + H_2O_{(l)} \rightleftharpoons HSO^-_3 + H_3O^+_{(aq)}$$
$$HSO^-_{3(aq)} + H_2O_{(l)} \rightleftharpoons SO^{2-}_{3(aq)} + H_3O^+_{(aq)}$$

UNIT TEST — MATTER AS SOLUTIONS: ACIDS AND BASES

Use the following information to answer the next question.

A student dissolves a white solid in a test tube filled with water. The student noticed that the temperature of the solution increased as the solid dissolved.

1. The dissolving of the white solid can be described as an
   A. endothermic process in which the energy absorbed is greater than the energy released
   B. endothermic process in which the energy released is greater than the energy released
   C. exothermic process in which the energy absorbed is greater than the energy released
   D. exothermic process in which the energy released is greater than the energy absorbed

Use the following information to answer the next question.

These equations represent three solutions prepared by dissolving a solid in a sample of water.

I. $NaNO_{3(s)} \rightarrow Na^+_{(aq)} + NO^-_{3(aq)}$

II. $C_{12}H_{22}O_{11(s)} \rightarrow C_{12}H_{22}O_{11(aq)}$

III. $NaOH_{(s)} \rightarrow Na^+_{(aq)} + OH^-_{(aq)}$

2. An electrolyte is shown in which of the given equations?
   A. I and II   B. I and III
   C. II and III   D. I, II, and III

Use the following information to answer the next multipart question.

3. The concentrations of several minerals in a sample of natural spring water are shown in the given chart.

Minerals	Concentration (ppm)
Calcium $\left(Ca^{2+}_{(aq)}\right)$	78
Magnesium $\left(Mg^{2+}_{(aq)}\right)$	24
Sodium $\left(Na^+_{(aq)}\right)$	5
Potassium $\left(K^+_{(aq)}\right)$	1

Written Response

a) What mass of magnesium ions is present in 250 mL of the given sample of spring water?

_____

_____

b) What is the molar concentration of calcium ions?

_____

_____

c) Express the sodium concentration as a percentage weight per volume.

_____

_____

_____

_____

_____

_____

_____

Use the following information to answer the next question.

> The laboratory technician at a school wants to make 4.00 L of a 0.125 mol/L solution through dilution of a more concentrated 1.50 mol/L solution.

4. What initial volume of the concentrated solution is required?

   A. 0.167 L   **B.** 0.333 L

   C. 24.0 L   **D.** 48.0 L

5. What is the total ion concentration in a 0.060 M solution of aluminum sulfate?

   A. 0.12 M   **B.** 0.18 M

   C. 0.30 M   **D.** 0.36 M

Use the following information to answer the next question.

> Solid $CaCl_{2(s)}$ is added to 100.0 mL of $H_2O_{(l)}$ until the solution becomes saturated. The solution is represented by the equation $CaCl_{2(s)} \rightleftharpoons Ca^{2+}_{(aq)} + 2Cl^-_{(aq)}$.

6. Which of the following statements about the saturated solution is **true**?

   A. $CaCl_{2(s)}$ is crystallizing but not dissolving.

   B. $CaCl_{2(s)}$ is dissolving but not crystallizing.

   C. The dissolving and crystallizing of $CaCl_{2(s)}$ has stopped.

   D. The rate at which $CaCl_{2(s)}$ is dissolving is equal to the rate at which $CaCl_{2(s)}$ is crystallizing.

7. Which of the following techniques is the **best** way of preparing 100 mL of a 0.0500 mol/L sodium carbonate $Na_2CO_{3(aq)}$ standard solution?

   A. Carefully pipette 10 mL of a 0.0500 mol/L sodium carbonate stock solution into a 100 mL volumetric flask, and then add water to the 100 mL mark.

   B. Carefully pour 0.500 mol/L sodium carbonate stock solution into a 100 mL graduated cylinder to the 10 mL mark, and then add water to the 100 mL mark.

   C. Dissolve 0.530 g of solid sodium carbonate in a 200 mL beaker, add water to the 100 mL mark, and then carefully transfer the solution to a 100 mL volumetric flask.

   D. In a 50 mL beaker, dissolve 0.530 g of solid calcium carbonate in deionized water, carefully transfer the solution to a 100 mL volumetric flask, and then add water to the 100 mL mark.

8. Which of the following statements describes an acidic solution?

   A. It is slippery.

   B. It has a pH less than 7.0.

   C. It turns red litmus paper blue.

   D. It does not react with alkali metals.

9. For a neutral solution at room temperature, which of the following relationships is **false**?

   A. pH > 7.0

   B. pOH = 7.0

   C. $\left[H_3O^+_{(aq)}\right] = \left[OH^-_{(aq)}\right]$

   D. $\left[H_3O^+_{(aq)}\right] = 1.00 \times 10^{-7}$ mol/L

10. Which of the following statements about a basic solution at 25°C is **true**?

    A. $\left[OH^-_{(aq)}\right] > \left[H_3O^+_{(aq)}\right]$

    B. $\left[OH^-_{(aq)}\right] = \left[H_3O^+_{(aq)}\right]$

    C. $\left[H^+_{(aq)}\right] = \left[OH^-_{(aq)}\right]$

    D. $\left[H^+_{(aq)}\right] > \left[OH^-_{(aq)}\right]$

11. Tomato juice has a pH of 4.10. What is the hydronium ion concentration of tomato juice?

    A. 4.1×10^7 mol/L

    B. 4.1×10^{-7} mol/L

    C. 7.9×10^{-4} mol/L

    D. 7.9×10^{-5} mol/L

Use the following information to answer the next question.

> $HI_{(aq)}$ is a strong acid that completely ionizes when in aqueous solution according to the following equation:
>
> $HI_{(aq)} + H_2O_{(l)} \rightarrow H_3O^+_{(aq)} + I^-_{(aq)}$

12. If a 50 mL solution contains 0.655 g of $HI_{(aq)}$, what is the pH of the solution?

    A. 0.16   B. 0.99

    C. 2.29   D. 13.10

Numerical Response

13. The pH of a 1.0 mol/L solution of $HCl_{(aq)}$ is _____. (Record your answer as a three-digit number.)

Use the following information to answer the next question.

> Two samples of a solution were tested with the indicators chlorophenol red and phenolphtalein. Chlorophenol red turned red and phenolphthalein remained colourless when added to the solution.

14. The pH for the solution is **most likely**

    A. 5.0   B. 8.0

    C. 10.0   D. 12.0

15. $CH_3COOH_{(aq)}$ acts as an Arrhenius acid in which of the following reactions?

    A. $CH_3COO^-_{(aq)} + H_3O^+_{(aq)}$
       $\rightleftharpoons CH_3COOH^+_{(aq)} + H_2O_{(l)}$

    B. $CH_3COOH_{(aq)} + H_2O_{(l)}$
       $\rightleftharpoons H_3O^+_{(aq)} + CH_3COO^-_{(aq)}$

    C. $CH_3COOH_{(aq)} + 2H_2O_{(l)}$
       $\rightleftharpoons CH_3COOH^-_{2(aq)} + H_3O^+_{(aq)}$

    D. $CH_3COOH_{(aq)} + H^+_{(aq)} + OH^-_{(aq)}$
       $\rightleftharpoons H_2O_{(l)} + H^+_{(aq)} + CH_3COO^-_{(aq)}$

Written Response

16. Using $HSO^-_{4(aq)}$ as a reactant in an aqueous solution, predict the products and identify if $HSO^-_{4(aq)}$ behaves as modified Arrhenius acid or base, or is amphiprotic.

    _____
    _____
    _____
    _____
    _____
    _____
    _____

17. The production of salt and water from the reaction of the hydrogen ions from an acid and the hydroxide ions from a base is known as

    A. neutralization   B. precipitation

    C. dissociation   D. desalination

18. The **main** difference between a strong acid and a strong base is the

    A. degree of ionization

    B. concentration in solution

    C. degree of electrical conduction

    D. identity of ions present in solution

Use the following information to answer the next question.

A scientist is working with two solutions of equal concentration. Both solutions turn red litmus paper blue and conduct electricity. However, solution 1 has low conductivity and solution 2 has high conductivity.

Written Response

19. Explain whether each solution is an acid or a base, has a pH less than or greater than 7, and is a weak or strong electrolyte.

    _____

    _____

    _____

    _____

    _____

20. Which of the following chemical species can be described as a polyprotic acid?

    A. $HNO_{3(aq)}$

    B. $HPO_{4(aq)}^{2-}$

    C. $H_2SO_{4(aq)}$

    D. $Ba(OH)_{2(aq)}$

ANSWERS AND SOLUTIONS — UNIT TEST

1. D	4. B	9. A	14. B	19. WR
2. B	5. C	10. A	15. B	20. C
3. a) WR	6. D	11. D	16. WR	
b) WR	7. D	12. B	17. A	
c) WR	8. B	13. 0.00	18. D	

1. D

The temperature of the test tube increases, so energy is released when the solid dissolves. Therefore, this is an exothermic process. In an exothermic process, the energy absorbed to break apart the solute is less than the energy released as the ions bind to water.

2. B

Electrolytes are substances that conduct electricity when dissolved in water. The conductivity of a solution is determined by the concentration of dissolved ions. The substances $NaNO_{3(s)}$ and $NaOH_{(s)}$ are electrolytes, and $C_{12}H_{22}O_{11(s)}$ is a non-electrolyte. Therefore, only equations I and III show electrolytes.

3. a) WR

It is helpful to be familiar with concentrations and their units when solving solution concentration problems.

- ppm—mg/L
- %(w/v)—g/100 mL
- %(w/w)—g/100 g
- %(v/v)—mL/100 mL

The concentration of $Mg^{2+}_{(aq)}$ in the given sample of spring water is 24 ppm.

By definition, 24 ppm = 24 mg/L = $\dfrac{24 \text{ mg}}{1\,000 \text{ mL}}$.

Use a cancellation calculation.

$m_{Mg} = 250 \text{ mL} \times \dfrac{24 \text{ mg}}{1\,000 \text{ mL}}$

$= 6.0 \text{ mg}$

There are 6.0 mg of $Mg^{2+}_{(aq)}$ present in 250 mL of the sample of spring water.

b) WR

It is helpful to be familiar with concentrations and their units when solving solution concentration problems.

- ppm—mg/L
- %(w/v)—g/100 mL
- %(w/w)—g/100 g
- %(v/v)—mL/100 mL

Unit cancellation calculations are sufficient to do any solution calculations.

$\left[Ca^{2+}_{(aq)} \right] = 78$ ppm

$= \dfrac{78 \text{ mg Ca}^{2+}}{L} = \dfrac{0.078 \text{ g Ca}^{2+}}{L}$

$\left[Ca^{2+}_{(aq)} \right] = \dfrac{0.078 \text{ g}}{L} \times \dfrac{1 \text{ mol}}{40.08 \text{ g}}$

$= 1.9 \times 10^{-3}$ mol/L

c) WR

- ppm → mg/L
- %(w/v) → $\dfrac{(\text{solute (g)}) \times 100\%}{(\text{solution(mL)})} \to \% \dfrac{g}{mL}$

  The units for this concentration do not divide out. This unit is the percent of solute per volume of solution.

Step 1
Convert parts per million (ppm) to milligrams per litre (mg/L).

5 ppm = 5 mg/ L

$= 5$ mg/1 000 mL

Step 2
Convert mg/L to g/L.

$\dfrac{5 \text{ mg}}{1\,000 \text{ mL}} = \dfrac{5 \times 10^{-3} \text{ g}}{1\,000 \text{ mL}}$

Step 3
Find the %(w/v) for sodium ions:

$\left[Na^{+}_{(aq)} \right] = \dfrac{5 \times 10^{-3} \text{ g}}{1\,000 \text{ mL}} \times 100\%$

$= 5 \times 10^{-4}\%(\text{g/mL})$

The sodium ion concentration is $5 \times 10^{-4}\%$(g/mL).

4. B

This is a dilution problem. The moles before and after dilution are the same.

$$n_i = n_f$$
$$V_i c_i = V_f c_f$$
$$(V_i)(1.50 \text{ mol}/\text{L}) = (4.00 \text{ L})(0.125 \text{ mol}/\text{L})$$
$$V_i = \frac{(4.00 \text{ L})(0.125 \text{ mol/L})}{(1.50 \text{ mol/L})}$$
$$= \frac{0.500 \text{ mol}}{1.50 \text{ mol}/\text{L}}$$
$$= 0.333 \text{ L}$$

Therefore, to prepare 4.00 L of a 0.125 mol/L solution, the lab technician needs to dilute 0.333 L of 1.50 mol/L solution. This can be done by adding distilled water.

5. C

Step 1

Write a balanced dissociation equation for aluminum sulfate.

The aluminum ion has a charge of 3+ and the sulfate ion has a charge of 2−. The balanced dissociation equation for aluminum sulfate is as follows:

$$Al_2(SO_4)_{3(s)} \rightarrow 2Al^{3+}_{(aq)} + 3SO^{2-}_{4(aq)}.$$

Step 2

Calculate the total concentration of aluminum ions in the solution.

$$[Al^{3+}] = 0.060 \text{ M } Al_2(SO_4)_3$$
$$\times \frac{2 \text{ M } Al^{3+}}{1 \text{ M } Al_2(SO_4)_3} = 0.12 \text{ M}.$$

Step 3

Calculate the total concentration of sulfate ions in the solution.

$$[SO^{2-}_4] = 0.060 \text{ M } Al_2(SO_4)_3$$
$$\times \frac{3 \text{ M } SO^{2-}_4}{1 \text{ M } Al_2(SO_4)_3} = 0.18 \text{ M}.$$

Step 4

Add the total concentration of aluminum ions and sulfate ions.

0.12 M + 0.18 M = 0.30 M

The total ion concentration in an aluminum sulfate solution is 0.30 M.

6. D

A saturated solution contains both dissolved and undissolved solute. When a solution becomes saturated, it is referred to as an equilibrium reaction. When the $CaCl_{2(s)}$ solution becomes saturated, the rate at which $CaCl_{2(s)}$ is dissolving is equal to the rate at which $CaCl_{2(s)}$ is crystallizing. The solution is in a state of equilibrium.

7. D

In order to prepare a standard solution of a solid solute, the first step is to calculate the mass of solute required.

$$n_{Na_2CO_3} = 0.100 \text{ L} \times 0.0500\frac{\text{mol}}{\text{L}}$$
$$= 0.005\ 00 \text{ mol}$$
$$m_{Na_2CO_3} = 0.005\ 00 \text{ mol} \times \frac{105.99 \text{ g}}{\text{mol}}$$
$$= 0.530 \text{ g}$$

This solution requires 0.530 g of $Na_2CO_{3(s)}$ to make 100 mL of a 0.0500 mol/L aqueous solution. Whenever a standard solution is prepared, it is best to dissolve the solute, if it is solid and crystalline, in half the final solvent volume with the aid of a glass stirring rod.

8. B

All acids have a pH less than 7.0.

Basic solutions are slippery and turn red litmus paper blue. Acids react with alkali metals to produce hydrogen gas and a salt.

9. A

In a neutral solution at room temperature, $[H_3O^+] = [OH^-] = 1.00 \times 10^{-7} \text{mol/L}$. Both the pH and the pOH of the solution will be equal to 7.

10. A

A base solution will always have $[OH^-_{(aq)}] > [H_3O^+_{(aq)}]$. This is true for any temperature at which water is liquid.

11. D

Use the mathematical definition of pH to solve for $[H_3O^+_{(aq)}]$.

$$-\log[H_3H3O(aq)+] = pH$$
$$\log[H_3H3O(aq)+] = -pH$$
$$[H_3O^+_{(aq)}] = 10^{-pH}$$
$$= 10^{-4.10}$$
$$= 7.9 \times 10^{-5} \text{ mol/L}$$

The hydronium ion concentration of tomato juice is 7.9×10^{-5} mol/L.

12. B

Step 1

Calculate the moles of HI in the solution.

$$n_{HI} = (0.655 \text{ g})\left(\frac{1 \text{ mol}}{127.91 \text{ g}}\right)$$
$$= 5.12 \times 10^{-3} \text{ mol}$$

Step 2

Calculate the moles of the hydronium ions.

Since the relationship of moles of HI and H_3O^+ is 1:1, $n_{H_3O^+} = 5.12 \times 10^{-3}$ mol.

Step 3

Find the concentration of hydronium ions.

$$[H_3O^+] = \frac{n_{H_3O^+}}{V_{\text{solution}}}$$
$$= \frac{5.12 \times 10^{-3} \text{ mol}}{0.0500 \text{ L}}$$
$$= 0.102 \text{ mol/L}$$

Step 4

Calculate the pH.

$$pH = -\log[H_3O^+]$$
$$= -\log(0.102)$$
$$= 0.99$$

Thus, the pH of the solution is 0.99.

13. 0.00

Because hydrochloric acid ionizes completely, the pH of a 1.0 mol/L $HCl_{(aq)}$ can be found using the following equation:

$$pH = -\log[H^+_{(aq)}]$$
$$pH = -\log(1.0 \text{ mol/L})$$
$$pH = -\log(10^0 \text{ mol/L})$$
$$pH = 0.00$$

The number of decimal places in a pH value is the same as the number of significant digits in the hydrogen ion concentration.

14. B

Chlorophenol red (pH range 5.2–6.8) turns red, which indicates the solution has a pH > 6.8. Phenolphthalein (pH range 8.2–10.0) remains colourless, which indicates the solution has a pH > 8.2. The solution has a pH in the range of 6.8–8.2. The pH value of 8.0 is most likely.

15. B

$CH_3COOH_{(aq)}$ undergoes acid ionization (hydrolysis) when in aqueous solution. Ionization is defined as the reaction of a chemical entity (ion or molecule) with water to produce $H_3O^+_{(aq)}$ or $OH^-_{(aq)}$. Arrhenius acids produce $H_3O^+_{(aq)}$ (or $H^+_{(aq)}$) ions during ionization reactions.

16. WR

In order to determine whether or not bisulfate ions will behave as modified Arrhenius acids or bases in aqueous solution, two separate reaction equations must be written, one with hydronium ions as a product, the other with hydroxide ions as a product.

In the first case with hydronium ions as a product, the reaction equation is as follows:

$$HSO_4^-{}_{(aq)} + H_2O_{(l)} \rightarrow H_3O^+_{(aq)} + SO_4^{2-}{}_{(aq)}$$

Sulfate ($SO_4^{2-}{}_{(aq)}$) ions are commonly found in solutions. It is reasonable to predict that hydrogen sulfate will donate a proton to water. This will increase the hydronium concentration and lower the pH, which are actions attributable to an acid.

Now, consider the second case in which bisulfate is behaving as a base producing hydroxide ions. The balanced equation for that reaction is as follows:

$$HSO_4^-{}_{(aq)} + H_2O_{(l)} \rightarrow OH^-_{(aq)} + H_2SO_{4(aq)}$$

The formation of sulfuric acid ($H_2SO_{4(aq)}$) should decrease the concentration of hydronium ions, raising the pH; thus, it is reasonable to predict that hydrogen sulfate can also behave as a base in aqueous solution.

Since both acid and base predictions seem viable, it can be concluded that the hydrogen sulfate ion is amphiprotic, meaning it can behave as either an acid or a base in solution.

17. **A**

A neutralization reaction produces salt and water when an acid and a base are combined in solution. Acids dissociate in aqueous solution to create hydrogen or hydronium ions, whereas bases dissociate and create hydroxide ions. The hydrogen or hydronium ions combine with the hydroxide ions to form water, and the remaining ions in the solution combine to form a salt. This reaction of acids and bases results in a solution with a pH that is more neutral than either the original acid or base reactants.

18. **D**

Strong acids and strong bases dissociate completely in water, but acids produce a large number of $H^+_{(aq)}$ ions and bases produce a large number of hydroxide ions $\left(OH^-_{(aq)}\right)$. The identity of the ions produced by dissociation differs in acids and bases.

19. **WR**

Solutions 1 and 2 both turn red litmus paper blue. Therefore, both solutions have a pH greater than 7 and can be described as bases (or alkaline solutions). The higher conductivity of solution 1 indicates that it is a strong electrolyte, while solution 2 has the conductive characteristics of a weak electrolyte. Because the solutions are of equal concentration, solution 1 is a strong base and solution 2 is a weak base.

20. **C**

Polyprotic acids have more than one hydrogen atom that can ionize and react with water to produce $H_3O^+_{(aq)}$. From the list of compounds given, sulfuric acid ($H_2SO_{4(aq)}$) is the only polyprotic species. The following chemical equations illustrate how sulfuric acid can donate two protons.

$$H_2SO_{4(aq)} + H_2O_{(l)} \rightarrow HSO^-_{4(aq)} + H_3O^+_{(aq)}$$
$$HSO^-_{4(aq)} + H_2O_{(l)} \rightarrow SO^{2-}_{4(aq)} + H_3O^+_{(aq)}$$

Chemical Change

QUANTITATIVE RELATIONSHIPS IN CHEMICAL CHANGE

Table of Correlations

Outcome		Practice Questions	Unit Test Questions	Practice Test 1	Practice Test 2
1	Explain how balanced chemical equations indicate the quantitative relationships between reactants and products involved in chemical changes				
20-D1.1k	*predict the product(s) of a chemical reaction based upon the reaction type*	1, 2, 3, 4a, 4b, 4c, 4d, 4e, 5	1	13, 14	2
20-D1.2k	*recall the balancing of chemical equations in terms of atoms, molecules and moles*	6a, 6b, 7	2, 3	20, 27	6
20-D1.3k	*contrast quantitative and qualitative analysis*	8, 9			31
20-D1.4k	*write balanced ionic and net ionic equations, including identification of spectator ions, for reactions taking place in aqueous solutions*	10, 11, 12, 13, 14, 15	4, 5a, 5b	15a, 15b	7
20-D1.5k	*calculate the quantities of reactants and/or products involved in chemical reactions, using gravimetric, solution or gas stoichiometry.*	16, 17, 18, 19a, 19b, 19c, 20, 21, 22, 23, 24	6, 7, 8, 9, 10	16, 17a, 17b, 17c	8, 9a, 9b, 10
2	Use stoichiometry in quantitative analysis				
20-D2.1k	*explain chemical principles (i.e., conservation of mass in a chemical change), using quantitative analysis*	25, 26	11		
20-D2.2k	*identify limiting and excess reagents in chemical reactions*	27	12		11
20-D2.3k	*define theoretical yields and actual yields*	28a, 28b, 29, 30, 31, 32	13		
20-D2.4k	*explain the discrepancy between theoretical and actual yields*	33	14a, 14b		
20-D2.5k	*draw and interpret titration curves, using data from titration experiments involving strong monoprotic acids and strong monoprotic bases*	34a, 34b	15	25a, 25b	29a, 29b
20-D2.6k	*describe the function and choice of indicators in titrations*	35, 36	16		
20-D2.7k	*identify equivalence points on strong monoprotic acid – strong monoprotic base titration curves and differentiate between the indicator end point and the equivalence point.*	37, 38	17		

20-D1.1k predict the product(s) of a chemical reaction based upon the reaction type

TYPES OF REACTIONS

The following are examples of different types of reactions.

FORMATION REACTIONS

In a formation reaction, two or more simple substances combine to form a new and more complex substance, which is generally denoted by this equation:

$X + Y \rightarrow XY$

For example, aluminum atoms and oxygen atoms combine to form aluminum oxide.

$4Al_{(s)} + 3O_{2(g)} \rightarrow 2Al_2O_{3(s)}$

DECOMPOSITION REACTIONS

Decomposition reactions are the opposite of formation reactions. Typically, a more complex substance breaks down into two or more simple substances as shown in this equation:

$XY \rightarrow X + Y$

For example, water decomposes into diatomic hydrogen and oxygen molecules.

$2H_2O_{(g)} \rightarrow 2H_{2(g)} + O_{2(g)}$

SINGLE-REPLACEMENT REACTIONS

In a single-replacement reaction, one element replaces another in a reactant compound to form a new product compound as follows:

$AB + C \rightarrow CB + A$, where C is a metal or metalloid.

These reactions are also called substitution reactions.

If C is a metal, the electropositive element (cation) in the reactant compound is usually replaced by the metal and the cation that is being replaced will be precipitated or generated in its elemental form.

For example, silver nitrate and copper react to form copper nitrate and silver atoms.

$2AgNO_{3(aq)} + Cu_{(s)} \rightarrow Cu(NO_3)_{2(aq)} + 2Ag_{(s)}$

Another form of a single-replacement reaction takes the form of $AB + C \rightarrow AC + B$, where C is a non-metal.

If C is a non-metal, it represents the electronegative element (anion) of the reactant compound that is replaced by the new reactant element to form a new product compound. The anion that is being replaced will be precipitated or generated in its elemental form.

For example, potassium iodide and chlorine gas react to form potassium chloride and iodine.

$2KI_{(aq)} + Cl_{2(g)} \rightarrow 2KCl_{(aq)} + I_{2(aq)}$

DOUBLE-REPLACEMENT REACTIONS

When the anion and cation of two different molecules switch their places to form two new compounds, the process is called a double-replacement reaction.

$AB + CD \rightarrow AD + CB$

For example, sodium iodide and lead nitrate react to form lead iodide and sodium nitrate.

$2NaI_{(aq)} + Pb(NO_3)_{2(aq)} \rightarrow PbI_{2(s)} + 2NaNO_{3(aq)}$

COMPLETE COMBUSTION REACTIONS

When a hydrocarbon burns completely in a sufficient supply of oxygen, it is called complete combustion. If the products are limited to only carbon dioxide and water and there is no formation of any other byproducts, it is referred to as complete combustion or ideal combustion. This process is almost impossible to achieve in practice. Complete hydrocarbon combustion occurs according to the following equation:

$C_xH_y + \left(x + \dfrac{y}{4}\right)O_{2(g)} \rightarrow xCO_{2(g)} + \dfrac{y}{2}H_2O_{(g)}$

For example, propane and oxygen combust, producing carbon dioxide and water.

$C_3H_{8(g)} + 5O_{2(g)} \rightarrow 3CO_{2(g)} + 4H_2O_{(g)}$

If the supply of oxygen is insufficient, the combustion process will be incomplete and the product mixture will contain various byproducts such as carbon monoxide, elemental carbon (soot), along with water, carbon dioxide, and some unreacted hydrocarbons. This situation is called **incomplete combustion** and often presents environmental hazards.

Use the following information to answer the next question.

Galvanized nails are used extensively because they do not rust. An experiment is designed to determine the mass of the zinc coating on hot-dipped galvanized nails, using the given reaction.

$Zn_{(s)} + 2HCl_{(aq)} \rightarrow ZnCl_{2(aq)} + H_{2(g)}$

1. This reaction could be classified as a
   A. formation
   B. decomposition
   C. single replacement
   D. double replacement

2. The reaction of $Ba(OH)_{2(aq)}$ and $H_2SO_{4(aq)}$ produces the precipitate
   A. $Ba(OH)_{2(s)}$ B. $BaSO_{4(s)}$
   C. $H_2SO_{4(s)}$ D. $H_2O_{(s)}$

Use the following information to answer the next question.

The mantle of a camping lantern is covered in thorium hydroxide and ceric nitrate. These substances burn when the mantle is ignited, providing a catalytic surface for the pressurized fuel-air combustion. The equation for this reaction before any burning takes place is $Th(OH)_{4(s)} \rightarrow ThO_{2(s)} + 2H_2O_{(g)}$.

3. This reaction is **best** classified as a
   A. formation reaction
   B. decomposition reaction
   C. single-replacement reaction
   D. double-replacement reaction

Use the following information to answer the next multipart question.

4. | For each of the following reactions, predict the resulting products and identify what type of reaction is shown.

Written Response

a) $H_2O_{(l)} + CO_{2(g)} \rightarrow$
   _____
   _____

b) $Mg(OH)_{2(aq)} + HNO_{3(aq)} \rightarrow$
   _____
   _____

c) $H_2O_{(l)} \rightarrow$
   _____
   _____

d) $Ca_{(s)} + H_2O_{(l)} \rightarrow$
   _____
   _____

e) $Cu_{(s)} + AgNO_{3(aq)} \rightarrow$
   _____
   _____

Written Response

5. Predict the products of the reaction $Ag(NO)_{3(aq)} + NaCl_{(aq)}$, and identify the type of reaction that takes place.
   _____
   _____
   _____
   _____
   _____

20-D1.2k recall the balancing of chemical equations in terms of atoms, molecules and moles

BALANCING CHEMICAL EQUATIONS

When chemical reaction equations are balanced, there will be an equal number of atoms (or number of moles of atoms) of each type on each side of the reaction equation.

Example

$$C_3H_{8(g)} + 5O_{2(g)} \rightarrow 3CO_{2(g)} + 4H_2O_{(g)}$$

On each side of the equation, there are 3 carbon atoms (or 3 moles of carbon atoms), 8 hydrogen atoms (or 8 moles of hydrogen atoms), and 10 oxygen atoms (or 10 moles of oxygen atoms).

On the left side, there is 1 molecule of $C_3H_{8(g)}$ (or 1 mole of $C_3H_{8(g)}$ molecules) and 5 molecules of $O_{2(g)}$ (or 5 moles of $O_{2(g)}$ molecules).

On the right side, there are 3 $CO_{2(g)}$ molecules (or 3 moles of $CO_{2(g)}$ molecules) and 4 molecules of $H_2O_{(g)}$ (or 4 moles of $H_2O_{(g)}$ molecules).

Use the following information to answer the next multipart question.

6. Hydrochloric acid ($HCl_{(aq)}$) is produced in the stomach to aid in the breakdown and digestion of food. Excess stomach acid, however, can irritate the lower esophagus causing heartburn. Milk of magnesia, a suspension of $Mg(OH)_{2(s)}$ in water, can usually provide effective relief from heartburn pain.

a) Which of the following equations is a balanced equation for the reaction of milk of magnesia with excess stomach acid?

   A. $HCl_{(aq)} + Mg(OH)_{2(s)}$
      $\rightarrow H_2O_{(l)} + MgCl_{(aq)}$

   B. $2HCl_{(aq)} + Mg(OH)_{2(s)}$
      $\rightarrow 2H_2O_{(l)} + MgCl_{2(aq)}$

   C. $2HCl_{(aq)} + Mg(OH)_{2(s)}$
      $\rightarrow 2H_2O_{(l)} + 2MgCl_{(aq)}$

   D. $2HCl_{(aq)} + 2Mg(OH)_{2(s)}$
      $\rightarrow H_2O_{(l)} + 2MgCl_{(aq)}$

b) How many moles of stomach acid are neutralized for every mole of magnesium hydroxide in milk of magnesia?

   A. 1 mol   **B.** 2 mol

   C. 3 mol   **D.** 4 mol

Use the following information to answer the next question.

When a piece of copper wire was placed into a solution of silver nitrate, a black solid was observed to quickly form on the surface of the wire. This solid was later determined to be silver metal.

Written Response

7. Write the balanced equation for this reaction, and state how many moles of silver would be produced for every one mole of copper consumed.

_____

_____

20-D1.3k contrast quantitative and qualitative analysis

EXAMINING CHEMICAL SPECIES

The chemical properties of a substance can be analyzed in a variety of ways, but all methods of analysis can be classified into two broad categories: qualitative and quantitative analysis. These two ways of examining substances encompass all the means of observation, measurement, and physical manipulation required to verify, substantiate, discredit, or disprove a chemical hypothesis.

QUALITATIVE ANALYSIS

Qualitative analysis typically involves the use of one or more of the five senses to make an observation. For safety reasons, sight is the most commonly used sense, but the other four senses can be used to draw significant conclusions as well. The lists that follow provide examples of experimental procedures that rely on the use of one or more of the senses for analysis.

Sight

- When trying to produce a precipitate from a solution, the sense of sight is used to observe the formation of a solid.
- Observing the color of a solution is necessary in order to perform titration experiments with indicator solutions.
- Flame tests use the color of the flame generated by a substance to determine the presence or absence of certain metal elements. For example, calcium burns with a deep red color, while sodium burns with a bright yellow flame.
- The shapes and forms of some substances, such as crystals, reveal much about the geometric properties of constituent molecules and elements.

Hearing

- Listening to the resonant sounds of some substances can reveal details about their densities and structures. A tuning fork, for example, changes tone depending upon the elasticity of the metal from which it is made.
- Acoustic resonance can be used to detect interference patterns.
- Geiger counters make characteristic popping noises for every radioactive particle they detect.

Touch

- Although this method of experimentation is not advisable unless one already knows the identity of the sample, a basic substance can be identified by touch. Bases have a tendency to saponify the oils on the skin, which makes them feel slippery or soapy.
- Ductility and malleability are both physical properties of samples that can be assessed through touch.
- The textures of some minerals and samples can be used to draw valid chemical conclusions. For example, the Mohs hardness scale is a ten-point scale ranking the hardness of solids. Ordering on the Mohs scale is determined by which substance can scratch another substance. A piece of talc $(Mg_3Si_4O_{10}(OH)_2)$, for instance, is soft, feels greasy to the touch, and can easily be scratched by a fingernail. On the Mohs hardness scale, talc has a hardness of 1.

Smell

- Many organic compounds, particularly complex aromatic ones, are easily detected due to their pungent odours. For example, most organic molecules that contain the functional group thiol have characteristically powerful smells.
- Some dangerous and toxic compounds can be detected using smell, as in the case of hydrogen sulfide, which smells of rotten eggs.
- Smell can be used to detect the presence of esters, which are usually sweet smelling and fragrant.

Taste

- The pH of an unknown sample can sometimes be estimated by taste. The sour taste of citrus fruits indicates that they have juice with a low pH, while the chalky, soapy taste of milk of magnesia suggests that it is a basic solution.
- An investigative scientist can tell the difference between mudstone and siltstone by tasting them. The mudstone will taste creamy, while the siltstone will feel gritty and taste slightly bitter.
- There are no naturally occurring, sweet-tasting substances that are poisonous to humans.

QUANTITATIVE ANALYSIS

In analytical chemistry, quantitative analysis involves answering the questions "how much" or "how many" and generally involves the use of instruments and measuring equipment. Of the two types of analysis, quantitative analysis is the one that predominantly deals with numbers, figures, and units.

Experimental scientists can work with tools as simple as rulers and graduated cylinders and as complicated as mass spectrometers and the Large Hadron Collider to find values of distance, volume, mass, or any other property of a substance that can be expressed numerically. Data collected using quantitative analysis is used in stoichiometric and volumetric computations to draw scientific conclusions.

Use the following information to answer the next question.

The enzyme multiplied immunoassay technique (EMIT) can be used to detect the presence (but not concentration) of a particular substance in urine, serum, or plasma. The EMIT is used in laboratories to screen for the presence of illicit drugs such as marijuana, barbiturates, amphetamines, and opiates.

8. The type of analysis that EMIT exemplifies is a
   A. titration analysis
   B. qualitative analysis
   C. gravimetric analysis
   D. quantitative analysis

Use the following information to answer the next question.

In 1995, chemists Frank Sherwood (Sherry) Rowland, Mario Molina, and Paul Crutzen shared the Nobel Prize in chemistry for the discovery of the ozone-damaging effects of chlorofluorocarbon compounds (CFCs).

9. Which of the following types of analysis is used in the present-day detection to determine the presence of CFCs in the atmosphere?
   A. Qualitative analysis
   B. Quantitative analysis
   C. Titration analysis of rainwater
   D. Titration analysis of glacial ice

20-D1.4k write balanced ionic and net ionic equations, including identification of spectator ions, for reactions taking place in aqueous solutions

WRITING NET IONIC EQUATIONS

Electrolytes in solution will exist in dissociated (ionic) or ionized (strong acid) form. In either case, there will be free ions in solution.

To take a formula equation and change it into ionic and net ionic equations, begin by identifying electrolytes and determining whether or not they are dissolved. If they are, then write them as free ions to produce the ionic equation. Then, identify and remove the spectator ions (the ions that do not change) from the ionic equation. This produces the net ionic equation.

Example
In the reaction of aqueous silver nitrate with solid copper, solid silver metal will precipitate out of the solution, leaving the remaining dissociated ions in aqueous form. In this example, the copper ionizes into cations in solution, and silver precipitates out. The nitrate ions do not change state, charge, concentration, or in fact, react chemically at all, so they are called spectator ions.

The formula equation for the reaction includes all the species involved.
$$2AgNO_{3(aq)} + Cu_{(s)} \rightarrow Cu(NO_3)_{2(aq)} + 2Ag_{(s)}$$

On the reactant side of the equation, however, the silver nitrate is dissociated into silver cations and polyatomic nitrate anions. Similarly, on the product side of the reaction, copper(II) nitrate exists in aqueous solution as dissociated ions, not as an ionic compound. As an ionic equation, the reaction is expressed as follows:

$$2Ag^+_{(aq)} + 2NO^-_{3(aq)} + Cu_{(s)}$$
$$\rightarrow Cu^{2+}_{(aq)} + 2NO^-_{3(aq)} + 2Ag_{(s)}$$

Since $2NO^-_{3(aq)}$ does not change in the reaction, it is a spectator ion. On both the product and reactant sides of the equation, the coefficient, charge, and state of matter of the nitrate ions are identical. Because the nitrate ions do not participate in the reaction and undergo no chemical changes, they are considered spectator ions and are cancelled out to produce a net ionic equation.

$$2Ag^+_{(aq)} + Cu_{(s)} \rightarrow Cu^{2+}_{(aq)} + 2Ag_{(s)}$$

Example

In a reaction of aqueous sodium iodide solution and aqueous lead(II) nitrate solution, a lead(II) iodide precipitate is observed.

The formula equation for the reaction is written as follows:

$$2NaI_{(aq)} + Pb(NO_3)_{2(aq)} \rightarrow PbI_{2(s)} + 2NaNO_{3(aq)}$$

In order to express the reaction in terms of the net ionic equation, all the aqueous ionic species must be shown in dissociated form.

$$2Na^+_{(aq)} + 2I^-_{(aq)} + Pb^{2+}_{(aq)} + 2NO^-_{3(aq)}$$
$$\rightarrow PbI_{2(s)} + 2Na^+_{(aq)} + 2NO^-_{3(aq)}$$

Since $2Na^+_{(aq)}$ and $2NO^-_{3(aq)}$ are unchanged on both sides of the equation, they undergo no chemical change in the reaction; they are spectator ions.

Spectator ions are cancelled out to produce the net ionic equation.

$$Pb^{2+}_{(aq)} + 2I^-_{(aq)} \rightarrow PbI_{2(s)}$$

---

10. Which of the following equations shows the net ionic equation representing the reaction between $HCl_{(aq)}$ and $NaOH_{(aq)}$?

A. $H^+_{(aq)} + OH^-_{(aq)} \rightarrow H_2O_{(l)}$

B. $Na^+_{(aq)} + Cl^-_{(aq)} \rightarrow NaCl_{(aq)}$

C. $HCl_{(aq)} + NaOH_{(aq)} \rightarrow NaCl_{(aq)} + H_2O_{(l)}$

D. $H^+_{(aq)} + Cl^-_{(aq)} + Na^+_{(aq)} + OH^-_{(aq)}$
$\rightarrow Na^+_{(aq)} + Cl^-_{(aq)} + H_2O_{(l)}$

Use the following information to answer the next question.

The concentration of $NaOH_{(aq)}$ in a soap sample was established by titrating it with $HCl_{(aq)}$.

11. The dissolved ions present in this titration were

A. $H^+_{(aq)}$, $OH^-_{(aq)}$, and $Cl^-_{(aq)}$

B. $Na^+_{(aq)}$, $Cl^-_{(aq)}$, and $H_2O_{(l)}$

C. $H_2O_{(l)}$, $H^+_{(aq)}$, and $OH^-_{(aq)}$

D. $Na^+_{(aq)}$, $OH^-_{(aq)}$, $H^+_{(aq)}$, and $Cl^-_{(aq)}$

Use the following information to answer the next question.

Equal volumes of $Ca(NO_3)_2$ and Na_2CO_3 solutions are mixed.

12. Which of the following equations shows the net ionic equation representing the precipitation of $CaCO_3$?

A. $Ca^{2+}_{(aq)} + CO^{2-}_{3(aq)} \rightarrow CaCO_{3(s)}$

B. $Ca(NO_3)_{2(aq)} + Na_2CO_{3(aq)}$
$\rightarrow CaCO_{3(s)} + 2NaNO_{3(s)}$

C. $CaCO_{3(s)} + 2NaNO_{3(aq)}$
$\rightarrow Ca(NO_3)_{2(aq)} + Na_2CO_{3(aq)}$

D. $Ca^{2+}_{(aq)} + 2NO^-_{3(aq)} + 2Na^+_{(aq)} + CO^{2-}_{3(aq)}$
$\rightarrow CaCO_{3(s)} + 2Na^+_{(aq)} + 2NO^-_{3(aq)}$

13. Which of the following equations represents the formula equation for the precipitation reaction between $Pb(NO_3)_{2(aq)}$ and $NaCl_{(aq)}$?

    A. $Pb^{2+}_{(aq)} + 2Cl^-_{(aq)} \rightarrow PbCl_{2(s)}$

    B. $Na^+_{(aq)} + NO^-_{3(aq)} \rightarrow NaNO_{3(aq)}$

    C. $Pb(NO_3)_{2(aq)} + 2NaCl_{(aq)}$
       $\rightarrow PbCl_{2(s)} + 2NaNO_{3(aq)}$

    D. $Pb^{2+}_{(aq)} + 2NO^-_{3(aq)} + 2Na^+_{(aq)} + 2Cl^-_{(aq)}$
       $\rightarrow PbCl_{2(s)} + 2Na^+_{(aq)} + 2NO^-_{3(aq)}$

14. Which of the following equations represents the net ionic equation for the precipitation of $CaSO_{4(s)}$ when $CaCl_{2(aq)}$ and $Na_2SO_{4(aq)}$ are mixed?

    A. $Ca^{2+}_{(aq)} + 2Cl^-_{(aq)} + 2Na^+_{(aq)} + SO^{2-}_{4(aq)}$
       $\rightarrow 2Na^+_{(aq)} + 2Cl^-_{(aq)} + CaSO_{4(s)}$

    B. $CaCl_{2(aq)} + Na_2SO_{4(aq)}$
       $\rightarrow 2NaCl_{(aq)} + CaSO_{4(s)}$

    C. $2Na^+_{(aq)} + SO^{2-}_{4(aq)} \rightarrow Na_2SO_{4(aq)}$

    D. $Ca^{2+}_{(aq)} + SO^{2-}_{4(aq)} \rightarrow CaSO_{4(s)}$

15. Which of the following equations is the complete ionic equation for the reaction between $K_2SO_{4(aq)}$ and $Sr(OH)_{2(aq)}$?

    A. $Sr^{2+}_{(aq)} + SO^{2-}_{4(aq)} \rightarrow SrSO_{4(s)}$

    B. $Sr^{2+}_{(aq)} + 2OH^-_{(aq)} \rightarrow Sr(OH)_{2(s)}$

    C. $K_2SO_{4(aq)} + Sr(OH)_{2(aq)}$
       $\rightarrow SrSO_{4(aq)} + 2KOH_{(aq)}$

    D. $2K^+_{(aq)} + SO^{2-}_{4(aq)} + Sr^{2+}_{(aq)} + 2OH^-_{(aq)}$
       $\rightarrow 2K^+_{(aq)} + 2OH^-_{(aq)} + Sr(SO)_{4(s)}$

20-D1.5k calculate the quantities of reactants and/ or products involved in chemical reactions, using gravimetric, solution or gas stoichiometry.

STOICHIOMETRY

The quantities of reactants or products involved in chemical reactions can be calculated using gravimetric, solution, or gas stoichiometry.

GRAVIMETRIC STOICHIOMETRY

Gravimetric stoichiometry calculations involve the masses of the substances, either products or reactants, in a particular reaction.

Example

In a precipitation reaction, $KOH_{(aq)}$ reacts with excess $Sn(NO_3)_{2(aq)}$ to produce a precipitate.

If the mass of precipitate is 2.57 g, what mass of $KOH_{(s)}$ was present in the original $KOH_{(aq)}$ solution?

Solution

Step 1
Write the reaction equation.
A solubility chart will show that the precipitate will be $Sn(OH)_{2(s)}$.
$2KOH_{(aq)} + Sn(NO_3)_{2(aq)}$
$\rightarrow Sn(OH)_{2(s)} + 2KNO_{3(aq)}$

Step 2
Determine the known and unknown values.

	$KOH_{(aq)}$	$Sn(OH)_{2(s)}$
Moles	n_2	n_1
Mass	?	2.57 g
Molar mass	56.11 g/mol	152.73 g/mol

This shows you need to find the number of moles, n_1, for the substance whose mass is given.

Step 3
Calculate the number of moles of $Sn(OH)_2$ present in the precipitate.

$$n_1 = 2.57\ g \times \frac{1\ mol}{152.73\ g} = 0.0168\ mol$$

Step 4

Use the mole ratio to find the moles of the required substance KOH, n_2.

The balanced equation indicates that 2 moles of KOH are required for every mole of $Sn(OH)_2$ produced.

$$n_2 = 0.0168 \text{ mol} \times \frac{2}{1} = 0.0336 \text{ mol}$$

Step 5

Convert n_2 into the mass of KOH.

$$m = 0.0336 \text{ mol} \times \frac{56.11 \text{ g}}{\text{mol}} = 1.89 \text{ g}$$

There was 1.89 g of KOH in the original solution.

SOLUTION STOICHIOMETRY

Solution stoichiometry questions involve substances in solution. In this case, the specific substance concentration and volumes of solution are used in order to calculate the quantity of a particular substance.

Example

In an experiment, 25.0 mL of 0.100 mol/L sulfuric acid is neutralized completely with 10.0 mL of potassium hydroxide solution.

What is the concentration of the potassium hydroxide solution?

Solution

Step 1

Write a reaction equation.

$$H_2SO_{4(aq)} + 2KOH_{(aq)} \rightarrow K_2SO_{4(aq)} + 2H_2O_{(l)}$$

Step 2

Find the moles of the substance for which you have both concentration and volume, n_1. Use the mole ratio to find moles of the required substance, n_2, and convert this to concentration.

	$H_2SO_{4(aq)}$	$KOH_{(aq)}$
Moles	n_1	n_2
Concentration	0.100 mol/L	?
Volume	25.0 mL	10.0 mL

Step 3

Calculate the moles of H_2SO_4 consumed.

$$n_1 = 0.100 \text{ mol/L} \times 0.0250 \text{ L}$$
$$= 0.002\ 50 \text{ mol}$$

Step 4

Calculate the moles of KOH using the mole ratio in a balanced equation.

$$n_2 = 0.002\ 50 \text{ mol} \times \frac{2}{1}$$
$$= 0.005\ 00 \text{ mol}$$
$$[KOH_{(aq)}] = \frac{0.00500 \text{ mol}}{0.0100 \text{ L}}$$
$$= 0.500 \text{ mol/L}$$

It is possible to work directly with millilitres (mL) and get millimoles (mmol) instead of moles (mol) for n_1 and n_2, but do not use this unless you are very comfortable with the units.

GAS STOICHIOMETRY

Gravimetric and solution stoichiometry questions are always very similar, but gas stoichiometry questions will vary in approach. Always find the number of moles first. Then, multiply by the mole ratio, and finally convert the final number of moles into the required quantity. In gas stoichiometry questions, volumes, pressures, and temperatures as well as gas volumes (molar volumes) and the ideal gas law are all possible factors in any calculation.

Example

In a combustion reaction, 150 g of methanol $(CH_3OH_{(l)})$ are completely burned.

What volume of $CO_{2(g)}$ at 95.0 kPa and 20.0°C will be produced?

Solution

Step 1

Write the reaction equation.

$$2CH_3OH_{(l)} + 3O_{2(g)} \rightarrow 2CO_{2(g)} + 4H_2O_{(l)}$$

Step 2

Determine the known and unknown values.

	$CH_3OH_{(l)}$	$CO_{2(g)}$
Moles	n_1	n_2
Given	150 g	95.0 kPa 20.0 °C
Molar mass	32.05 g/mol	44.01 g/mol

Step 3

Calculate the moles of methanol consumed, n_1.

$$n_1 = 150 \text{ g} \times \left(\frac{1}{32.05 \text{ g/mol}}\right) = 4.68 \text{ mol}$$

Step 4
Calculate the moles of CO_2 produced, n_2.

$$n_2 = 4.68 \text{ mol} \times \frac{2}{2} = 4.68 \text{ mol}$$

Step 5
Assume ideal gas conditions to calculate the volume of $CO_{2(g)}$.

$$V = \frac{nRT}{P}$$

$$= \frac{4.68 \text{ mol} \times (8.314 \text{kPa} \cdot \text{L/mol} \cdot \text{K}) \times 293 \text{ K}}{95.0 \text{ kPa}}$$

$$= 120 \text{ L}$$

The volume of $CO_{2(g)}$ produced will be 120 L.

Use the following information to answer the next question.

Scientists often analyze different sources of water to determine their chloride concentrations. The majority of chloride present in natural bodies of water derives from dissolved rocks and minerals, although human activity can elevate these levels. High concentrations of chloride can be damaging to pipes, bridges, and agricultural crops. Chloride analysis can be done by titration with 0.0040 mol/L $AgNO_{3(aq)}$.

16. If three 100 mL samples of water required an average volume of 26.8 mL of $AgNO_{3(aq)}$ titrant for a complete reaction, then the concentration of chloride ions in the water samples was
    A. 1.1 mol/L

    B. 1.1×10^{-1} mol/L

    C. 1.1×10^{-2} mol/L

    D. 1.1×10^{-3} mol/L

Use the following information to answer the next question.

In oxygen-poor environments, such as stagnant swamps, decay is promoted by anaerobic bacteria. These bacteria obtain their energy by splitting methane and carbon dioxide from carbohydrates.

$$C_6H_{12}O_{6(s)} \rightarrow 3CO_{2(g)} + 3CH_{4(g)}$$

The net effect is often a buildup of carbon-rich residue. These environments can eventually become sources of fossil fuels such as coal or even natural gas.

17. If 100 kg of glucose is broken down, the mass of methane gas produced would be
    A. 2.97 kg   B. 8.91 kg

    C. 13.4 kg   D. 26.7 kg

Use the following information to answer the next question.

Today's cars contain very advanced airbags. The supplemental restraint system (SRS) uses gold-plated, corrosion-resistant electrical connectors to improve conductivity. This allows the airbag to inflate at a faster rate than airbags that employ other types of connectors. Upon impact, a pendulum-type device swings to close an electrical switch, which initiates the simple decomposition reaction of sodium azide. This reaction produces the gas that inflates the bag.

$$2NaN_{3(s)} \rightarrow 2Na_{(s)} + 3N_{2(g)}$$

18. If the volume of an inflated airbag is 35.0 L at SATP, the mass of sodium azide required to fully inflate the airbag upon reaction is

   A. 61.2 g   B. 91.8 g

   C. 122 g   D. 138 g

Use the following information to answer the next multipart question.

19. The chemical 3-(methylimino)butan-2-one is added to food as a flavouring agent. It is prepared from small quantities of butane-2,3-dione, methylamine hydrochloride, and a suitable base.

$$H_3C-\overset{O}{\overset{\|}{C}}-\overset{O}{\overset{\|}{C}}-CH_3 \xrightarrow[\text{Strong base}]{CH_3NH_2 \cdot HCl} H_3C-\overset{O}{\overset{\|}{C}}-\overset{\overset{CH_3}{\overset{N}{\|}}}{C}-CH_3$$

This reaction can also be shown by the following balanced equation:

$$C_4H_6O_2 + CH_3NH_2 \cdot HCl$$
$$\rightarrow C_5H_9NO + H_2O$$

Numerical Response

a) The mass of 3-(methylimino)butan-2-one (C_5H_9NO) that could be produced when 0.70 g of butane-2,3-dione $(C_4H_6O_2)$ is reacted is $a.b \times 10^{-c}$ g. The values of a, b, and c respectively are _____, _____, and _____. (Record your answer as a three-digit number.)

b) What is the theoretical yield of 3-(methylimino)butan-2-one, C_5H_9NO (the product), obtained from the reaction of 0.35 g of butane-2,3-dione, $C_4H_6O_2$ (the reactant), with excess methylamine hydrochloride, $CH_3NH_2 \cdot HCl$?

   A. 0.36 g   B. 0.41 g

   C. 0.56 g   D. 4.1 g

c) If 0.56 g of 3-(methylimino)butan-2-one (C_5H_9NO) is obtained when 0.70 g of butane-2,3-dione $(C_4H_6O_2)$ is reacted, the percentage yield of the experiment is

   A. 56%   B. 65%

   C. 69%   D. 78%

Calcium carbonate ($CaCO_{3(s)}$) is found in marble and limestone buildings and structures. Acid rain poses a problem because it reacts with $CaCO_{3(s)}$ to cause the deterioration of these structures. An example of this reaction is shown.

$$CaCO_{3(s)} + 2HCl_{(aq)}$$
$$\rightarrow CaCl_{2(aq)} + H_2O_{(l)} + CO_{2(g)}$$

20. The volume of rain with a $H^+_{(aq)}$ concentration of 1.00×10^{-4} mol/L that would be required to dissolve 3.50 g of $CaCO_{3(s)}$ is

  A. 7.00 L   **B.** 70.0 L

  C. 700 L   **D.** 7.00 kL

The complete neutralization of a 200 mL sample of acidic rainwater requires 43.2 mL of 0.001 05 mol/L $KOH_{(aq)}$.

21. Assuming that all the acid in the rainwater is H_2SO_4, what is the concentration of $H_2SO_{4(aq)}$ in this sample?

  A. 1.13×10^{-4} mol/L

  B. 2.27×10^{-4} mol/L

  C. 2.27×10^{-5} mol/L

  D. 5.25×10^{-3} mol/L

In the given reaction, sodium bicarbonate, $NaHCO_{3(s)}$, can be used to neutralize excess stomach acid.

$$NaHCO_{3(s)} + HCl_{(aq)}$$
$$\rightarrow NaCl_{(aq)} + CO_{2(g)} + H_2O_{(l)}$$

22. What mass of sodium bicarbonate is needed to completely neutralize 75 mL of 0.110 mol/L $HCl_{(aq)}$?

  A. 0.70 g   **B.** 0.57 g

  C. 0.17 g   **D.** 0.12 g

An environmental chemist analyzes the effluent (waste material) released from an industrial process. He finds that the effluent contains benzoic acid (C_6H_5COOH), a monoprotic acid. The concentration of benzoic acid must be monitored to ensure that it does not exceed environmentally safe levels.
A 100 mL effluent sample is titrated with 0.0155 mol/L NaOH. The initial and final burette readings of the analysis are 28.7 mL and 40.2 mL, respectively.

23. The concentration of the benzoic acid in the effluent is

  A. 9.10×10^{-3} mol/L

  B. 1.78×10^{-3} mol/L

  C. 1.09×10^{-2} mol/L

  D. 0.135 mol/L

Many tonnes of hydrochloric acid are produced every year. $HCl_{(aq)}$ is used in the manufacture of pharmaceuticals, alkyl chlorides, and rubber. It is also used to clean metals before galvanizing them and in simple titrations in chemistry labs.

24. If a 15 mL sample of $KOH_{(aq)}$ is completely neutralized by 8.5 mL of 0.190 mol/L $HCl_{(aq)}$, then the molar concentration of the $KOH_{(aq)}$ is

  A. 0.08 mol/L   **B.** 0.11 mol/L

  C. 0.13 mol/L   **D.** 0.18 mol/L

20-D2.1k explain chemical principles (i.e., conservation of mass in a chemical change), using quantitative analysis

CONSERVATION OF MASS

In a chemical reaction, mass is conserved. This means that the mass of products equals the mass of reactants.

Example

$$2AgNO_{3(aq)} + Cu_{(s)} \rightarrow Cu(NO_3)_{2(aq)} + 2Ag_{(s)}$$

The mass of $AgNO_{3(aq)}$ and $Cu_{(s)}$ equals the mass of $Cu(NO_3)_{2(aq)}$ and $Ag_{(s)}$. This can be explained by the fact that there are an equal number of moles of each element before and after the reaction. If this reaction was performed with excess $Cu_{(s)}$ and the concentration of $AgNO_{3(aq)}$ was known, when the reaction goes to completion, all the $AgNO_3$ would be used, some of the $Cu_{(s)}$ would be used, and $Cu(NO_3)_{2(aq)}$ and $Ag_{(s)}$ would be produced. The mass of $AgNO_3$ will be known from the solution concentration and volume.

The $Ag_{(s)}$ that forms on the surface of the piece of copper can be carefully removed, washed, dried, and its mass can be determined. After the silver is removed, the $Cu_{(s)}$ mass can be determined and compared to the original mass. Finally, the $Cu^{2+}_{(aq)}$ could be removed from the solution by precipitation with excess $NaOH_{(aq)}$. The mass of $Cu(OH)_{2(s)}$ precipitate could be used to calculate the mass of $Cu(NO_3)_2$ in the solution using gravimetric stoichiometry. This should verify the law of conservation of mass with some experimental error.

---

25. When 45.90 g of sodium metal reacts with 70.90 g of chlorine gas, 116.8 g of solid sodium chloride is formed.
    This occurrence demonstrates the law of
    A. mass action
    B. multiple proportions
    C. definite composition
    D. conservation of mass

Use the following information to answer the next question.

> To determine the amount of a sample of an unknown gas in moles, Jose measured the mass, temperature, and pressure of the gas sample.

26. In order to determine the molar mass, the Jose will also require the
    A. temperature and pressure measurements
    B. mass and temperature measurements
    C. mass and pressure measurements
    D. measurement of volume

20-D2.2k identify limiting and excess reagents in chemical reactions

LIMITING AND EXCESS REAGENTS

A chemical equation represents the stoichiometric relation between reactants and products, as shown in the following example:

i. $CO_{2(g)} + H_2O_{(l)} \rightarrow H_2CO_{3(aq)}$
    Here, one mole of carbon dioxide reacts with one mole of water to produce one mole of carbonic acid.

ii. $4Al_{(s)} + 3O_{2(g)} \rightarrow 2Al_2O_{3(s)}$
    Here, four moles of aluminum and three moles of oxygen react to produce two moles of aluminum oxide.

Suppose that in equation II, seven moles of oxygen are supplied along with four moles of aluminum. In this case one reagent (Al) is present in less than the stoichiometric amount, while the other reactant (O_2) is in excess. An excess reagent is present in a greater quantity (measured, for example, as the number of moles times the mole ratio of the reactants) than is necessary to consume the other reactant. The reactant in the lesser amount is the limiting reagent. It is the limiting reactant that determines the theoretical quantity of product formed. In this example, even with the extra oxygen present, there are still just four moles of aluminum. From the balanced equation, three moles of oxygen are needed to consume the four moles of aluminum, leaving four moles of oxygen in excess. The four moles of aluminum will determine the amount of product—in this case, it will remain as two moles of aluminum oxide.

The concept of a limiting reagent is frequently applied in industry, when one of the reactants is very expensive compared to other reactants. The cheaper reactants are added in excess in order to ensure that as much of the costlier material as possible is converted into product.

Use the following information to answer the next question.

> A student mixes 300 mL of 0.100 mol/L $BaCl_{2(aq)}$ and 200 mL of 0.110 mol/L $Na_2CO_{3(aq)}$.

27. The limiting reagent in the given reaction is
    A. $Na_2CO_{3(aq)}$
    B. $BaCO_{3(s)}$
    C. $BaCl_{2(aq)}$
    D. $NaCl_{(aq)}$

20-D2.3k define theoretical yields and actual yields

THEORETICAL AND PERCENTAGE YIELDS

The theoretical yield of a chemical reaction is the quantity of product that would be expected to be formed if all the limiting reagent is consumed. It is calculated from stoichiometry.

The actual yield is the actual quantity of product collected. In most cases, the actual yield will be less than the theoretical yield.

The most common way to report the outcome of an experiment is to use this formula:

$$\text{percentage yield} = \frac{\text{actual yield}}{\text{theoretical yield}} \times 100\%$$

Example

In an experiment, 300 g of copper sulfide reacts with oxygen to produce 112 g of copper.

$$CuS_{(s)} + O_{2(g)} \rightarrow Cu_{(s)} + SO_{2(g)}$$

Calculate the theoretical yield and the actual yield of copper produced if the percentage yield of the reaction was 56%.

Solution

Step 1

Calculate the molar mass of CuS.
   Cu = 63.55 g/mol
   S = 32.07 g/mol
CuS = 63.55 + 32.07 = 95.62 g/mol

Step 2

Calculate the moles of CuS in the 300 g used.

$$\text{moles of CuS} = \frac{300 \text{ g}}{95.62 \text{ g/mol}} = 3.14 \text{ mol}$$

Step 3

From the balanced equation, calculate the theoretical moles and mass of copper produced. The balanced equation indicates that 1 mole of copper will be produced per mole of copper sulfide used.

- The theoretical moles of copper being produced are 3.14 moles.
- The theoretical mass of copper produced would then be
  3.14 mol × 63.55 g/mol = 199.5 g

Step 4

Calculate the actual mass from the theoretical mass and the percentage yield.

$$\% \text{ yield} = \frac{\text{actual yield}}{\text{theoretical yield}} \times 100$$

actual yield = 56% × 199.5 g

= 111.7 g

= 112 g

The actual yield of copper was 112 g.

Use the following information to answer the next multipart question.

28. Methyl hydrate ($CH_3OH_{(l)}$), commonly known as gasoline antifreeze, is added to automobile gas tanks in winter to aid in the cleaner combustion of gasoline that has been contaminated by water condensation. The IUPAC name for methyl hydrate is methanol. It is produced by the chemical reaction

$$CO_{(g)} + 2H_{2(g)} \rightarrow CH_3OH_{(l)}$$

The reaction is carried out using 70.0 kg of $CO_{(g)}$ in combination with 9.00 kg of $H_{2(g)}$.

a) Assuming the reaction goes to completion, which of the following statements identifies the limiting reagent and the amount of $CH_3OH_{(l)}$ produced in this situation?

A. $CO_{(g)}$ is the limiting reagent, and 2.50×10^3 mol of CH_3OH is produced.

B. $CO_{(g)}$ is the limiting reagent, and 2.23×10^3 mol of CH_3OH is produced.

C. $H_{2(g)}$ is the limiting reagent, and 2.50×10^3 mol of CH_3OH is produced.

D. $H_{2(g)}$ is the limiting reagent, and 2.23×10^3 mol of CH_3OH is produced.

b) If 9.00 kg of $H_{2(g)}$ were consumed to produce an actual yield of 59.2 kg of $CH_3OH_{(l)}$, what is the percentage yield for this reaction?

A. 84.6%   **B.** 82.9%

C. 73.9%   **D.** 65.8%

Use the following information to answer the next question.

A student mixes 300.0 mL of 0.100 mol/L $BaCl_{2(aq)}$ and 200.0 mL of 0.110 mol/L $Na_2CO_{3(aq)}$.

29. What mass of precipitate actually forms if the experimental yield is 78% of the predicted yield?

A. 1.0 g   **B.** 2.0 g

C. 2.5 g   **D.** 3.4 g

30. The quantity of product that is predicted as a result of a stoichiometric calculation is known as the

A. actual yield

B. percent yield

C. fractional yield

D. theoretical yield

31. The actual yield of an experiment is the

A. mass of product obtained from the reaction

B. mass of the products expected from the reaction

C. difference between the mass of the reactants and the mass of the products

D. difference between the expected mass and the measured mass of the product

Use the following information to answer the next question.

A student mixes two solutions together, and a precipitate forms. The student calculates a theoretical yield of 14.3 g. After the student washes and dries the precipitate, it is found to have a mass of 11.7 g.

32. What was the percentage yield?

A. 1.67%   **B.** 22.2%

C. 81.8%   **D.** 122%

20-D2.4k explain the discrepancy between theoretical and actual yields

Reaction Yields

Actual yields will be less than theoretical yields for many reasons including the following:

- Impurities found in the reactants
- Uncertainty in measurements
- Some of the precipitate substance actually dissolves.
- Washing the precipitate with water to clean it causes a little bit to dissolve.
- Small amounts of solid stick to spatulas and stirring rods.

A theoretical yield assumes that a reaction goes to completion. However, this may not happen in an actual reaction for the following reasons:

- The reaction may be thought to be complete because it is a slow reaction.
- Some reactions never go to completion; they reach a state of dynamic equilibrium before doing so.

Example

An experiment to convert 300 g of copper sulfide into copper proceeded with a 56% yield to give 112 g of copper.

$$CuS_{(s)} + O_{2(g)} \rightarrow Cu_{(s)} + SO_{2(g)}$$

Suggest some reasons for the poor yield if the usual yield is found to be 85%.

Solution

If there is not enough oxygen supplied, then not all the copper sulfide will react. If the copper sulfide contained other impurities that did not react, then the final amount of copper would be less and there would have been less copper sulfide to begin with. Depending upon how carefully the copper was collected and weighed, some losses could be accounted for here as well.

Use the following information to answer the next question.

A common technique to increase the purity of compounds is recrystallization. In a lab experiment, a sample that consists of mainly compound A with trace amounts of impurity B undergoes a recrystallization procedure. The sample is dissolved in warm solvent to form a nearly saturated solution. Then, the solution is cooled down slowly using an ice bath. As the temperature drops, the solubility of compound A in the solution also drops, and crystals are formed in the solution. These crystals contain less impurity B than the initial sample used in the experiment. The solution containing the solid crystals is passed through filter paper, and the crystals are recovered and weighed. Since the recovery of the sample is calculated to be 105%, it is concluded that the experiment is flawed.

33. Which of the following observations would **most likely** explain why the recovery rate was calculated to be greater than 100%?

   A. The initial sample was not 100% pure.

   B. The recovered crystals were not completely dry when weighed.

   C. Some particles of compound A were dragged through the pores of the filter paper.

   D. At the temperature at which the filtering procedure was done, compound A was slightly soluble in the solvent.

20-D2.5k draw and interpret titration curves, using data from titration experiments involving strong monoprotic acids and strong monoprotic bases

TITRATIONS

In order to determine the concentration of an unknown reactant in solution, a reagent with a known volume and concentration is added to the solution. The solution with the unknown reactant is the **analyte** and the reagent being added to the solution is the **titrant**. In the case of strong monoprotic acids and strong monoprotic bases, when there is an equal amount of titrant and analytic present the titration reaches the **equivalence point** (pH = 7).

STRONG ACID-STRONG BASE TITRATIONS

As a strong acid is added to a strong base, or as a strong base is added to a strong acid, initially the pH does not change dramatically. There is always a significant amount of the initial acid or base present. Once the number of moles of acid is equal to the number of moles of base in the solution, the titration has reached its equivalence point.

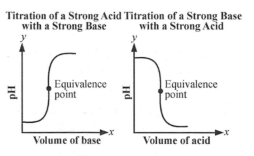

Just before the equivalence point, the pH of the analyte begins to change rapidly (the steep part of the curve) as the original base or acid is used up. The pH levels out again after the equivalence point as the pH of the solution approaches the pH of the titrant.

Use the following information to answer the next multipart question.

34. A technician performed a titration to determine the concentration of a 27.0 mL sample of $NaOH_{(aq)}$. A few drops of phenol red indicator were added to the base, which was then titrated with a 0.24 mol/L solution of $HCl_{(aq)}$ until the indicator changed colour from red to orange.

Volume of Acid Used	
Final burette reading (mL)	25.8
Initial burette reading (mL)	7.8

Numerical Response

a) What is the concentration of the $NaOH_{(aq)}$ solution? _____ mol/L. (Record your three-digit answer.)

Written Response

b) Sketch a titration curve for the titration of aqueous sodium hydroxide with hydrochloric acid, and label the equivalence point on the curve.

_____
_____
_____
_____
_____
_____
_____
_____

20-D2.6k describe the function and choice of indicators in titrations

INDICATORS IN TITRATIONS

In most titrations, there is no visible evidence that indicates when the equivalence point occurs. Therefore, indicators that change colour at a specific pH range are added to the solution being titrated to determine the equivalence point.

Indicators are chosen so that the equivalence point is in the middle of the transition range for the indicator. For example, bromothymol blue changes colour depending on the pH range as follows:

- Below pH 6.0, it is yellow.
- Above pH 7.6, it is blue.
- Between 6.0 and 7.6, it is various shades of green.

Bromothymol blue is an ideal indicator for a monoprotic strong acid-strong base titration since the equivalence point is in the middle of the transition range. When titrating, a lab worker would attempt to get a green bromothymol blue endpoint.

Phenolphthalein is another commonly used indicator in titrations. Although it changes pH at a range of 8.2 to 10.0 (slightly above an equivalence point of 7), it still changes colour near the equivalence point on the steep part of the titration curve.

35. If a sample of HCl is titrated with NaOH to its endpoint, the **best** choice for an indicator is

    A. methyl orange

    B. indigo carmine

    C. alizarin yellow

    D. bromothymol blue

Use the following information to answer the next question.

A basic substance was titrated with HCl. The equivalence point occurred when the pH reached 3.5.

36. A suitable indicator for this endpoint is

    A. chlorophenol red

    B. bromothymol blue

    C. methyl orange

    D. thymol blue

20-D2.7k identify equivalence points on strong monoprotic acid – strong monoprotic base titration curves and differentiate between the indicator end point and the equivalence point.

TITRATION TERMINOLOGY

When discussing the analysis of titration experiments, it is important to remember some key terms.

The **equivalence point** is the point at which the number of moles of titrant is stoichiometrically equal to the number of moles of analyte.

The **endpoint** is the point at which there is a sudden change in a physical property, such as indicator colour, pH, absorbency, or conductivity. For an acid-base indicator, the point at which the indicator changes colour in the titration is the endpoint.

A strong acid-strong base titration has a green bromothymol blue endpoint. This can be verified on an indicator chart. The equivalence point of a strong acid-strong base titration occurs when the pH is equal to 7.0. Bromothymol blue is green at this point.

Example

    Describe when the equivalence point for the titration of a 10.0 mL sample of 0.10 mol/L $HCl_{(aq)}$ with 0.50 mol/L $NaOH_{(aq)}$ occurs.

Solution

    Step 1
    Write the balanced equation that represents the titration.
    $HCl_{(aq)} + NaOH_{(aq)} \rightarrow NaCl_{(aq)} + H_2O_{(l)}$

Step 2

Determine the equivalence point.
The equivalence point occurs when there is a stoichiometrically equal amount of $HCl_{(aq)}$ and $NaOH_{(aq)}$.

$$n_{HCl_{(aq)}} = 0.10 \text{ mol/L} \times 0.0100 \text{ L}$$
$$= 0.0010 \text{ mol}$$

The stoichiometric ratio of HCl:NaOH is 1:1. Therefore, the equivalence point can be determined as follows:

$$n_{NaOH_{(aq)}} = 0.0010 \text{ mol HCl} \times \frac{1 \text{ mol NaOH}}{1 \text{ mol HCl}}$$

$$V_{NaOH_{(aq)}} = \frac{0.0010 \text{ mol}}{0.50 \text{ mol/L}}$$
$$= 0.0020 \text{ L}$$
$$= 2.0 \text{ mL}$$

The equivalence point occurs when 2.0 mL of $NaOH_{(aq)}$ has been added. At this point, the solution is neutral (has a pH equal to 7) because the moles of $HCl_{(aq)}$ are equal to the moles of $NaOH_{(aq)}$. On a titration curve, the equivalence point is the midpoint of the steep vertical rise.

---

37. A sample of NaOH is titrated with HCl. Which of the following statements about this reaction is **true** at the equivalence point?

A. The number of moles of HCl added is equivalent to the initial number of moles of NaOH present.

B. There are more hydrogen ions than hydroxide ions in the solution.

C. Sodium chloride would precipitate in the Erlenmeyer flask.

D. Litmus paper would turn from blue to pink.

Use the following information to answer the next question.

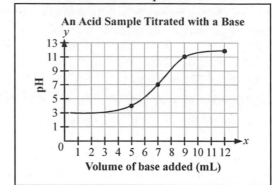

38. The pH at the equivalence point on the given titration curve is

A. 4   **B.** 7

C. 11   **D.** 12

ANSWERS AND SOLUTIONS
QUANTITATIVE RELATIONSHIPS IN CHEMICAL CHANGE

1.	C	b)	B	16.	D	24.	B	33.	B
2.	B	7.	WR	17.	D	25.	D	34. a)	0.16
3.	B	8.	B	18.	A	26.	D		b) WR
4. a)	WR	9.	A	19. a)	881	27.	A	35.	D
	b) WR	10.	A		b) B	28. a)	D	36.	C
	c) WR	11.	D		c) C		b) B	37.	A
	d) WR	12.	A	20.	C	29.	D	38.	B
	e) WR	13.	C	21.	A	30.	D		
5.	WR	14.	D	22.	A	31.	A		
6. a)	B	15.	D	23.	B	32.	C		

1. C

Single-replacement reactions have the form of $A + BC \rightarrow AC + B$. That is, entity A replaces ion B in compound BC. This forms a new compound, AC, and the element, B. In this case, Zn displaces the H^+ ions in HCl to form a new compound, $ZnCl_2$, and $H_{2(g)}$. This reaction is a single-replacement reaction.

2. B

The complete neutralization of $H_2SO_{4(aq)}$ and $Ba(OH)_{2(aq)}$ results in the release of $Ba^{2+}_{(aq)}$ and $SO^{2-}_{4(aq)}$ ions. These combine to produce a $BaSO_{4(s)}$ precipitate.

A solubility table will show that most sulfate compounds are highly soluble, except for those containing Ca^{2+}, Sr^{2+}, Ba^{2+}, Ra^{2+}, Pb^{2+}, and Ag^+.

3. B

When a compound is broken down into other compounds, a decomposition has taken place.

A simple decomposition has occurred if the products are all elements.

4. a) WR

The reaction will produce $H_2CO_{3(aq)}$. This is a formation or synthesis reaction.

b) WR

The reaction will produce $Mg(NO_3)_{2(aq)} + H_2O_{(l)}$. This is a double displacement reaction.

c) WR

The reaction will produce $2H_{2(g)} + O_{2(g)}$. This is a decomposition reaction.

d) WR

The reaction will produce $Ca(OH)_{2(s)} + H_{2(g)}$. This is a single displacement reaction.

e) WR

The reaction will likely produce $Ag_{(s)} + Cu(NO_3)_{2(aq)}$, since Cu(II) is more common than Cu(I). This is a single displacement reaction.

5. WR

$Ag(NO)_{3(aq)} + NaCl_{(aq)} \rightarrow AgCl_{(s)} + Na(NO)_{3(aq)}$

This reaction is a double-displacement reaction since the anions and cations were exchanged during the reaction. Because the $Cl^-_{(aq)}$ ion has a low solubility with $Ag^+_{(aq)}$, an $AgCl_{(s)}$ precipitate will form.

6. a) B

Step 1

Write the reaction of $HCl_{(aq)}$ and $Mg(OH)_{2(s)}$.

$HCl_{(aq)} + Mg(OH)_{2(s)} \rightarrow H_2O_{(l)} + MgCl_{2(aq)}$

Step 2

Balance the atom or ion that is present in the greatest number.

In this case, balance either the OH^- or Cl^- ions.

$2HCl_{(aq)} + Mg(OH)_{2(s)} \rightarrow H_2O_{(l)} + MgCl_{2(aq)}$

Step 3

Balance the H^+ ions.

$2HCl_{(aq)} + Mg(OH)_{2(s)} \rightarrow 2H_2O_{(l)} + MgCl_{2(aq)}$

b) B

Step 1

Write a balanced equation.

The mole ratio of $HCl_{(aq)}$ to $Mg(OH)_{2(s)}$ is expressed in this neutralization reaction:

$$2HCl_{(aq)} + Mg(OH)_{2(s)} \rightarrow 2H_2O_{(l)} + MgCl_{2(aq)}$$

The coefficients of $HCl_{(aq)}$ and $Mg(OH)_{2(s)}$ are 2 and 1, respectively, in the balanced equation.

Step 2

Calculate the mole ratio.

$$\frac{n_{HCl}}{n_{Mg(OH)_2}} = \frac{2 \text{ mol}}{1 \text{ mol}} = \frac{2}{1} \text{ or } 2:1$$

Therefore, two moles of $HCl_{(aq)}$ are neutralized by one mole of $Mg(OH)_{2(s)}$.

7. WR

Write the balanced equation.

$$2AgNO_{3(aq)} + Cu_{(s)} \rightarrow 2Ag_{(s)} + Cu(NO_3)_{2(aq)}$$

For every one mole of copper consumed, two moles of silver will be produced.

8. B

An analysis that detects the presence of a chemical but not its concentration is a qualitative analysis.

A quantitative analysis determines the actual concentration of a substance known to be present in a given sample. Titration analysis determines the concentration of a known substance in a sample by measuring the volume of a particular reagent required to completely react with the sample. Gravimetric analysis determines the concentration of a known substance in a sample by measuring the mass of a precipitate formed by the reaction with a particular reagent.

9. A

A quantitative analysis is used to measure the actual amount (concentration, mass, or volume) of a substance known to be present in a particular sample, while a qualitative analysis simply detects the presence of a chemical species in a sample. The mere detection of some unknown amount of CFCs in the atmosphere is the result of a qualitative analysis.

Titration is a type of quantitative analysis that determines the amount of a known substance present in a sample by measuring the volume of another reagent required to react completely with it.

10. A

Step 1

Write the formula equation.

$$HCl_{(aq)} + NaOH_{(aq)} \rightarrow NaCl_{(aq)} + H_2O_{(l)}$$

Step 2

Write the complete ionic equation.

$$H^+_{(aq)} + Cl^-_{(aq)} + Na^+_{(aq)} + OH^-_{(aq)}$$
$$\rightarrow Na^+_{(aq)} + Cl^-_{(aq)} + H_2O_{(l)}$$

Step 3

Write the net ionic equation.

The unchanged ions on either side of the equation, called spectator ions, are usually removed from the net ionic equation.

$$H^+_{(aq)} + OH^-_{(aq)} \rightarrow H_2O_{(l)}$$

11. D

Both $NaOH_{(aq)}$ and $HCl_{(aq)}$ are strong electrolytes that dissociate completely in aqueous solution.

$$HCl_{(aq)} \rightarrow H^+_{(aq)} + Cl^-_{(aq)}$$
$$NaOH_{(aq)} \rightarrow Na^+_{(aq)} + OH^-_{(aq)}$$

The dissolved ions in the reaction are $H^+_{(aq)}$, $Cl^-_{(aq)}$, $Na^+_{(aq)}$, and $OH^-_{(aq)}$.

12. A

Step 1

Write the formula equation for the reaction.

$$Ca(NO_3)_{2(aq)} + Na_2CO_{3(aq)}$$
$$\rightarrow CaCO_{3(s)} + 2NaNO_{3(aq)}$$

Step 2

Write the complete ionic equation.

$$Ca^{2+}_{(aq)} + 2NO^-_{3(aq)} + 2Na^+_{(aq)} + CO^{2-}_{3(aq)}$$
$$\rightarrow CaCO_{3(s)} + 2Na^+_{(aq)} + 2NO^-_{3(aq)}$$

Step 3

Write the net ionic equation.

Spectator ions are removed from the net ionic equation.

$$Ca^{2+}_{(aq)} + CO^{2-}_{3(aq)} \rightarrow CaCO_{3(s)}$$

13. C

The formula equation for the reaction between $Pb(NO_3)_{2(aq)}$ and $NaCl_{(aq)}$ is given as follows:

$$Pb(NO_3)_{2(aq)} + 2NaCl_{(aq)} \rightarrow PbCl_{2(s)} + 2NaNO_{3(aq)}$$

14. D

Step 1

Write the formula equation for the given reaction.

$CaCl_{2(aq)} + Na_2SO_{4(aq)} \rightarrow 2NaCl_{(aq)} + CaSO_{4(s)}$

Step 2

Write the complete ionic equation.

$Ca^{2+}_{(aq)} + 2Cl^{-}_{(aq)} + 2Na^{+}_{(aq)} + SO^{2-}_{4(aq)}$

$\rightarrow 2Na^{+}_{(aq)} + 2Cl^{-}_{(aq)} + CaSO_{4(s)}$

Step 3

Write the net ionic equation.

The spectator ions, or the ions that do not change during the reaction, are cancelled from the complete ionic equation to obtain the net ionic equation.

$Ca^{2+}_{(aq)} + SO^{2-}_{4(aq)} \rightarrow CaSO_{4(s)}$

15. D

In a complete ionic equation, the aqueous ionic compounds are represented in ionic form as free ions in aqueous state. Precipitates are represented in solid state. The complete ionic equation is as follows:

$2K^{+}_{(aq)} + SO^{2-}_{4(aq)} + Sr^{2+}_{(aq)} + 2OH^{-}_{(aq)}$

$\rightarrow 2K^{+}_{(aq)} + 2OH^{-}_{(aq)} + Sr(SO)_{4(s)}$

16. D

Step 1

Write a balanced reaction equation that includes all the relevant data.

$AgNO_{3(aq)} + Cl^{-}_{(aq)} \rightarrow AgCl_{(s)} + NO^{-}_{3(aq)}$

Step 2

Calculate the number of moles of the given reactant or product (n_{given}).

Find the number of moles of $AgNO_3$ used.

$= 0.0268 \text{ L} \times 0.004 \text{ mol/L}$

$= 1.1 \times 10^{-4} \text{ moles}$

Step 3

Use the appropriate mole ratio to convert n_{given} into the number of moles of the required reactant or product ($n_{required}$).

$n_{Cl^-} = \frac{1}{1} n_{AgNO_3}$

$= \frac{1}{1} \times 1.1 \times 10^{-4} \text{ moles}$

Step 4

Determine the answer by converting the $n_{required}$ into a concentration.

$\left[Cl^{-}_{(aq)}\right] = \dfrac{1.1 \times 10^{-4} \text{ moles}}{0.1 \text{ L}}$

$= 1.1 \times 10^{-3} \text{ mol/L}$

The chloride ion concentration was 1.1×10^{-3} mol/L.

The equation $Ag^{+}_{(aq)} + Cl^{-}_{(aq)} \rightarrow AgCl_{(s)}$ could also be used.

17. D

Use the stoichiometric method.

$C_6H_{12}O_{6(s)} \rightarrow 3CO_{2(g)} + 3CH_{4(g)}$

Glucose ($C_6H_{12}O_{6(S)}$)
$M = 180.18$ g/mol
$m = 100$ kg
Methane($CH_{4(g)}$)
$M = 180.18$ g/mol
$m = 100$ kg

$n_{C_6H_{12}O_6} = 1.0 \times 10^5 \text{ g} \times \dfrac{\text{mol}}{180.18 \text{ g}}$

$= 555 \text{ mol}$

$n_{CH_4} = \dfrac{3}{1} n_{C_6H_{12}O_6}$

$= \dfrac{3}{1} \times 555 \text{ mol}$

$= 1.67 \times 10^3 \text{ mol}$

$m_{CH_4} = 1.67 \times 10^3 \text{ mol} \times \dfrac{16.05 \text{ g}}{\text{mol}}$

$= 26.7 \text{ kg}$

The anaerobic digestion of 100 kg of glucose should produce 26.7 kg of methane gas.

18. A

$2NaN_{3(s)} \rightarrow 2Na_{(s)} + 3N_{2(g)}$

The molecular weight of NaN_3 is 65.02 g/mol.

The volume of gas at SATP = 24.8 L/mol.

Step 1

Calculate the moles of N_2 required.

$n_{N_2} = 35.0 \text{ L} \times \dfrac{\text{mol}}{24.8 \text{ L}} = 1.41 \text{ mol}$

Step 2

Calculate the mass of NaN_3 required.

$$n_{NaN_3} = \frac{2}{3}n_{N_2} = \frac{2}{3} \times 1.41 \text{ mol} = 0.941 \text{ mol}$$

$$m_{NaN_3} = 0.941 \text{ mol} \times \frac{65.02 \text{ g}}{\text{mol}}$$

$$m_{NaN_3} = 61.2 \text{ g}$$

The decomposition of 61.2 g of $NaN_{3(s)}$ will provide 35.0 L of gas at SATP.

19. **a) 881**

Step 1

Find the molar mass of butane-2,3-dione ($C_4H_6O_2$).

$C_4 = 4(12.01) = 48.04$
$H_6 = 6(1.01) = 6.06$
$O_2 = 2(16.00) = \underline{32.00}$
total $= 86.10$ g/mol

Step 2

Find the number of moles of butane-2,3-dione that are being reacted.

$$n = \frac{m}{M}$$

$$n = \frac{0.7 \text{ g}}{86.10 \text{ g/mol}}$$

$$n = 0.0081 \text{ mol}$$

Step 3

Find the molar mass of 3-(methylimino)butan-2-one (C_5H_9NO).

$C_5 = 5(12.01) = 60.05$
$H_9 = 9(1.01) = 9.09$
$N = 1(14.01) = 14.01$
$O = 1(16.00) = \underline{16.00}$
total $= 99.15$ g/mol

Step 4

Solve for the expected mass of 3-(methylimino)butan-2-one.

$m = n \times M$
$m = 0.0081 \text{ mol} \times 99.15 \text{ g/mol}$
$m = 0.81 \text{ g or } 8.1 \times 10^{-1} \text{ g}$

When the answer is expressed as $a.b \times 10^{-C}$ g, the values of a, b, and c respectively are 8, 8, and 1.

b) B

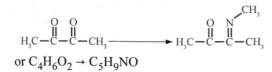

or $C_4H_6O_2 \rightarrow C_5H_9NO$

$$n_{reactant} = 0.35 \text{ g} \times \frac{\text{mol}}{86.10 \text{ g}}$$
$$= 0.0041 \text{ mol}$$

$$n_{product} = \frac{1}{1}n_{reactant}$$
$$= \frac{1}{1} \times 0.0041 \text{ mol}$$

$$m_{product} = 0.0041 \text{ mol} \times \frac{99.15 \text{ g}}{\text{mol}}$$
$$= 0.41 \text{ g}$$

The predicted mass (theoretical yield) of the product of this reaction is 0.41 g.

c) C

Step 1

Find the molar mass of butane-2,3-dione ($C_4H_6O_2$).

$C_4 = 4(12.01) = 48.04$
$H_6 = 6(1.01) = 6.06$
$O_2 = 2(16.00) = \underline{32.00}$
total $= 86.10$ g/mol

Step 2

Find the number of moles of butane-2,3-dione that are being reacted.

$$n = \frac{m}{M}$$

$$n = \frac{0.7 \text{ g}}{86.10 \text{ g/mol}}$$

$$n = 0.0081 \text{ mol}$$

Step 3

Find the molar mass of 3-(methylimino)butan-2-one (C_5H_9NO).

$C_5 = 5(12.01) = 60.05$
$H_9 = 9(1.01) = 9.09$
$N = 1(14.01) = 14.01$
$O = 1(16.00) = \underline{16.00}$
total $= 99.15$ g/mol

Step 4

Solve for the expected mass of 3-(methylimino)butan-2-one.

$m = n \times M$
$m = 0.0081 \text{ mol} \times 99.15 \text{ g/mol}$
$m = 0.81 \text{ g}$

Step 5

Determine the percentage yield by dividing the amount of 3-(methylimino)butan-2-one that was actually produced in the experiment by the amount that is predicted by the theoretical stoichiometric calculation. Then, multiply the value by 100.

$$\text{percentage yield} = \frac{\text{mass obtained}}{\text{mass predicted}} \times 100\%$$

In this case, the percentage yield is

$$\frac{0.56 \text{ g}}{0.81 \text{ g}} \times 100\% = 69\%.$$

The percentage yield of the reaction is 69%.

20. C

Use a stoichiometric calculation to solve this problem.

$$CaCO_{3(s)} + 2H^+_{(aq)} \rightarrow Ca^{2+}_{(aq)} + H_2O_{(l)} + CO_{2(g)}$$

Step 1

Calculate the number of moles of calcium carbonate.

$$n_{CaCO_3} = \frac{3.50 \text{ g}}{M_{CaCO_3}}$$

$$n_{CaCO_3} = \frac{3.50 \text{ g}}{100.09 \text{ g/mol}}$$

$$n_{CaCO_3} = 0.0350 \text{ mol}$$

Step 2

Equate the number of moles of H^+ required by using the stoichiometric relation.

$$n_{H^+} = 2n_{CaCO_3} = 2(0.0350 \text{ mol}) = 0.0700 \text{ mol}$$

Step 3

Convert moles into volume with the concentration data.

$$V_{H^+} = \frac{0.0700 \text{ mol}}{1.00 \times 10^{-4} \text{ mol/L}}$$
$$= 700 \text{ L}$$

The volume of acid rain with a $\left[H^+_{(aq)}\right]$ of

1.00×10^{-4} mol/L needed to dissolve 3.50 g of $CaCO_{(s)}$ is 700 L.

21. A

Use the stoichiometric method to solve this problem.

Step 1

Write the reaction equation.

$$2KOH_{(aq)} + H_2SO_{4(aq)} \rightarrow Na_2SO_{4(aq)} + H_2O_{(l)}$$
$$0.001 \ 05 \text{ mol/L} = \left[KOH_{(aq)}\right]$$

Step 2

Determine the number of moles of $KOH_{(aq)}$.

$$n_{KOH} = 0.0432 \text{ L} \times \frac{0.001 \ 05 \text{ mol}}{L}$$
$$= 0.0454 \text{ mmol}$$

or 4.54×10^{-5} mol

Step 3

Calculate the number of moles of $H_2SO_{4(aq)}$ using the mole ratio in a balanced equation.

Since the molar ratio of $KOH_{(aq)}$:$H_2SO_{4(aq)}$ is 2:1, the number of moles of $H_2SO_{4(aq)}$ is half the number of moles of potassium hydroxide.

$$n_{H_2SO_4} = \frac{1}{2}n_{KOH}$$
$$= \frac{1}{2} \times 0.0454 \text{ mmol}$$
$$= 0.0227 \text{ mmol}$$

Step 4

Calculate the concentration of $H_2SO_{4(aq)}$.

$$\left[H_2SO_{4(aq)}\right] = \frac{0.0227 \text{ mmol}}{200 \text{ mL}} = \frac{2.27 \times 10^{-5} \text{ mol}}{0.200 \text{ L}}$$
$$= 1.13 \times 10^{-4} \text{ mol/L}$$

The concentration of $H_2SO_{4(aq)}$ in the rainwater was 1.13×10^{-4} mol/L.

22. A

Use the stoichiometric method to calculate the mass of $NaHCO_{3(s)}$ required.

$$NaHCO_{3(s)} + HCl_{(aq)} \rightarrow NaCl_{(aq)} + CO_{2(g)} + H_2O_{(l)}$$
$$NaHCO_3 (MW = 84.01 \text{ g/mol})$$

Step 1

Calculate the moles of $HCl_{(aq)}$ present.

$$n_{HCl} = 0.075 \text{ L} \times 0.110 \text{ mol/L}$$
$$= 0.0083 \text{ mol}$$

Step 2

Use the balanced equation to determine how many moles of $NaHCO_{3(s)}$ are present.

$$n_{NaHCO_3} = n_{HCl} = 0.0083 \text{ mol}$$

Step 3

Determine the mass of the $NaHCO_{3(s)}$.

$$Mass_{NaHCO_3} = 0.0083 \text{ mol}$$
$$\times 84.01 \text{ g/mol}$$
$$= 0.70 \text{ g}$$

23. B

A stoichiometric calculation is used to solve most acid-base titration problems.

Step 1
Write the balanced equation.
$$C_6H_5COOH_{(aq)} + NaOH_{(aq)}$$
$$\rightarrow C_6H_5COONa_{(aq)} + H_2O_{(l)}$$

Step 2
Calculate the number of moles of $NaOH_{(aq)}$ used.
$$n_{NaOH} = 0.0115\ L \times \frac{0.0155\ mol}{L}$$
$$= 1.78 \times 10^{-4}\ moles$$

Step 3
Calculate the number of moles of $C_6H_5COOH_{(aq)}$ used, based on the molar ratio.
$$n_{C_6H_5COOH} = \frac{1}{1}n_{NaOH}$$
$$= 1.78 \times 10^{-4}\ moles$$
Therefore,
$$[C_6H_5COOH_{(aq)}] = \frac{1.78 \times 10^{-4}\ mol}{0.100\ L}$$
$$= 1.78 \times 10^{-3}\ mol/L$$
The benzoic acid molar concentration in the effluent is 1.78×10^{-3} mol/L.

24. B

Employ the stoichiometric method to answer this acid-base titration problem.

Step 1
Write the balanced equation.
$$KOH_{(aq)} + HCl_{(aq)} \rightarrow KCl_{(aq)} + H_2O_{(l)}$$

Step 2
Calculate the number of moles of HCl.
$$n_{HCl} = 0.0085\ L \times \frac{0.190\ mol}{L}$$
$$= 1.6 \times 10^{-3}\ mol$$

Step 3
Calculate the number of moles of $KOH_{(aq)}$.
Based on the molar ratio, the number of moles of $KOH_{(aq)}$ to $HCl_{(aq)}$ is 1:1.
$$n_{KOH} = \frac{1}{1}n_{HCl}$$
$$= \frac{1}{1} \times 1.6 \times 10^{-3}\ mol$$
$$= 1.6 \times 10^{-3}\ mol$$

Step 4
Calculate the molar concentration of $KOH_{(aq)}$.
$$[KOH_{(aq)}] = \frac{1.6 \times 10^{-3}\ mol}{0.015\ L}$$
$$= 0.11\ mol/L$$

25. D

The total mass of the reactants is 45.90 g + 70.90 g, which is 116.8 g.

The mass of the products is also 116.8 g. Since there is no loss or gain of mass, mass is conserved.

26. D

Since the molar mass is the number of grams per mole, $M = \frac{m}{n}$, Jose needs to know the number of moles. The ideal gas law is $PV = nRT$, consisting of four variables and one constant, R. If mass, temperature, and pressure are known, that still leaves a volume measurement required for substitution into the formula.

27. A

An excess-limiting stoichiometric calculation is required when the quantities of two or more reactants are provided. The limiting reagent is the compound or element present in insufficient quantities to react completely after considering the appropriate mole ratio of the reactants.

Step 1
Write the predicted reaction of $BaCl_{2(aq)}$ and $Na_2CO_{3(aq)}$.
$$BaCl_{2(aq)} + Na_2CO_{3(aq)} \rightarrow BaCO_{3(s)} + 2NaCl_{(aq)}.$$

Step 2
Determine the number of moles of $BaCl_2$ and Na_2CO_3.

With a 1:1 mole ratio of reactants, the species present with the least amount is the limiting reagent.
$$n_{BaCl_2} = 0.300\ L \times \frac{0.100\ mol}{L}$$
$$= 0.030\ mol$$
$$n_{Na_2CO_3} = 0.200\ L \times \frac{0.110\ mol}{L}$$
$$= 0.0220\ mol$$
The limiting reagent is $Na_2CO_{3(aq)}$.

28. a) D

Use the method for determining excess and limiting reactants.

Step 1

Determine the amount of $H_{2(g)}$ available for reaction. The molar mass of $H_2\left(M_{H_2}\right)$ is $2(1.01 \text{ g/mol})$

$= 2.02 \text{ g/mol}$.

$$n_{H_2} = \frac{m}{M}$$

$$= \frac{9.00 \times 10^3 \text{ g}}{2.02 \text{ g/mol}}$$

$$= 4.46 \times 10^3 \text{ mol}$$

Step 2

Using the coefficient ratio of $CO_{(g)}$ to $H_{2(g)}$ in the balanced equation, determine the amount of $CO_{(g)}$ needed to react with all the $H_{2(g)}$ available.

$$CO_{(g)} + 2H_{2(g)} \rightarrow CH_3OH_{(l)}$$

$$\frac{n_{CO}}{n_{H_2}} = \frac{1}{2}$$

$$n_{CO \text{ needed}} = \frac{1}{2}\left(n_{H_2}\right)$$

$$= \frac{1}{2}\left(4.46 \times 10^3 \text{ mol}\right)$$

$$= 2.23 \times 10^3 \text{ mol}$$

Step 3

Calculate the amount of $CO_{(g)}$ available. The molar mass of CO is

$12.01 \text{ g/mol} + 16.00 \text{ g/mol} = 28.01 \text{ g/mol}$.

$$n_{CO \text{ available}} = \frac{m}{M}$$

$$= \frac{70.0 \text{ kg} \times \frac{10^3 \text{ g}}{1 \text{ kg}}}{28.01 \text{ g/mol}}$$

$$= 2.50 \times 10^3 \text{ mol}$$

Step 4

Identify the limiting and excess reagents.

Since there is more $CO_{(g)}$ available than is needed to fully consume the $H_{2(g)}$ present, $CO_{(g)}$ is the excess reagent and $H_{2(g)}$ is the limiting reagent.

Step 5

Using the coefficient ratio of $CH_3OH_{(l)}$ to $H_{2(g)}$ in the balanced equation, determine the amount of $CH_3OH_{(l)}$ produced when the limiting reagent, $H_{2(g)}$, is completely consumed.

$$\frac{n_{CH_3OH}}{n_{H_2}} = \frac{1}{2}$$

$$n_{CH_3OH} = \frac{1}{2}\left(n_{H_2}\right)$$

$$= \frac{1}{2}\left(4.46 \times 10^3 \text{ mol}\right)$$

$$= 2.23 \times 10^3 \text{ mol}$$

The limiting reagent in this reaction is $H_{2(g)}$ and $2.23 \times 10^3 \text{ mol}$ of $CH_3OH_{(l)}$ is produced.

b) B

Step 1

Convert the mass of $H_{2(g)}$ consumed in the reaction to moles.

$$n_{H_2} = \frac{9\ 000 \text{ g}}{2.02 \text{ (g/mol)}}$$

$$= 4\ 455 \text{ mol}$$

Step 2

Using the coefficients from the balanced chemical equation, calculate the moles of $CH_3OH_{(l)}$ produced in the reaction.

$$n_{CH_3OH} = \frac{1 \text{ mol } CH_3OH}{2 \text{ mol } H_2} \times n_{H_2}$$

$$= \frac{1}{2} \times 4\ 455 \text{ mol}$$

$$= 2\ 228 \text{ mol}$$

Step 3

Convert the moles of $CH_3OH_{(l)}$ to grams to find the mass.

$$m_{CH_3OH} = 2\ 228 \text{ mol} \times \frac{32.05 \text{ g}}{\text{mol}}$$

$$= 71.4 \text{ kg}$$

Step 4

Use the percentage yield formula to find the percentage yield of $CH_3OH_{(l)}$ in the reaction.

$$\% \text{ yield} = \frac{\text{mass obtained}}{\text{mass predicted}} \times 100\%$$

$$= \frac{59.2 \text{ kg}}{71.4 \text{ kg}} \times 100\%$$

$$= 82.9\%$$

The percentage yield of $CH_3OH_{(l)}$ is 82.9%.

29. D

The solution to this problem involves the stoichiometric method.

Step 1

Write a balanced equation for the reaction that occurs, and identify the formula for the precipitate.

A solubility table will show that $BaCO_3$ has low solubility, while $NaCl$ is soluble. The solid precipitate, therefore, is $BaCO_{3(s)}$.

$$BaCl_{2(aq)} + Na_2CO_{3(aq)} \rightarrow BaCO_{3(s)} + 2NaCl_{(aq)}$$

Step 2

Calculate the initial moles of $BaCl_2$ and Na_2CO_3 present.

$$n_{BaCl_2} = c_{BaCl_2} \times V_{BaCl_2}$$
$$= 0.100 \text{ mol}/L \times 0.3000 \text{ L}$$
$$= 0.0300 \text{ mol}$$

$$n_{Na_2CO_3} = c_{Na_2CO_3} \times V_{Na_2CO_3}$$
$$= 0.110 \text{ mol}/L \times 0.2000 \text{ L}$$
$$= 0.0220 \text{ mol}$$

Step 3

Determine the excess and limiting reactants.

Use the coefficient ratio of Na_2CO_3 to $BaCl_2$ in the balanced equation to determine the number of moles of Na_2CO_3 needed to completely react with the 0.0300 mol of $BaCl_2$ present.

$$\frac{n_{Na_2CO_3}}{n_{BaCl_2}} = \frac{1}{1}$$

$$n_{Na_2CO_3 \text{ (needed)}} = \frac{1}{1}\left(n_{BaCl_2}\right)$$
$$= \frac{1}{1}(0.0300 \text{ mol})$$
$$= 0.0300 \text{ mol}$$

Since 0.0300 mol of Na_2CO_3 are needed and only 0.0220 mol are present, Na_2CO_3 is the limiting reactant and $BaCl_2$ is the excess reactant.

Step 4

Use the moles of the limiting reactant $Na_2CO_{3(aq)}$ present and the coefficient ratio of the product $BaCO_{3(s)}$ to $Na_2CO_{3(aq)}$ in the balanced equation to calculate the predicted number of moles of $BaCO_{3(s)}$.

$$\frac{n_{BaCO_{3(s)}}}{n_{Na_2CO_{3(aq)}}} = \frac{1}{1}$$

$$n_{BaCO_{3(s)}} = \frac{1}{1}\left(n_{Na_2CO_{3(aq)}}\right)$$
$$= \frac{1}{1}(0.0220 \text{ mol})$$
$$= 0.0220 \text{ mol}$$

Step 5

Convert the predicted number of moles of the product $BaCO_{3(s)}$ to mass.

Determine the molar mass of $BaCO_3$ using the atomic masses of Ba, C, and O.

$$M_{BaCO_3} = 137.33 \text{ g}/\text{mol}$$
$$+12.01 \text{ g}/\text{mol}$$
$$+3(16.00 \text{ g}/\text{mol})$$
$$= 197.34 \text{ g}/\text{mol}$$

$$m_{BaCO_3} = n_{BaCO_3} \times M_{BaCO_3}$$
$$= (0.0220 \text{ mol})(197.34 \text{ g}/\text{mol})$$
$$= 4.34 \text{ g}$$

Step 6

Determine the actual mass of $BaCO_{3(s)}$ obtained.

$$\% \text{ yield} = \frac{\text{actual yield}}{\text{predicted yield}} \times 100\%$$

$$\text{actual yield} = \frac{\% \text{ yield}}{100\%} \times \text{predicted yield}$$
$$= \frac{78\%}{100\%} \times 4.34 \text{ g}$$
$$= 3.4 \text{ g}$$

The actual mass of the precipitate, $BaCO_{3(s)}$, produced in this reaction if the yield is 78% is 3.4 g.

30. D

The theoretical yield is the quantity of product that is predicted as a result of a stoichiometric calculation.

31. A

Actual yield is the mass of product obtained from the reaction.

32. C

The percentage yield is defined as the actual yield divided by the theoretical yield. The theoretical yield is usually obtained from stoichiometric calculations.

$$\% \text{ yield} = \frac{(\text{actual yield})}{(\text{theoretical yield})} \times 100\%$$
$$= \frac{11.7 \text{ g}}{14.3 \text{ g}} \times 100\%$$
$$= 81.8\%$$

33. B

Since the recovery rate should not exceed 100%, it must have been overestimated (likely an overestimation of the recovered product). If the recovered product was not completely dry at the time of weighing, some solvent may still have been present. Consequently, the product mass would have been overestimated. This error would have led to an overestimation of the product recovery which explains why the recovery rate was greater than 100%.

Impurities in the dissolved sample would remain dissolved and go through the filter. This would lead to a lower recovered product mass and a lower product recovery. If particles of compound A went through the filter, the recovered product mass would decrease and lead to a lower product recovery.

34. a) 0.16

Step 1
Write the equation.
$$NaOH_{(aq)} + HCl_{(aq)} \rightarrow H_2O_{(l)} + NaCl_{(aq)}$$

Step 2
Calculate the volume of HCl used.
= 25.8 mL − 7.8 mL = 18.0 mL or 0.018 L

Step 3
Calculate the moles of HCl used.
$$n_1 = c \times V$$
$$= (0.24 \text{ mol}/L) \times (0.018 \text{ L})$$
$$= 4.3 \times 10^{-3} \text{ mol}$$

Step 4
Calculate the moles of NaOH.
Use the balanced equation moles HCl = moles NaOH so that
$$n_{NaOH} = n_{HCl} = 4.3 \times 10^{-3} \text{ mol}.$$
$$\left[NaOH_{(aq)} \right] = \frac{n}{V} = \frac{4.3 \times 10^{-3} \text{ mol}}{0.027 \text{ L}}$$
$$= 0.16 \text{ mol/L}$$
The concentration of the $NaOH_{(aq)}$ solution was 0.16 mol/L.

b) WR

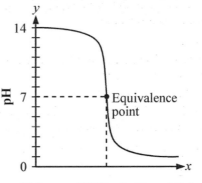

Volume of HCl solution added

The equivalence point should be marked where the pH is 7.0 and is located at the midpoint of the rapid rise in the curve.

35. D

Bromothymol blue is the best choice as an indicator in this instance because the midpoint of the rapid rise in the curve, is at pH 7. Bromothymol blue turns from yellow at pH 6.0 to blue at pH 7.6. At pH 7 bromothymol blue would be a dark green.

The other indicators either would not work or would not be the best choice.

36. C

If the endpoint occurs at a pH of 3.5, an indicator is needed whose color change occurs in the middle of the second rapid pH change. Methyl orange is yellow at pH 4.4 and red at pH 3.2. It will turn from yellow to a pale peach color at the endpoint.

37. A

The neutralization reaction is
$$HCl_{(aq)} + NaOH_{(aq)} \rightarrow NaCl_{(aq)} + H_2O_{(l)}$$

In the balanced equation, there is 1 mol of base for every 1 mol of acid. At the equivalence point, equal numbers of moles must have reacted. Since the equivalence point of a strong acid-strong base reaction will be at pH 7, the numbers of H^+ and OH^- ions must be equal.

Sodium chloride is highly soluble; therefore, it will not precipitate.

38. B

The equivalence point is the point during a titration when the number of moles of titrant added is equivalent to the number of moles of the substance initially being titrated.

In strong acid-strong base titrations, the equivalence point will equal 7 because adding equal moles of a base to an acid will create a neutral solution.

Unit Test — Quantitative Relationships in Chemical Change

Three pairs of test tubes, labelled either A or B, contain solutions according to the given chart.

Pair	Test Tube A	Test Tube B (in excess)
1	$AgNO_{3(aq)}$	$K_2CO_{3(aq)}$
2	$Pb(NO_3)_{2(aq)}$	$Na_2S_{(aq)}$
3	$BaCl_{2(aq)}$	$Na_2SO_{2(aq)}$

The type of reaction expected to occur between each pair of reactants is _____ *i* _____, and one of the products is a _____ *ii* _____.

1. The statement is completed by the information in which of the following tables?

A.

i	*ii*
formation	precipitate

B.

i	*il*
formation	solid metal

C.

i	*ii*
double replacement	precipitate

D.

i	*ii*
double replacement	solid metal

Ethyne, commonly known as acetylene, is commercially used for welding and cutting steel and other materials because it burns with a very hot flame.
The unbalanced equation for the complete combustion of acetylene is shown.
$$C_2H_{2(g)} + O_{2(g)} \rightarrow CO_{2(g)} + H_2O_{(g)}$$

Numerical Response

2. When the combustion reaction is balanced by using lowest whole number coefficients, the coefficients from left to right in the balanced equation are _____, _____, _____, and _____. (Record your answer as a four-digit number.)

Use the following information to answer the next question.

Methane gas and the products formed during its combustion are all greenhouse gases. Sources of methane include termites, which are believed to produce 16.5 million tons per year.

3. The balanced equation for the complete combustion of methane is

A. $2CH_{4(g)} + 4O_{2(g)}$
   $\rightarrow 2CO_{2(g)} + 4H_2O_{(g)}$

B. $CH_{4(g)} + 3O_{2(g)}$
   $\rightarrow 2CO_{2(g)} + 2H_2O_{(g)}$

C. $CH_{4(g)} + 2O_{2(g)} \rightarrow CO_{2(g)} + 2H_2O_{(g)}$

D. $CH_{4(g)} + 4O_{2(g)} \rightarrow CO_{2(g)} + 2H_2O_{(g)}$

Use the following information to answer the next question.

Acid rain affects lakes, rivers, and soil, as well as the wildlife that lives in these environments. The acidity of rain develops primarily from reactions of SO_2 and NO_2 in the atmosphere.

A titration using $KOH_{(aq)}$ was performed to measure the concentration of acid in a sample of rainwater. The acid present in the rainwater sample was $H_2SO_{4(aq)}$.

4. The balanced net ionic equation representing the reaction of $KOH_{(aq)}$ with $H_2SO_{4(aq)}$ is

A. $H^+_{(aq)} + OH^-_{(aq)} \rightarrow H_2O_{(l)}$

B. $2KOH_{(aq)} + H_2SO_{4(aq)}$
   $\rightarrow K_2SO_{4(aq)} + 2H_2O_{(l)}$

C. $2KOH_{(aq)} + H_2SO_{4(aq)}$
   $\rightarrow K_2S_{(aq)} + 2H_2O_{(l)} + 2O_{2(g)}$

D. $K^+_{(aq)} + OH^-_{(aq)} + H^+_{(aq)} + SO^{2-}_{4(aq)}$
   $\rightarrow K^+_{(aq)} + SO^{2-}_{(aq)} + H_2O_{(l)}$

Use the following information to answer the next multipart question.

5. Aqueous lead(II) nitrate, $Pb(NO_3)_{2(aq)}$, and aqueous sodium iodide, $NaI_{(aq)}$, react together to produce a yellow solid.

a) How many moles of aqueous sodium iodide react with every mole of aqueous lead(II) nitrate?

A. 0.5 mol   B. 1 mol

C. 2 mol   D. 3 mol

b) The spectator ions in the reaction between aqueous lead(II) nitrate and aqueous sodium iodide are

A. $Pb^{2+}_{(aq)}$ and $I^-_{(aq)}$

B. $Na^+_{(aq)}$ and $NO^-_{3(aq)}$

C. $Pb^{2+}_{(aq)}$ and $NO^-_{3(aq)}$

D. $Na^+_{(aq)}$ and $I^-_{(aq)}$

Use the following information to answer the next question.

In the canning industry, contaminant metal ion concentrations must be determined to ensure that food products meet safety standards. Tin(II) ion concentrations are measured after canning to see whether or not tin cans increase the tin(II) ion concentration to hazardous levels after storage.

Potassium phosphate can be used to precipitate any tin(II) ions that may enter the contents during this time, according to the given net ionic equation:

$$2PO_{4(aq)}^{3-} + 3Sn_{(aq)}^{2+} \rightarrow Sn_3(PO_4)_{2(s)}$$

The juice from a 2.00 L can is analyzed using 100 mL of aqueous potassium phosphate. It is found that 0.689 mg of tin(II) phosphate precipitated.

6. What is the tin(II) ion concentration in the juice?

   A. 3.79×10^{-5} mol/L

   B. 1.89×10^{-6} mol/L

   C. 1.26×10^{-6} mol/L

   D. 4.84×10^{-7} mol/L

Use the following information to answer the next question.

Primary standards are solutions of a known concentration used to calculate the concentration of other solutions.

For example, sodium carbonate solutions are primary standards used to calibrate the concentration of hydrochloric acid.

A student prepares a primary standard solution by dissolving 10.431 g of sodium carbonate into a slurry and then diluting it to 100.00 mL with a volumetric flask.

A 10.00 mL sample of stock hydrochloric acid is pipetted into an empty 250 mL beaker. The acid is diluted to 50.00 mL by adding distilled water. The acidic solution is then titrated with the sodium carbonate primary standard solution prepared.

The end point is reached after the addition of 21.49 mL of the sodium carbonate primary standard solution.

The neutralization reaction used for the titration is represented by the following balanced equation:

$$2HCl_{(aq)} + Na_2CO_{3(aq)}$$
$$\rightarrow 2NaCl_{(aq)} + H_2O_{(l)} + CO_{2(g)}$$

7. What is the concentration of the stock HCl solution?

   A. 0.0212 mol/L

   B. 0.0423 mol/L

   C. 2.12 mol/L

   D. 4.23 mol/L

Use the following information to answer the next question.

> Pure acetic acid is called glacial acetic acid. It is used by photographers to prepare stop baths for photographic film and print development. A 30.0 mL stop bath sample was titrated with 1.75 mol/L KOH to ensure it contained enough acetic acid. The volume of $KOH_{(aq)}$ used for each trial was 8.4 mL, 9.1 mL, 8.6 mL, and 8.5 mL.

8. What was the concentration of acetic acid in the stop bath?

   A. 0.015 mol/L **B.** 0.053 mol/L

   C. 0.30 mol/L **D.** 0.50 mol/L

Use the following information to answer the next question.

> Citric acid, which can be written as H_3Ct, is a triprotic acid. It is completely neutralized by aqueous sodium hydroxide. H_3Ct is a simplified formula for the acid showing the three acid hydrogens. Ct is the rest of the acid molecule and is treated as any compound ion would be.

Numerical Response

9. If 24.2 mL of 0.100 mol/L $NaOH_{(aq)}$ are required to completely neutralize a 25.0 mL aqueous solution of citric acid, then the acid concentration is _____ mmol/L. (Record your three-digit answer.)

Numerical Response

10. In a hard-water solution, 2.45 g of calcium carbonate precipitates from 1.00 L of water when it is treated with excess sodium carbonate. The Ca^{2+} ion concentration of the hard water is _____ mmol/L. (Record your three-digit answer.)

Use the following information to answer the next question.

> Titanium dioxide is used as a white pigment in paints, rubbers, plastics, and paper. Titanium dioxide is formed in this reaction.
>
> $TiCl_{4(g)} + O_{2(g)} \rightarrow TiO_{2(s)} + 2Cl_{2(g)}$

11. Which of the following statements is **true**?

    A. The mass of chlorine is exactly twice the mass of titanium dioxide.

    B. The masses of the products outweigh the masses of the reactants.

    C. The masses of the reactants outweigh the masses of the products.

    D. The combined mass of the products equals the combined mass of the reactants.

Use the following information to answer the next question.

> A student mixes 300.0 mL of barium chloride solution ($BaCl_{2(aq)}$) with 200.0 mL of sodium carbonate solution ($Na_2CO_{3(aq)}$). $BaCl_{2(aq)}$ has a molarity of 0.100 mol/L, and $Na_2CO_{3(aq)}$ has a molarity of 0.110 mol/L.

12. Which of the following tables identifies the limiting reagent in this reaction and the mass of precipitate formed?

A.	Limiting Reagent	Mass of Precipitate
	$BaCl_{2(aq)}$	5.92 g

B.	Limiting Reagent	Mass of Precipitate
	$BaCl_{2(aq)}$	4.34 g

C.	Limiting Reagent	Mass of Precipitate
	$Na_2CO_{3(aq)}$	5.92 g

D.	Limiting Reagent	Mass of Precipitate
	$Na_2CO_{3(aq)}$	4.34 g

Use the following information to answer the next question.

> When 3.00 mol of sodium are reacted with large amounts of chlorine gas, 145.8 g of sodium chloride are produced.

Written Response

13. Determine the percent yield for the reaction.

_____
_____
_____
_____
_____
_____
_____

Use the following information to answer the next multipart question.

14. Coloured glass can be made by adding small amounts of coloured metal impurities to clear glass. Calcium sulfate $(CaSO_{4(s)})$ is sometimes used to give glass a milky white colour. $CaSO_{4(s)}$ can be produced by reacting calcium chloride solution $(CaCl_{2(aq)})$ with sodium sulfate solution $(Na_2SO_{4(aq)})$. The balanced equation for the reaction is
$CaCl_{2(aq)} + Na_2SO_{4(aq)}$
$\rightarrow CaSO_{4(s)} + 2NaCl_{(aq)}$.

a) If the reaction produces 85.0% of the predicted yield and the initial concentration of the $CaCl_{2(aq)}$ solution is 2.33 mol/L, what volume of $CaCl_{2(aq)}$ solution is needed to react with excess the $Na_2SO_{4(aq)}$ in order to produce 400.0 g of $CaSO_{4(s)}$?

   A. 1.07 L   **B.** 1.26 L

   C. 1.48 L   **D.** 1.67 L

b) One possible reason the actual yield would be less than the theoretical yield could be that the
   A. volume of $CaCl_{2(aq)}$ added was more than what was needed
   B. concentration of $CaCl2_{(aq)}$ added was greater than 2.33 mol/L
   C. precipitate $CaSO_{4(s)}$ was not completely dry before it was weighed
   D. amount of $Na_2SO_{4(aq)}$ was not in excess but rather it was a limiting reagent

15. Which of the following titration curves shows a 10.00 mL sample of 0.20 mol/L hydrochloric acid titrated with a 0.20 mol/L solution of sodium hydroxide?

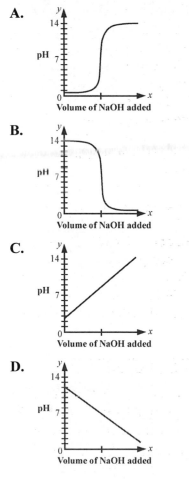

Use the following information to answer the next question.

A student titrates a sample of $HNO_{3(aq)}$, a strong acid with $NaOH_{(aq)}$, a strong base.

Written Response

16. Explain whether the student should use the indicator methyl orange or phenol red for the titration, and indicate the colour the indicator will turn at the end point.

_____

_____

_____

_____

_____

Use the following information to answer the next question.

The indicator phenolphthalein is added to the titration of $HCl_{(aq)}$ with $KOH_{(aq)}$.
The titration is represented by the equation
$HCl_{(aq)} + KOH_{(aq)} \rightarrow KCl_{(aq)} + H_2O_{(l)}$.
The _____*i*_____ is the point where the mol of H^+ = mol OH^-, and the _____*ii*_____ is the point where phenolphthalein turns pink.

17. The given statement is completed by the information in which of the following tables?

A.

i	ii
endpoint	equivalence point

B.

i	ii
endpoint	neutralization point

C.

i	ii
equivalence point	endpoint

D.

i	ii
equivalence point	neutralization point

ANSWERS AND SOLUTIONS — UNIT TEST

1. C	b) B	10. 24.5	b) D
2. 2542	6. B	11. D	15. A
3. C	7. D	12. D	16. WR
4. A	8. D	13. WR	17. C
5. a) C	9. 32.3	14. a) C	

1. C

Each pair of reactant compounds combines during a double replacement reaction to make a precipitate (a low solubility product): one of $Ag_2CO3_{(s)}$, $PbS_{(s)}$, and $BaSO_{4(s)}$. The solubility of an ionic compound is easy to determine using a solubility chart.

2. 2542

When balancing the complete combustion reaction of $C_2H_{2(g)}$, double the number of moles of acetylene to ensure there will be equal numbers of moles of $H_2O_{(g)}$ and moles of O on both sides of the equation.

$$2C_2H_{2(g)} + 5O_{2(g)} \rightarrow 4CO_{2(g)} + 2H_2O_{(g)}$$

3. C

The products of the complete combustion of a hydrocarbon compound are $CO_{2(g)}$ and $H_2O_{(g)}$. Remember to balance the C and H in $CO_{2(g)}$ and $H_2O_{(g)}$, respectively, before balancing the O in $O_{2(g)}$. The balanced equation is as follows:

$$CH_{4(g)} + 2O_{2(g)} \rightarrow CO_{2(g)} + 2H_2O_{(g)}$$

4. A

Strong acids and strong bases dissociate completely in solution to form the ions $K^+_{(aq)}$, $OH^-_{(aq)}$, $H^+_{(aq)}$, and $SO^{2-}_{4(aq)}$, with $K^+_{(aq)}$ and $SO^{2-}_{4(aq)}$ being spectator ions. Spectator ions are removed from net ionic equations. The net ionic equation for the reaction of a strong acid and strong base is $H^+_{(aq)} + OH^-_{(aq)} \rightarrow H_2O_{(l)}$.

5. a) C

Step 1

Write the balanced equation representing the reaction. The mole ratio of $Pb(NO_3)_{2(aq)}$ to $NaI_{(aq)}$ is expressed in this double replacement reaction:

$$Pb(NO_3)_{2(aq)} + 2NaI_{(aq)} \rightarrow PbI_{2(s)} + 2NaNO_{3(aq)}$$

The coefficients of $Pb(NO_3)_{2(aq)}$ and $NaI_{(aq)}$ are 1 and 2, respectively, in the balanced equation.

Step 2

Calculate the mole ratio.

$$\frac{n_{NaI}}{n_{PB(NO_3)_2}} = \frac{2 \text{ mol}}{1 \text{ mol}} = \frac{2}{1} \text{ or } 2{:}1$$

Therefore, two moles of $NaI_{(aq)}$ react with one mole of $Pb(NO_3)_{2(aq)}$.

b) B

The two reactants dissociate to produce the ions $Pb^{2+}_{(aq)}$, $NO^-_{3(aq)}$, $Na^+_{(aq)}$ and $I^-_{(aq)}$. $Pb^{2+}_{(aq)}$ and $I^-_{(aq)}$ react to produce the precipitate $PbI_{2(s)}$. $Na^+_{(aq)}$ and $NO^-_{3(aq)}$ are spectator ions in this reaction.

6. B

Step 1

Using the net ionic equation, calculate the molar mass of tin(II) phosphate.

$$2PO^{3-}_{4(aq)} + 3Sn^{2+}_{(aq)} \rightarrow Sn_3(PO_4)_{2(s)}$$

$Sn_3(PO_4)_2$: (M = 546.07 g/mol)

Step 2

Calculate the moles of tin(II) phosphate precipitated.

$$n_{Sn_3PO_4} = 6.89 \times 10 \text{ g}^{-4} \times \frac{\text{mol}}{546.07 \text{ g}}$$
$$= 1.26 \times 10^{-6} \text{ mol}$$

Step 3

Use the molar ratios of the equation to find the concentration of tin(II) ions present.

$$n_{Sn^{2+}} = \frac{3}{1} n_{Sn_3PO_4}$$
$$= \frac{3}{1} \times 1.26 \times 10^{-6} \text{ mol}$$
$$= 3.78 \times 10^{-6} \text{ mol}$$

Step 4

Calculate the concentration of tin(II) ions.

$$\left[Sn_{(aq)}^{2+}\right] = \frac{3.78 \times 10^{-6} \text{ mol}}{2.00 \text{ L}}$$
$$= 1.89 \times 10^{-6} \text{ mol/L}$$

(This may also be stated as 1.89μ mol/L.)

The $Sn_{(aq)}^{2+}$ molar concentration is

1.89×10^{-6} mol/L.

7. D

Step 1

Calculate the concentration of the primary standard prepared.

$$c_{Na_2CO_3} = \frac{n_{Na_2CO_3}}{V_{Na_2CO_3}}$$
$$= \frac{(10.431 \text{ g})\left(\frac{1 \text{ mol}}{105.99 \text{ g}}\right)}{0.100\ 00 \text{ L}}$$
$$= 0.984\ 15 \text{ mol} / \text{L}$$

Step 2

Determine the number of moles of Na_2CO_3 consumed in the titration.

$$n_{Na_2CO_3}$$
$$= c_{Na_2CO_3} V_{Na_2CO_3}$$
$$= \left(\frac{0.984\ 15 \text{ mol}}{1 \text{ L}}\right)(21.49 \text{ mL})\left(\frac{1 \text{ L}}{1\ 000 \text{ mL}}\right)$$
$$= 0.021\ 15 \text{ mol}$$

Step 3

Determine the number of moles of HCl present in the sample.

The moles of HCl in the sample can be determined using the coefficients of HCl and Na_2CO_3 in the balanced equation.

$$n_{HCl}$$
$$= \left(0.021\ 15 \text{ mol Na}_2\text{CO}_3\right)\left(\frac{2 \text{ mol HCl}}{1 \text{ mol Na}_2\text{CO}_3}\right)$$
$$= 0.042\ 30 \text{ mol HCl}$$

Step 4

Determine the molar concentration of HCl in the original 10.00 mL sample of the stock solution.

$$c_{HCl} = \frac{n_{HCl}}{V_{HCl}}$$
$$= \frac{0.042\ 30 \text{ mol}}{0.010\ 00 \text{ L}}$$
$$= 4.230 \text{ mol/L}$$

The concentration of the stock HCl solution is 4.230 mol/L.

8. D

The stoichiometric method is needed here.

$$CH_3COOH_{(aq)} + KOH_{(aq)}$$
$$\rightarrow KCH_3COO_{(aq)} + H_2O_{(l)}$$

Step 1

Calculate the average volume of KOH from the three closest titration results.

$$V_{KOH} = \frac{8.4 \text{ mL} + 8.6 \text{ mL} + 8.5 \text{ mL}}{3}$$
$$= 8.5 \text{ mL}$$

Step 2

Calculate the moles of KOH used.

$$n_{KOH} = 0.0085 \text{ L} \times \frac{1.75 \text{ mol}}{\text{L}}$$
$$= 0.015 \text{ mol}$$

Step 3

From the balanced equation, calculate the CH_3COOH needed.

$$n_{CH_3COOH} = \frac{1}{1} n_{KOH}$$
$$n_{CH_3COOH} = \frac{1}{1} \times 0.015 \text{ mol}$$
$$= 0.015 \text{ mol}$$

Step 4

Calculate the concentration of acetic acid in the 30 mL (0.030 L) sample.

$$\left[CH_3COOH_{(aq)}\right] = \frac{0.015 \text{ mol}}{0.030 \text{ L}}$$
$$= 0.50 \text{ mol/L}$$

The molar concentration of acetic acid in the stop bath is 0.50 mol/L.

9. 32.3

Use the stoichiometric method.

Step 1

Write a balanced reaction equation that includes all the relevant data.

$$H_3Ct_{(aq)} + 3NaOH_{(aq)} \rightarrow Na_3Ct_{(aq)} + 3H_2O_{(l)}$$

Step 2

Calculate the number of moles of the given reactant or product (n_{given}).

$$n_{NaOH} = 0.0242 \text{ L} \times 0.100 \text{ mol/L}$$
$$= 2.42 \times 10^{-3} \text{ mol}$$

Step 3

Use the appropriate mole ratio to convert n_{given} into the number of moles of required reactant or product ($n_{required}$).

$$n_{Na_3Ct} = \frac{1}{3}n_{NaOH}$$
$$= \frac{1}{3} \times 2.42 \times 10^{-3} \text{ mol}$$
$$= 8.07 \times 10^{-4} \text{ mol}$$

Step 4

Determine the answer by converting the $n_{required}$ into a concentration.

$$[H_3Ct_{(aq)}] = \frac{8.07 \times 10^{-4} \text{ mol}}{0.025 \text{ L}}$$
$$= 0.0323 \text{ mol/L}$$

The citric acid concentration is 32.3 mmol/L.

10. 24.5

Use the stoichiometric method.

$$Ca^{2+}_{(aq)} + CO^{2-}_{3(aq)} \rightarrow CaCO_{3(s)}$$

First, calculate the molar mass of calcium carbonate.
$CaCO_{3(s)}$ (MW 100.09 g/mol)

There is 2.45 g of calcium carbonate in 1.00 L hard water. Use this information to calculate the concentration of $Ca^{2+}_{(aq)}$ ions in the water.

$$[Ca^{2+}_{(aq)}] = ?$$
$$n_{CaCO_3} = 2.45 \text{ g} \times \frac{mol}{100.09 \text{ g}}$$
$$= 0.0245 \text{ mol}$$
$$n_{Ca^{2+}} = \frac{1}{1}n_{CaCO_3}$$
$$= \frac{1}{1} \times 0.0245 \text{ mol}$$
$$= 0.0245 \text{ mol}$$
$$[Ca^{2+}_{(aq)}] = \frac{0.0245 \text{ mol}}{1.00 \text{ L}}$$
$$= 0.0245 \text{ mol/L}$$

The molar concentration of the $Ca^{2+}_{(aq)}$ is 0.0245 mol/L or 24.5 mmol/L.

11. D

The law of conservation of mass states that the mass of the products of a chemical reaction equals the mass of the reactants. When you balance a chemical reaction by ensuring equal numbers of atoms are on both sides of a chemical equation, you are applying the law of conservation of mass.

12. D

Step 1

Use an excess limiting stoichiometric calculation to find the answer.

Balance the reaction equation.
$$BaCl_{2(aq)} + Na_2CO_{3(aq)} \rightarrow BaCO_{3(s)} + 2NaCl_{(aq)}$$

Define the reactants and the products of the reaction.

$BaCl_{2(aq)}$: V = 300.0 mL
  : c = 0.100 mol/L
$Na_2CO_{3(aq)}$: V = 200.0 mL
  : c = 0.110 mol/L
$BaCO_{3(s)}$: m = ?
  : M = 197.34 g/mol

Step 2

Calculate the number of moles of $BaCl_2$ initially present in the reactant mixture.

$$n_{BaCl_2 \text{ present}} = c \times V$$
$$= \frac{0.100 \text{ mol}}{1 \text{ L}} \times 0.3000 \text{ L}$$
$$= 0.0300 \text{ mol}$$

Step 3

Using the coefficient ratio of Na_2CO_3 to $BaCl_2$ in the balanced reaction equation, calculate the number of moles of Na_2CO_3 needed to react completely with 0.0300 mol of $BaCl_2$.

$$\frac{n_{Na_2CO_3}}{n_{BaCl_2}} = \frac{1}{1}$$
$$n_{Na_2CO_3 \text{ needed}} = \frac{1}{1}(n_{BaCl_2})$$
$$= \frac{1}{1}(0.0300 \text{ mol})$$
$$= 0.0300 \text{ mol}$$

Step 4

Calculate the number of moles of Na_2CO_3 initially present in the reactant mixture.

$$n_{Na_2CO_3 \text{ present}} = c \times V$$
$$= \frac{0.110 \text{ mol}}{1 \text{ L}} \times 0.2000 \text{ L}$$
$$= 0.0220 \text{ mol}$$

Step 5

Identify the limiting and excess reagents in this situation.

Since the amount of Na_2CO_3 actually present in the initial mixture is less than what is needed to completely react with all the $BaCl_2$ present, Na_2CO_3 is the limiting reagent and $BaCl_2$ is the excess reagent. The amount of limiting reactant, Na_2CO_3, present (0.0220 mol) is used to calculate the amount of the product, $BaCO_{3(s)}$, obtained.

Step 6

Using the coefficient ratio of $BaCO_3$ to Na_2CO_3 in the balanced equation, determine the number of moles of $BaCO_3$ produced when the limiting reagent, Na_2CO_3, is completely consumed.

$$\frac{n_{BaCO_3}}{n_{Na_2CO_3}} = \frac{1}{1}$$

$$n_{BaCO_3} = \frac{1}{1}\left(n_{Na_2CO_3}\right)$$

$$= \frac{1}{1}(0.0220 \text{ mol})$$

$$= 0.0220 \text{ mol}$$

Step 7

Convert the number of moles of $BaCO_{3(s)}$ to mass in grams.

$$m_{BaCO_{3(s)}} = n \times M$$

$$= 0.0220 \text{ mol} \times \frac{197.34 \text{ g}}{1 \text{ mol}}$$

$$= 4.34 \text{ g}$$

The mass of $BaCO_{3(s)}$ predicted is 4.34 g.

13. **WR**

To determine percent yield, the actual and theoretical yields are needed. The actual yield for this reaction was 145.8 g of sodium chloride. The theoretical yield must be calculated using stoichiometry.

Step 1

Write a balanced equation for the reaction.

$$2Na_{(s)} + Cl_{2(g)} \rightarrow 2NaCl_{(s)}$$

Step 2

Determine the given and unknown substances involved in the reaction.

Given: 3.00 mol Na
Unknown: ? g NaCl

Step 3

Set up a mole ratio using coefficients of the balanced equation for the two substances.

$$\frac{n_{Na_{(s)}}}{n_{NaCl_{(s)}}} = \frac{2}{2}$$

Step 4

Substitute the values into the mole ratio for the given and unknown.

$$\frac{3.00 \text{ mol}}{n_{NaCl_{(s)}}} = \frac{2}{2}$$

Step 5

Solve the equation for the unknown number of moles.

$$\frac{3.00 \text{ mol}}{n_{NaCl_{(s)}}} = \frac{2}{2}$$

$$n_{NaCl_{(s)}} = \frac{2}{2}(3.00 \text{ mol})$$

$$n_{NaCl_{(s)}} = 3.00 \text{ mol}$$

Since the mole ratios are the same, 3.00 mol of NaCl will be produced.

Step 6

Convert unknown moles into mass by multiplying by the unknown's molar mass.

The molar mass of NaCl is

Na = 1×22.99 g/mol
Cl = $\underline{1 \times 35.45 \text{ g/mol}}$
       58.44 g/mol

$$m = n \times M$$

$$= (3.00 \text{ mol})(58.44 \text{ g/mol})$$

$$= 175.3 \text{ g of NaCl}$$

This amount of NaCl represents the theoretical yield.

Step 7

Use the formula for percent yield and the value of the theoretical yield.

$$\text{Percent yield} = \frac{\text{actual yield}}{\text{theoretical yield}} \times 100\%$$

$$= \frac{145.8 \text{ g}}{175.3 \text{ g}} \times 100\%$$

$$= 83.2\%$$

The percent yield for this reaction was 83.2%.

14. **a) C**

Step 1

Calculate the predicted yield of $CaSO_4$.

$$\% \text{ yield} = \frac{\text{actual yield}}{\text{predicted yield}} \times 100\%$$

$$\text{Predicted yield} = \frac{\text{actual yield}}{\% \text{ yield}} \times 100\%$$

$$= \frac{400.0 \text{ g}}{85.0\%} \times 100\%$$

$$= 470.6 \text{ g}$$

Step 2

Write the balanced equation for the reaction.

$$CaCl_{2(aq)} + Na_2SO_{4(aq)} \rightarrow CaSO_{4(s)} + 2NaCl_{(aq)}$$

Step 3

Calculate the molar mass of $CaSO_4$ from the atomic masses of calcium (Ca), sulfur (S), and oxygen (O).

$$M_{CaSO_4} = \begin{pmatrix} 40.08 \text{ g/mol} \\ + \ \ 32.07 \text{ g/mol} \\ + \ 4(16.00 \text{ g/mol}) \end{pmatrix}$$
$$= 136.15 \text{ g/mol}$$

Calculate the number of moles of $CaSO_4$ using the mass of the predicted yield and the molar mass.

$$n_{CaSO_4} = \frac{m_{CaSO_4}}{M_{CaSO_4}}$$
$$= \frac{470.6 \text{ g}}{136.15 \text{ g/mol}}$$
$$= 3.456 \text{ mol}$$

Step 4

Using the coefficient ratio of $CaCl_2$ to $CaSO_4$ in the balanced equation, determine the moles of $CaCl_2$ needed for the reaction.

$$\frac{n_{CaCl_2}}{n_{CaSO_4}} = \frac{1}{1}$$
$$n_{CaCl_2} = \frac{1}{1}\left(n_{CaSO_4}\right)$$
$$= \frac{1}{1}(3.456 \text{ mol})$$
$$= 3.456 \text{ mol}$$

Step 5

Calculate the volume of 2.33 mol/L $CaCl_{2(aq)}$ solution needed to provide 3.456 mol.

$$V_{CaCl_{2(aq)}} = \frac{n_{CaCl_{2(aq)}}}{c_{CaCl_{2(aq)}}}$$
$$= \frac{3.456 \text{ mol}}{2.33 \text{ mol/L}}$$
$$= 1.48 \text{ L}$$

The reaction would require 1.48 L of 2.33 mol/L $CaCl_{2(aq)}$ solution to produce 400.0 g of $CaSO_{4(s)}$ with an 85.0% yield.

b) D

One reason the actual yield was less than the theoretical yield could be because the $Na_2SO_{4(aq)}$ solution was not in excess. If the $Na_2SO_{4(aq)}$ was a limiting reagent then all of the moles of $CaCl_{2(aq)}$ would not react resulting in less $CaSO_{4(s)}$.
Not drying the precipitate completely, excess $CaSO_{4(s)}$, or a higher concentration of $CaCl_2$ would all indicate reasons for the actual yield being larger than it should be.

15. A

A titration curve has a steep section (a rapid pH decrease) when a strong base is added to a strong acid sample. This is because the graph is logarithmic (based on powers of ten) and not a straight line (linear).

16. WR

The pH is equal to 7 at the equivalence point of a strong acid-strong base at the pH range of 3.2 to 4.4. Phenol red changes colour at the pH range 6.6 to 8.0. Phenol red would be a better choice for this titration because it changes colour near the equivalence point. Phenol red will change from yellow to orange at the equivalence point.

17. C

In an acid-base titration, the equivalence point is the point at which the mol of H^+ is equal to OH^- (stoichiometrically equal). The endpoint is the point at which the indicator phenolphthalein changes colour, from colourless to pink.

NOTES

KEY Strategies for Success on Tests

TEST PREPARATION AND TEST-TAKING SKILLS

THINGS TO CONSIDER WHEN TAKING A TEST

- It is normal to feel anxious before you write a test. You can manage this anxiety by:
    - Thinking positive thoughts. Imagine yourself doing well on the test.
    - Making a conscious effort to relax by taking several slow, deep, controlled breaths. Concentrate on the air going in and out of your body.

- Before you begin the test, ask questions if you are unsure of anything.

- Jot down key words or phrases from any instructions your teacher gives you.

- Look over the entire test to find out the number and kinds of questions on the test.

- Read each question closely and reread if necessary.

- Pay close attention to key vocabulary words. Sometimes these are **bolded** or *italicized*, and they are usually important words in the question.

- If you are putting your answers on an answer sheet, mark your answers carefully. Always print clearly. If you wish to change an answer, erase the mark completely and then ensure your final answer is darker than the one you have erased.

- Use highlighting to note directions, key words, and vocabulary that you find confusing or that are important to answering the question.

- Double-check to make sure you have answered everything before handing in your test.

When taking tests, students often overlook the easy words. Failure to pay close attention to these words can result in an incorrect answer. One way to avoid this is to be aware of these words and to underline, circle, or highlight them while you are taking the test.

Even though some words are easy to understand, they can change the meaning of the entire question, so it is important that you pay attention to them. Here are some examples:

all	always	most likely	probably	best	not
difference	usually	except	most	unlikely	likely

Example

1. Which of the following equations is **not** considered abiotic?

    A. wind

    B. bacteria

    C. sunlight

    D. precipitation

HELPFUL STRATEGIES FOR ANSWERING MULTIPLE-CHOICE QUESTIONS

A multiple-choice question gives you some information, and then asks you to select an answer from four choices. Each question has one correct answer. The other answers are distractors, which are incorrect. Below are some strategies to help you when answering multiple-choice questions.

- Quickly skim through the entire test. Find out how many questions there are and plan your time accordingly.

- Read and reread questions carefully. Underline key words and try to think of an answer before looking at the choices.

- If there is a graphic, look at the graphic, read the question, and go back to the graphic. Then, you may want to underline the important information from the question.

- Carefully read the choices. Read the question first and then each answer that goes with it.

- When choosing an answer, try to eliminate those choices that are clearly wrong or do not make sense.

- Some questions may ask you to select the best answer. These questions will always include words like *best*, *most appropriate*, or *most likely*. All of the answers will be correct to some degree, but one of the choices will be better than the others in some way. Carefully read all four choices before choosing the answer you think is the best.

- If you do not know the answer, or if the question does not make sense to you, it is better to guess than to leave it blank.

- Do not spend too much time on any one question. Make a mark (*) beside a difficult question and come back to it later. If you are leaving a question to come back to later, make sure you also leave the space on the answer sheet, if you are using one.

- Remember to go back to the difficult questions at the end of the test; sometimes clues are given throughout the test that will provide you with answers.

- Note any negative words like *no* or *not* and be sure your choice fits the question.

- Before changing an answer, be sure you have a very good reason to do so.

- Do not look for patterns on your answer sheet, if you are using one.

HELPFUL STRATEGIES FOR ANSWERING OPEN-RESPONSE QUESTIONS

A written response requires you to respond to a question or directive such as **explain**, **predict**, **list**, **describe**, **show your work**, **solve**, or **calculate.** In preparing for open-response tasks you may wish to:

- Read and reread the question carefully.
- Recognize and pay close attention to directing words such as *explain*, *show your work*, and *describe*.
- Underline key words and phrases that indicate what is required in your answer, such as *explain*, *estimate*, *answer*, *calculate*, or *show your work*.
- Write down rough, point-form notes regarding the information you want to include in your answer.
- Think about what you want to say and organize information and ideas in a coherent and concise manner within the time limit you have for the question.
- Be sure to answer every part of the question that is asked.
- Include as much information as you can when you are asked to explain your thinking.
- Include a picture or diagram if it will help to explain your thinking.
- Try to put your final answer to a problem in a complete sentence to be sure it is reasonable.
- Reread your response to ensure you have answered the question.
- Think: Does your answer make sense?
- Listen: Does it sound right?
- Use appropriate subject vocabulary and terms in your response.

ABOUT SCIENCE TESTS

What You Need to Know about Science Tests

To do well on a science test, you need to understand and apply your knowledge of scientific concepts. Reading skills can also make a difference in how well you perform. Reading skills can help you follow instructions and find key words, as well as read graphs, diagrams, and tables.

Science tests usually have two types of questions: knowledge questions and skill questions. Knowledge questions test for your understanding of science ideas. Skill questions test how you would use your science knowledge.

How You Can Prepare for Science Tests

Below are some strategies that are particular to preparing for and writing science tests.

- Note-taking is a good way to review and study important information from your class notes and textbook.

- Sketch a picture of the process or idea being described in a question. Drawing is helpful for learning and remembering concepts.

- Check your answer to practice questions the require formulas by working backward to the beginning. You can find the beginning by going step-by-step in reverse order.

- When answering questions with graphics (pictures, diagrams, tables, or graphs), read the test question carefully.

   –Read the title of the graphic and any key words.
   –Read the test question carefully to figure out what information you need to find in the graphic.
   –Go back to the graphic to find the information you need.

- Always pay close attention when pressing the keys on your calculator. Repeat the procedure a second time to be sure you pressed the correct keys.

TEST PREPARATION COUNTDOWN

If you develop a plan for studying and test preparation, you will perform well on tests.

Here is a general plan to follow seven days before you write a test.

Countdown: 7 Days before the Test

1. Use "Finding Out About the Test" to help you make your own personal test preparation plan.

2. Review the following information:
    - Areas to be included on the test
    - Types of test items
    - General and specific test tips

3. Start preparing for the test at least 7 days before the test. Develop your test preparation plan and set time aside to prepare and study.

Countdown: 6, 5, 4, 3, 2 Days before the Test

1. Review old homework assignments, quizzes, and tests.

2. Rework problems on quizzes and tests to make sure you still know how to solve them.

3. Correct any errors made on quizzes and tests.

4. Review key concepts, processes, formulas, and vocabulary.

5. Create practice test questions for yourself and then answer them. Work out many sample problems.

Countdown: The Night before the Test

1. The night before the test is for final preparation, which includes reviewing and gathering material needed for the test before going to bed.

2. Most important is getting a good night's rest and knowing you have done everything possible to do well on the test.

Test Day

1. Eat a healthy and nutritious breakfast.

2. Ensure you have all the necessary materials.

3. Think positive thoughts: "I can do this." "I am ready." "I know I can do well."

4. Arrive at your school early so you are not rushing, which can cause you anxiety and stress.

SUMMARY OF HOW TO BE SUCCESSFUL DURING A TEST

You may find some of the following strategies useful for writing a test.

- Take two or three deep breaths to help you relax.
- Read the directions carefully and underline, circle, or highlight any important words.
- Look over the entire test to understand what you will need to do.
- Budget your time.
- Begin with an easy question, or a question you know you can answer correctly, rather than following the numerical question order of the test.
- If you cannot remember how to answer a question, try repeating the deep breathing and physical relaxation activities first. Then, move on to visualization and positive self-talk to get yourself going.
- When answering a question with graphics (pictures, diagrams, tables, or graphs), look at the question carefully.
  - Read the title of the graphic and any key words.
  - Read the test question carefully to figure out what information you need to find in the graphic.
  - Go back to the graphic to find the information you need.
- Write down anything you remember about the subject on the reverse side of your test paper. This activity sometimes helps to remind you that you do know something and you are capable of writing the test.
- Look over your test when you have finished and double-check your answers to be sure you did not forget anything.

NOTES

Practice
TEST

PRACTICE TEST 1

Use the following information to answer the next question.

Nitrous oxide (N_2O), also known as laughing gas, is one of several byproducts of nitrogen assimilation in bacteria and algae. Similar to $NO_{(g)}$, $N_2O_{(g)}$ is also a greenhouse gas that can damage the stratospheric ozone layer.

1. What types of bonding interactions between individual N_2O molecules are **most likely** to occur?
   A. London dispersion forces and dipole-dipole attractions
   B. Network covalent bonds and dispersion forces
   C. Ionic bonds and dipole-dipole attractions
   D. Hydrogen bonds and dispersion forces

Use the following information to answer the next question.

Oxygen and sulfur belong to the same group on the periodic table. Both react with hydrogen to form H_2O and H_2S, respectively. However, the two compounds differ in their volatility. Hydrogen sulfide is a gas while water is a liquid under standard conditions of temperature and pressure.

2. The difference in the volatility of $H_2O_{(l)}$ and $H_2S_{(g)}$ **most likely** occurs as a result of
   A. hydrogen bonding in $H_2S_{(g)}$
   B. hydrogen bonding in $H_2O_{(l)}$
   C. stronger dispersion forces in $H_2S_{(g)}$
   D. stronger dispersion forces in $H_2O_{(l)}$

Use the following information to answer the next question.

The following table shows the boiling points of three silicon tetrahalides.

Compound Formula	Boiling Point (°C)
$SiCl_4$	57.7
$SiBr_4$	153
SiI_4	287

3. The trend in the boiling points of these three compounds is **best** explained by saying that as the halogen atoms bonded to silicon get larger, the
   A. polarity of the molecules decreases
   B. intermolecular forces get stronger because of the increase in the number of electrons
   C. increase in the bond lengths within the molecules results in an increase in bond strength
   D. intramolecular covalent bonds get stronger because of an increase in the number of shared electrons

Use the following information to answer the next multipart question.

4. The hypervalent molecule CLi_6 was observed for the first time in the gas phase in 1992. This observation was significant because of the unusual bonding within the molecule.

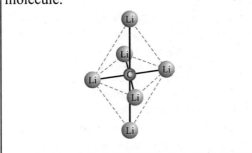

a) According to the Lewis bonding theory, how many electrons does carbon appear to have surrounding it?

   A. 6   **B.** 8

   C. 10   **D.** 12

b) The number of electrons surrounding the carbon atom

   A. conform to the octet rule

   B. appear to violate the octet rule

   C. show that CLi_6 is very unstable

   D. show that lithium has no valence electrons

Use the following information to answer the next question.

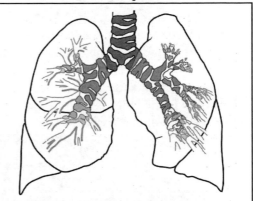

Gas exchange in the lungs occurs across the membranes of tiny sacs called alveoli. Upon inhalation, the alveoli fill with air, approximately 20 % of which is oxygen. In this case, the air behaves as an ideal gas at body temperature (37° C), and the absolute pressure of the alveolus is 100 kPa. Avogadro's number is 6.022×10^{23} particles/mol.

5. If the volume of an alveolus is approximately 8.00×10^{-6} mL, approximately how many oxygen molecules occupy one alveolus?

   A. 2.24×10^{15}

   B. 1.87×10^{14}

   C. 3.74×10^{13}

   D. 4.44×10^{12}

*Use the following information to
answer the next question.*

The demand valve on a diver's mouthpiece continually adjusts the pressure of the air being released into the diver's mouth. At 10 m under water, air crosses the demand valve when the pressure in the lungs is roughly twice the air pressure on the surface.

6. Assuming the temperature and the percentage of oxygen in the diver's lungs is the same while diving as it is at the surface, when the diver is at a depth of 10 m, the alveoli in her lungs will contain

   A. twice the amount of oxygen as they would at the surface

   B. the same amount of oxygen as they would at the surface

   C. one-half the amount of oxygen as they would at the surface

   D. one-quarter the amount of oxygen as they would at the surface

*Use the following information to
answer the next multipart question.*

7. Many refrigeration and air-conditioning devices contain chlorofluorocarbons (CFCs). However, CFCs are known to deplete ozone in the atmosphere. Hydrofluorocarbons (HFCs) are a promising, ozone-friendly substitute for CFCs. The compound 1,1,1,2-tetrafluoroethane, CH_2FCF_3, is one alternative currently being used in home refrigeration and automobile air-conditioning units.

Earth's atmosphere consists of nitrogen, oxygen, argon, water vapour, and various trace gases. CFCs are among the most notorious of these trace gases and now account for roughly 3 ppb (parts per billion by volume) of the atmosphere.

a) Which of the following experiment types would be used to measure the concentration of CFC in the atmosphere?

   A. Logical test

   B. Diagnostic test

   C. Qualitative analysis

   D. Quantitative analysis

b) The intramolecular bonding in CH_2FCF_3 is caused by

   A. a simultaneous attraction of neutrons by the atomic nuclei

   B. a mutual attraction of electrons by the atomic nuclei

   C. an exchange of alpha particles between atoms

   D. a mutual attraction of protons by electrons

c) If dissolved in water, CH_2FCF_3 would

   A. conduct electricity

   B. dissociate into ions

   C. become an electrolyte

   D. become a non-electrolyte

8. Which of the following tables identifies the type of intramoleculuar bonding in $CaCl_{2(s)}$ and the structure formed by the compound?

A.
Bond	Shape
Ionic	Crystal lattice

B.
Bond	Shape
Ionic	Polar molecule

C.
Bond	Shape
Covalent	Crystal lattice

D.
Bond	Shape
Covalent	Polar molecule

Use the following information to answer the next multipart question.

9. Kimchi is a popular Korean pickled dish made by fermenting a combination of radishes, turnips, onions, Chinese cabbages, and salt.

Numerical Response

a) If the salt in kimchi has a 3.00% concentration by mass, the mass of salt contained in a 500 g portion of kimchi, is _____ g. (Record your three-digit answer.)

b) A 48.0 mL sample of kimchi juice has a salt concentration of 0.400 mol/L. If this sample is diluted with water to a new final volume of 100 mL, then the concentration of the salt in the kimchi juice would be $a.bc \times 10^{-d}$ mol/L. The values of a, b, c and d are _____, _____, _____ and _____. (Record your four-digit answer.)

Numerical Response

10. The mass of helium gas that is present in a 10.0 L tank, at 101.325 kPa and 25.0°C is _____ g. (Record your three-digit answer.)

Use the following information to answer the next question.

 Film photography uses silver bromide to form images on paper. Silver bromide is slightly soluble in water, and when saturated, the solution is described by the equation $AgBr_{(s)} \rightleftharpoons Ag^+_{(aq)} + Br^-_{(aq)}$.

11. In this equilibrium equation, the rate of dissolution is
   A. equal to the rate of crystallization
   B. less than the rate of crystallization
   C. greater than the rate of crystallization
   D. independent of the rate of crystallization

Numerical Response

12. Coffee, bananas, spinach, and squash all have a hydrogen ion concentration of about 10^{-5} mol/L. This hydrogen ion concentration corresponds to a pH of _____. (Record your one-digit answer.)

Use the following information to
answer the next question.

> Ammonium perchlorate ($NH_4ClO_{4(s)}$) is a component of the fuel used in solid booster rockets in American space shuttles. When it is heated above 200°C, $NH_4ClO_{4(s)}$ decomposes instead of melting. In the decomposition reaction, all of the hydrogen in $NH_4ClO_{4(s)}$ is released as water vapour, and the remaining products are pure elements.

13. Which of the following equations correctly represents the decomposition of $NH_4ClO_{4(s)}$?

   A. $NH_4ClO_{4(s)}$
   $\rightarrow 2H_2O_{(g)} + N_{(g)} + Cl_{(g)} + O_{2(g)}$

   B. $NH_4ClO_{4(s)}$
   $\rightarrow 2H_2O_{(g)} + N_{(g)} + Cl_{(g)} + 2O_{(g)}$

   C. $2NH_4ClO_{4(s)}$
   $\rightarrow 4H_2O_{(g)} + N_{2(g)} + Cl_{2(g)} + 2O_{2(g)}$

   D. $2NH_4ClO_{4(s)}$
   $\rightarrow 4H_2O_{(g)} + N_{2(g)} + 2Cl_{(g)} + 2O_{2(g)}$

Use the following information to
answer the next question.

> Ammonium perchlorate ($NH_4ClO_{4(s)}$) is the main component of the fuel for the solid rocket boosters used by American space shuttles. It is also used as a propellant in Sidewinder air-to-air missiles and Tomahawk cruise missiles. $NH_4ClO_{4(s)}$ is highly effective as a propellant because of its rapid rate of decomposition.
>
> When ammonium perchlorate decomposes, it produces water vapour along with nitrogen, oxygen, and chlorine in their elemental forms.
>
> Aluminum powder ($Al_{(s)}$) improves the efficiency of NH_4ClO_4 as a propellant by engaging in formation reactions with the elemental oxygen ($O_{2(g)}$) and chlorine ($Cl_{2(g)}$) produced during the decomposition reaction. These formation reactions release vast quantities of thermal energy.

14. When $O_{2(g)}$ and $Cl_{2(g)}$ from the decomposition of $NH_4ClO_{4(S)}$ react with $Al_{(s)}$, two substances formed are

   A. AlO and AlCl

   B. AlO_2 and Al_2Cl_3

   C. Al_2O_3 and $AlCl_3$

   D. Al_3O_2 and Al_2Cl_4

Use the following information to answer the next multipart question.

15. Potassium chromate and lead(II) acetate can be combined to form lead(II) chromate, as shown in the given equation.

$$K_2CrO_{4(aq)} + Pb(CH_3COO)_{2(aq)}$$
$$\rightarrow PbCrO_{4(s)} + 2KCH_3COO_{(aq)}$$

Because of its resistance to mechanical wear, light, and heat, lead(II) chromate (or chrome yellow) is the pigment used for the yellow lane markers on highways. However, since lead is toxic and oxidized chromium is carcinogenic, the use of alternative pigments is preferred.

a) What are the spectator ions in the reaction of potassium chromate and lead(II) acetate in aqueous solution?

A. Pb^{2+} and K^+

B. K^+ and CrO_4^{2-}

C. K^+ and CH_3COO^-

D. Pb^{2+} and CH_3COO^-

Numerical Response

b) If 200 kg of lead(II) chromate is produced from the reaction of 1 000 L of $K_2CrO_{4(aq)}$ and excess lead(II) acetate, the concentration of potassium chromate is $a.bc \times 10^{-d}$ mol/L. The values of a, b, c, and d are _____, _____, _____, and _____. (Record your four-digit answer.)

Use the following information to answer the next question.

Methanol is used as a fuel in race cars, and it has the potential to replace gasoline in regular automobiles. Methanol can be manufactured by reacting carbon monoxide with hydrogen, as shown in the given reaction.

$$2H_{2(g)} + CO_{(g)} \rightarrow CH_3OH_{(l)}$$

Numerical Response

16. If 70.0 kg of $CO_{(g)}$ is combined with 9.00 kg of $H_{2(g)}$, how much methanol will be produced? _____ kg

Use the following information to answer the next multipart question.

17. Ethyne, which is commonly known as acetylene, is used commercially for welding and cutting steel and other materials because it burns with a very hot flame. Prior to 1955, the sole means of producing ethyne $(C_2H_{2(g)})$ was by reacting calcium carbide $(CaC_{2(s)})$ with water, as shown in the given chemical equation.

$$CaC_{2(s)} + 2H_2O_{(l)}$$
$$\rightarrow C_2H_{2(g)} + Ca(OH)_{2(s)}$$

Numerical Response

a) If 4.30 kg of calcium carbide is reacted, the mass of acetylene produced is _____ kg.

b) If 4.30 kg of calcium carbide is reacted, the mass of $Ca(OH)_2$ that forms in the reaction is _____ kg.

c) The solubility of the calcium hydroxide produced is 0.185 g / 100 mL at 0°C. Expressed as a molar solubility, this concentration is $a.bc \times 10^{-d}$ mol/L. The values of a, b, c and d are _____, _____, _____ and _____. (Record your four-digit answer.)

Use the following information to answer the next question.

Svante Arrhenius's doctoral thesis centerd on the electrical conductivity of liquid solutions. Arrhenius theorized that only those solutions containing ions were electrically conductive. Ions can be produced through one of two processes that are often mistaken for one another: ionization and dissociation. Whereas ionization produces ions in solution either by breaking molecular bonds or by charging neutral atoms, dissociation releases the ionic attraction between already existing ions. The radical aspect of his thesis was the suggestion that electrical conductivity was based on dissociated ions. Ions that dissociate tend to form complexes within the solution based on intermolecular dynamics that can facilitate the movement of charged particles and therefore conduct electricity.

18. According to the Arrhenius theory, which of the following statements concerning the electrical conductivity of strong and weak acid solutions is **true**?

A. Weak acids conduct electricity well.

B. Strong acids conduct electricity well.

C. Weak acids do not conduct electricity.

D. Strong acids conduct electricity poorly.

Use the following information to answer the next question.

Sodium borohydride can be used to whiten and deacidify old papers, which is effective in preserving valuable historical documents.

19. If the pH value of a certain paper was 5 before sodium borohydride bleaching and 8 afterward, the corresponding hydrogen ion concentrations of these two pH values are

A. 10^{-9} mol/L and 10^{-6} mol/L

B. 10^{-5} mol/L and 10^{-8} mol/L

C. 10^{5} mol/L and 10^{8} mol/L

D. 10^{9} mol/L and 10^{6} mol/L

Use the following information to answer the next question.

Ethyne, which is commonly known as acetylene, is used commercially for welding and cutting steel and other materials because it burns with a very hot flame. The unbalanced equation for complete combustion of ethyne is as follows:

$$\_C_2H_{2(g)} + \_O_{2(g)} \rightarrow \_CO_{2(g)} + \_H_2O_{(g)}.$$

Written Response

20. Write a balanced equation for the combustion reaction of ethyne.

_____

_____

_____

_____

_____

Use the following information to answer the next question.

Three samples of a solution were tested with three different indicators. The results were recorded in the table below.

	Indicator Added	Resulting Colour
I	bromocresol green	yellow
II	cresol red	yellow
III	orange IV	yellow

21. The approximate pH of the solution is
   A. 1   B. 2
   C. 3   D. 4

Use the following information to answer the next question.

Phosgene ($COCl_{2(g)}$) is a toxic, volatile liquid used primarily in the manufacture of urethane foams, plastics, and coatings. It has also been used as a military chemical weapon. Air containing 0.500 mg/L of phosgene gas can be fatal.

Numerical Response

22. The lethal amount of phosgene in the air has a molar concentration of
$a.bc \times 10^{-d}$ mol/L. The values of a, b, c and d are _____, _____, _____ and _____. (Record your four-digit answer.)

Numerical Response

23. The volume in milliliters of 0.110 mol/L HCl neutralized by 0.236 g of magnesium hydroxide in a dose of milk of magnesia is _____mL. (Record your three-digit answer.)

Use the following information to answer the next question.

| In automobile engines, the reaction of nitrogen and oxygen at high temperature produces nitric oxide.
$$N_{2(g)} + O_{2(g)} \rightarrow 2NO_{(g)}$$
The type of bonding present within molecules of $NO_{(g)}$ is _____*i*_____ and is formed from _____*ii*_____. |
|---|

24. Which of the following tables contains the information that completes the given statement?

A.

i	*ii*
ionic	the attraction between oppositely charged ions

B.

i	*ii*
ionic	the sharing of electrons

C.

i	*ii*
covalent	the attraction between oppositely charged ions

D.

i	*ii*
covalent	the sharing of electrons

Use the following information to answer the next multipart question.

25.

A student titrates a 0.10 mol/L sample of $HCl_{(aq)}$ with a 0.10 mol/L $NaOH_{(aq)}$. The student adds the indicator bromathymol blue to the sample prior to starting the titration.

Written Response

a) Sketch a titration curve to represent the titration. Label the equivalence point on the titration curve.

b) What is the colour of the solution at the indicator endpoint? Did the student choose a good indicator for this titration? Explain your answer.

_____

_____

Written Response

26. Provide a laboratory procedure that would allow for the precipitation of all the Pb^{2+} ions from 500 mL of a contaminated waste solution that also contains $Ag^+_{(aq)}$ ions. Use a procedure that would yield data useful for calculating the $Pb^{2+}_{(aq)}$ ion concentration.

_____

_____

_____

_____

_____

Use the following information to answer the next question.

Magnesium hydroxide, or milk of magnesia, is an antacid. Magnesium hydroxide reacts with the hydrochloric acid present in stomach acid.

27. What is the balanced equation for this reaction?

A. $HCl_{(aq)} + Mg(OH)_{2(s)}$
$\rightarrow H_2O_{(l)} + MgCl_{(aq)}$

B. $HCl_{(aq)} + Mg(OH)_{2(s)}$
$\rightarrow H_2O_{(l)} + MgCl_{2(aq)}$

C. $2HCl_{(aq)} + Mg(OH)_{2(s)}$
$\rightarrow 2H_2O_{(l)} + MgCl_{2(aq)}$

D. $2HCl_{(aq)} + 2Mg(OH)_{2(s)}$
$\rightarrow H_2O_{(l)} + MgCl_{2(aq)}$

PRACTICE TEST 2

Use the following information to answer the next question.

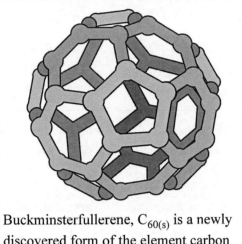

Buckminsterfullerene, $C_{60(s)}$ is a newly discovered form of the element carbon comprised of carbon atoms in an arrangement identical to the corners of each panel on a World Cup soccer ball. It is possible to fill the cavity of a $C_{60(s)}$ molecule with $He_{(g)}$ or $Ne_{(g)}$ (one atom) at 600°C and at a pressure of 3.00 atmospheres. These are, arguably, the first compounds containing helium and neon.

Numerical Response

1. Expressed as an absolute temperature, 600°C is _____ K. (Record your answer to three digits.)

2. What is the reverse reaction of a decomposition reaction?

   A. Single displacement reaction

   B. Combustion reaction

   C. Acid-base reaction

   D. Formation reaction

3. Which of the following graphs illustrates what happens to the rates of dissolving and precipitation when a solid is added to water and allowed to form a saturated solution?

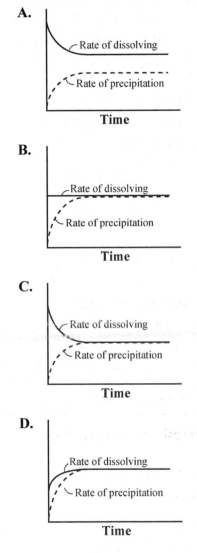

A.
Rate of dissolving
Rate of precipitation
Time

B.
Rate of dissolving
Rate of precipitation
Time

C.
Rate of dissolving
Rate of precipitation
Time

D.
Rate of dissolving
Rate of precipitation
Time

Use the following information to answer the next question.

> Visiting hockey teams have to cope with the lack of oxygen when playing the Colorado Avalanche at home. This is because atmospheric pressure is much lower in Denver, which is at a higher altitude than most other cities.

Numerical Response

4. The volume occupied by 1.00 mol of oxygen in Denver with an average pressure of 90.0 kPa at a temperature of 10°C is _____ L. (Record your three-digit answer.)

5. The pH of a 10.0 mol/L solution of sulfuric acid is

   A. −1.000   B. 0.000

   C. 1.000   D. 10.000

Use the following information to answer the next question.

> The use of gasohol, a mixture of ethanol (C_2H_5OH) and gasoline, has become prominent over the last two decades as the search for alternative energy sources to fossil fuels continues. Both corn and sugar cane are widely used to produce ethanol using the process of fermentation.

6. Which of the following equations correctly represents the complete combustion of ethanol?

   A. $C_2H_5OH + 3O_2 \rightarrow 2CO_2 + 3H_2O$

   B. $C_2H_5OH + 6O_2 \rightarrow 2CO_2 + 4H_2O$

   C. $2C_2H_5OH + 6O_2 \rightarrow 4CO_2 + 5H_2O$

   D. $2C_2H_5OH + 7O_2 \rightarrow 4CO_2 + 6H_2O$

Use the following information to answer the next question.

> A pair of test tubes, labelled A and B, contain solutions according to the given chart.

Test Tube A	Test Tube B (in excess)
3.50 g silver nitrate	Potassium carbonate

7. Which of the following tables identifies the precipitate that would result and a spectator ion in the reaction if test tubes A and B were combined?

A.

Precipitate	Spectator Ion
$AgCO_{3(s)}$	$K^+_{(aq)}$

B.

Precipitate	Spectator Ion
$AgCO_{3(s)}$	$CO_{3(aq)}^{2-}$

C.

Precipitate	Spectator Ion
$KNO_{3(s)}$	$K^+_{(aq)}$

D.

Precipitate	Spectator Ion
$KNO_{3(s)}$	$CO_{3(aq)}^{2-}$

Use the following information to answer the next question.

> In most modern cars, the gas that fills the air bags during a crash comes from the simple decomposition of sodium azide ($NaN_{3(s)}$).
> $2NaN_{3(s)} \rightarrow 2Na_{(s)} + 3N_{2(g)}$
> Specifications dictate that 80 L of gas must inflate the bag at temperatures as low as −60 °C at a pressure of 1.0 atm.

Numerical Response

8. The mass of $NaN_{3(s)}$ that must decompose to produce 80 L of gas at −60 °C is $a.b \times 10^c$ g. The values for *a*, *b* and *c* are _____, _____ and _____. (Record your three-digit answer.)

Use the following information to answer the next multipart question.

9. Alkaloids, such as nicotine ($M = 162.26$ g/mol), can react with acid to produce a nicotine salt ($M = 198.72$ g/mol).

Nicotine   Nicotine Salt

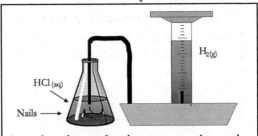

In a reaction, 60.0 mg of nicotine is mixed with 10.0 mL of a 1.00×10^{-3} mol/L $HCl_{(aq)}$, as represented by the balanced equation given.

a) The limiting reagent for this reaction is
  A. hydrochloric acid
  B. nicotine salt
  C. alkaloid
  D. nicotine

Numerical Response

b) The theoretical mass of the nicotine salt that should form in the reaction is _____ mg. (Record your three-digit answer.)

Use the following information to answer the next question.

A student is conducting an experiment in chemistry class. Sufficient 6 mol/L $HCl_{(aq)}$ is added to a flask to cover the zinc-galvanized nails. The $H_{2(g)}$ formed in the reaction can be trapped and its pressure and volume determined. The reaction of 10 g of the galvanized nails with $HCl_{(aq)}$ yields 0.325 L of H_2 after 5 min. The temperature is measured to be 20.0°C and the pressure due to $P_{H_2} = 720$ torr.

Numerical Response

10. The mass of zinc that dissolves from the galvanized nails is $a.bc \times 10^{-d}$ g. The values of a, b, c, and d are _____, _____, _____, and _____. (Record your four-digit answer.)

Use the following information to answer the next question.

Copper(II) oxide is a black solid with an ionic structure that melts above 1 200°C with some loss of oxygen. It can be formed by heating copper in air. This reaction is represented as follows:
$2Cu_{(s)} + O_{2(g)} \rightarrow 2CuO_{(s)}$

11. If 50.0 g of copper are combined with 80.0 g of oxygen in a reactor to form copper(II) oxide according to the given reaction, what is the remaining mass of the excess reagent?
  A. 12.6 g   **B.** 13.6 g
  C. 67.4 g   **D.** 268 g

Use the following information to answer the next question.

Acetic acid is a weak acid that can be found in many foods and drinks including wine and vinegar. It is present as 5% aqueous solution in vinegar and is responsible for the sour taste of spoilt wine.

12. If a suitable electric current were applied to an acetic acid solution, then the acetic acid would

 A. not conduct the electric current

 B. conduct the electric current efficiently

 C. not conduct the electric current as well as distilled water would

 D. conduct the electric current inefficiently but better than distilled water

Use the following information to answer the next multipart question.

13.

A tea company states in an advertisement that a 235 mL (8 fluid oz) cup of tea contains 40.0 mg of caffeine, which is almost 60 % less than the same volume of coffee.

Numerical Response

a) The concentration of caffeine in the tea expressed as a percentage weight per volume is _____%. (Record your three-digit answer.)

b) Caffeine has a molar mass of 194.19 g/mol. The molar concentration of caffeine for one serving of the tea in the advertisement, expressed in scientific notation, is $a.b \times 10^{-c}$ mol/L. What are the values for a, b, and c, respectively? _____(Record your answer as a three-digit number.)

Use the following information to answer the next question.

Margarine is manufactured by hydrogenating a hot mixture of fats and oils. Different varieties of margarine contain largely different amounts of air and moisture.

A student conducted an experiment to determine the amount of water and oil within a sample of margarine, which separate into two distinct layers upon heating. The student recorded the following observations after melting two 14.0 g samples of different margarines.

Margarine	Mass of $H_2O_{(g)}$	Mass of Oil
Regular	3.00 g	11.0 g
Light	6.00 g	8.00 g

Written Response

14. What is the difference in water content between the two samples of margarine, expressed as mass percent of the sample?

_____

_____

_____

_____

_____

Phospholipids are special fatty acid esters that constitute most cell membranes. One of the most abundant fatty acid residues in mammalian cells is derived from palmitic acid ($C_{16}H_{32}O_2$), which has a molar mass of 256.48 g/mol.

15. The approximate mass percentage of each element in palmitic acid as measured by mass is
   A. 75% C, 13% H, and 12% O
   B. 75% C, 12% H, and 13% O
   C. 79% C, 8% H, and 13% O
   D. 77% C, 6% H, and 7% O

16. What is the mass of $Na_2CO_{3(aq)}$ needed to prepare 100 mL of a 0.100 mol/L solution?
   A. 10.6 g   B. 1.06 g
   C. 0.100 g   D. 0.0100 g

Use the following information to answer the next multipart question.

17. Lactic acid ($C_3H_6O_3$) is a weak acid found in milk and is important to several biochemical processes.

a) A 1.0 M aqueous solution of lactic acid would be a
   A. non-electrolyte
   B. strong electrolyte
   C. poor conductor of electricity
   D. good conductor of electricity

b) An aqueous solution of lactic acid could be **best** described as having
   A. a very low pH
   B. an acidic pH > 7
   C. all lactic acid molecules completely dissociated
   D. dissociated and non-dissociated lactic acid molecules

Use the following information to answer the next question.

The hyperbaric chamber is used by professional sports teams to treat their injured players. It is believed that hyperbaric oxygen therapy speeds up the healing process. This may have to do with the extra supply of oxygen to injured cells during treatment.

18. Taking into account that standard pressure is about 100 kPa, what would happen to the amount of oxygen available to cells if the chamber's pressure was 120 kPa?
   A. The oxygen level in the cells would decrease by about 20% because the same amount of oxygen would take up 20% more space.
   B. The oxygen level in the cells would increase by about 20% because the same amount of oxygen would take up 20% more space.
   C. The oxygen level in the cells would decrease by about 20% because the same amount of oxygen would take up 20% less space.
   D. The oxygen level in the cells would increase by about 20% because the same amount of oxygen would take up 20% less space.

Use the following information to answer the next question.

The amount of energy required to split one mole of water into hydrogen and oxygen is seven times higher than the amount of energy required to vapourize one mole of water at its boiling point.

19. The forces that are overcome in vapourizing water are
   A. ionic bonds
   B. covalent bonds
   C. intermolecular bonds
   D. intramolecular bonds

*Use the following information to
answer the next question.*

The molecule *beta*-carotene is a strongly
coloured pigment found in most fruits and
plants. It is a precursor to vitamin A.

20. *Beta*-carotene is a non-polar, molecular
substance that is expected to
   A. have low solubility in water
   B. be highly reactive in water
   C. be highly soluble in water
   D. dissociate in water

*Use the following information to
answer the next question.*

An exothermic reaction occurs wen an
unknown ionic compound is dissolved
in water.

21. Which of the following statements **best**
describes the changes in energy that occur
during the dissolving process?
   A. The energy released when breaking
   the bonds in the reactants is greater
   than the energy consumed in bond
   formation in the products.
   B. The energy released when breaking
   the bonds in the reactants is less than
   the energy consumed in bond
   formation in the products.
   C. The energy consumed to break the
   bonds in the reactants is greater than
   the energy released from bond
   formation in the products.
   D. The energy consumed to break the
   bonds in the reactants is less than the
   energy released from bond formation
   in the products.

*Use the following information to
answer the next question.*

 Chlorine, Cl_2, is
used in great
quantities as a
bleach for the pulp
and paper industry
and as a disinfectant
for municipal water
supplies.
The boiling point of chlorine is $-34.6°C$.

22. The electrons involved in the bonding
within chlorine molecules are
   A. completely transferred from one
   atom to another
   B. inner shell electrons only
   C. unequally shared
   D. equally shared

*Use the following information to
answer the next question.*

Commercial glass is hard and generally
quite chemically resistant.
The predominant constituent of glass is
silicon dioxide, SiO_2. Hydrofluoric acid,
HF, is commonly used for the acid etching
of glass. An example of this reaction
is given.
$$SiO_2 + 4HF \rightarrow SiF_4 + 2H_2O$$

23. A plausible explanation as to why fluorine
forms a stronger bond with silicon than
oxygen is that
   A. fluorine is a halogen
   B. fluorine-silicon bonds are non-polar
   C. fluorine has fewer lone pairs of
   electrons than oxygen
   D. fluorine has a higher
   electronegativity than oxygen, and
   thus has a stronger attraction for the
   silicon electrons

24. Which of the following compounds contains a polar covalent bond?
   A. NaCl   B. HCl
   C. NaK   D. Cl_2

25. What characteristic of a water molecule accounts for its polarity?
   A. its cohesiveness
   B. its ability to act as a solvent
   C. its unequal sharing of electrons
   D. the hydrogen bonding to neighbouring water molecules

Use the following information to answer the next multipart question.

26. A student compares these four molecular compounds.
$CH_3CH_2NH_2$ (ethylamine), $CH_3CH_2CH_3$ (propane), CH_3CH_2OH (ethanol), and CH_3CH_2F (fluoroethane)

Written Response

a) Construct a table that summarizes the total number of bonding electrons, the polarity, and the types of intermolecular bonds present in each of the compounds.

_____
_____
_____
_____

b) List the compounds from the lowest expected boiling point to the highest expected boiling point. Explain your answer.

_____
_____
_____
_____
_____
_____

27. A pH of 8 corresponds to a solution in which
   A. $[H_3O^+_{(aq)}] = 10^{-8}$ mol/L and $[OH^-_{(aq)}] = 10^{-6}$ mol/L
   B. $[H_3O^+_{(aq)}] = 10^8$ mol/L and $[OH^-_{(aq)}] = 10^6$ mol/L
   C. $[H_3O^+_{(aq)}] = [OH^-_{(aq)}] = 10^{-8}$ mol/L
   D. $[H_3O^+_{(aq)}] = [OH^-_{(aq)}] = 10^8$ mol/L

Use the following information to answer the next question.

A sample of helium gas is contained in a 2.00 L balloon at a pressure of 3.00 atm and a temperature of 10.0°C. When the temperature of the balloon was increased to 25.0°C, the volume of the balloon increased to 3.00 L.

Numerical Response

28. The final pressure of the helium gas in the balloon is _____ atm. (Record your three-digit answer.)

Use the following information to answer the next multipart question.

29.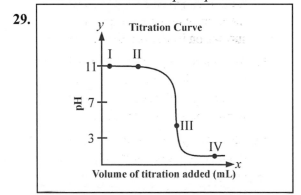

a) The equivalence point of the titration is represented by which number on the titration curve?
   A. I   B. II
   C. III   D. IV

b) Which of the following tables identifies the species involved in the titration and a suitable indicator that could be used in the titration?

A.
Species Involved	Indicator
A strong acid titrated with a strong base.	Indigo carmine

B.
Species Involved	Indicator
A strong acid titrated with a strong base.	Phenolphthalein

C.
Species Involved	Indicator
A strong base titrated with a strong acid.	Indigo carmine

D.
Species Involved	Indicator
A strong base titrated with a strong acid.	Phenolphthalein

Use the following information to answer the next question.

Sulfuric acid ($H_2SO_{4(aq)}$) is used to manufacture fertilizers, plastics, pharmaceuticals, metals, paints, and numerous other products. The use of sulfuric acid is so extensive that economists can measure the economic health of a country by how much sulfuric acid the country uses.

30. One characteristic of sulfuric acid that makes it so useful in industry is that the acid is a
   A. good conductor of electricity
   B. poor conductor of electricity
   C. weak electrolyte
   D. non-electrolyte

Use the following information to answer the next question.

Diabetes mellitus is a group of disorders that lead to the elevation of glucose in the blood. It is usually characterized by excess glucose excretion in the urine. Urinalysis is often performed on those suspected of having diabetes mellitus. Colorimetric strip tests are used to assess urinary glucose. Like litmus in some ways, the glucose test strips become a specific color if abnormal amounts of glucose are present.

31. The colorimetric strips used to analyze the urine sample test
   A. gravimetrically
   B. quantitatively
   C. qualitatively
   D. physically

Use the following information to answer the next question.

The mineral magnetite (Fe_3O_4) is a naturally occurring black metal oxide. Its formation at high temperatures can be represented by the equation
$3Fe_{(s)} + 2O_{2(g)} \rightarrow Fe_3O_{4(s)}$.

32. The bonding between the iron and oxygen ions in the given equation is the result of a
   A. loss of electrons by Fe and a gain of electrons by O
   B. gain of electrons by Fe and a loss of electrons by O
   C. loss of electrons by Fe and a loss of electrons by O
   D. gain of electrons by Fe and a gain of electrons by O

ANSWERS AND SOLUTIONS — PRACTICE TEST 1

1. A	7. a) D	11. A	17. a) 1.75	22. 5066
2. B	b) B	12. 5	b) 4.97	23. 73.6
3. B	c) D	13. C	c) 2502	24. D
4. a) D	8. A	14. C	18. B	25. a) WR
b) B	9. a) 15.0	15. a) C	19. B	b) WR
5. C	b) 1921	b) 6191	20. WR	26. WR
6. A	10. 1.64	16. 71.5	21. C	27. C

1. A

All chemical matter contains circulating electrons. Therefore, all matter experiences London dispersion forces. Since N_2O is weakly polar, its molecules will also interact through dipole-dipole attractions.

This is the Lewis diagram of N_2O.

$$\overset{\delta^-}{:\ddot{O}} - N \equiv N$$

2. B

Intermolecular forces exert a great influence over the physical properties of molecular compounds. There are three varieties of intermolecular forces: dispersion forces, normal dipole-dipole interactions, and a special type of dipole-dipole interaction called hydrogen bonding.

Hydrogen bonding occurs only in substances that have a hydrogen atom covalently bonded to an oxygen, nitrogen, or fluorine atom. The relatively large difference in electronegativity between a hydrogen atom and an atom of oxygen, nitrogen, or fluorine makes H–O, H–N, and H–F bonds very polar. This results in a strong attraction between a hydrogen atom of one molecule and an oxygen, a nitrogen, or a fluorine atom of a neighboring molecule. This attraction is known as a hydrogen bond.

Hydrogen Bond

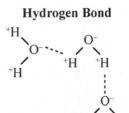

In liquid water, the attraction between a hydrogen atom of one water molecule and the oxygen atom of another is an example of a hydrogen bond. Hydrogen bonds are stronger than all other dipole-dipole interactions and much stronger than dispersion forces. Hydrogen bonds are the primary intermolecular interactions pulling H_2O molecules together in the liquid phase, and their high strength results in a low volatility for $H_2O_{(l)}$. The H–S bond is not polar enough to produce hydrogen bonding in $H_2S_{(g)}$, giving this compound weaker intermolecular interactions and a higher volatility than $H_2O_{(l)}$.

All molecules and atomic chemical entities experience dispersion forces. These intermolecular forces result from temporary dipoles created by moving electrons within molecules. Their relative strength is affected by the number of electrons and protons in the molecules involved. H_2S molecules have more electrons and protons than H_2O molecules so would experience stronger dispersion forces. This difference, however, becomes insignificant compared to the effect of hydrogen bonding in liquid water.

3. B

The three compounds listed all consist of molecules with tetrahedral shapes. Any dipoles between atoms of a tetrahedral molecule are cancelled out, making the molecules non-polar. The only interaction between the individual molecules of these compounds, intermolecular interactions, are London forces. The strength of London forces acting between two molecules is affected by the number of electrons in each molecule. As the halogen atoms surrounding a silicon atom get larger, there are more electrons, and the London forces get stronger. An increase in the attractive forces between molecules results in an increase in boiling point.

Since bonds within the molecules of these compounds, the intramolecular bonds, are not broken during boiling, the relative strengths of these bonds do not affect the boiling points.

4. a) D

If each atom in the molecule is bonded with a bonding pair of electrons, there should be $12e^-$ (six pairs of bonding e^-) surrounding the carbon.

b) B

The octet rule states that most of the representative elements tend to be most stable when they have eight electrons in their valence shells. Carbon normally obeys this rule, but in CLi_6, this is not the case.

5. C

Step 1
Convert the given units into the units of the ideal gas law $PV = nRT$.
$$37°C = (37 + 273.15)K$$
$$= 310.15K$$

$$8.00 \times 10^{-6} \text{ mL} \times \frac{1.00 \text{ L}}{1\,000 \text{ mL}}$$
$$= 8.00 \times 10^{-9} \text{ L}$$

Step 2
Apply the ideal gas law.
This equation can be solved for the number of moles (n) to give $n = \dfrac{PV}{RT}$.

Oxygen makes up about $\dfrac{1}{5}$ of the gases in air.

$$n_{O_2} = \frac{1}{5} n_{AIR}$$
$$n_{O_2} = \frac{1}{5} \times \frac{PV}{RT}$$
$$= \frac{1}{5} \times \frac{100 \text{ kPa} \times 8.00 \times 10^{-9} \text{ L}}{8.314 \frac{\text{kPa} \cdot \text{L}}{\text{mol} \cdot \text{K}} \times 310.15 \text{ K}}$$
$$= 6.20 \times 10^{-11} \text{ mol of } O_{2(g)}$$

Step 3
Convert moles of oxygen into molecules of oxygen using, n_A, Avogadro's number of molecules per mole of any gas.
$$\text{molecules}_{O_2} = n_{O_2} \times n_A$$
$$= \left(\begin{array}{c} 6.20 \times 10^{-11} \text{ mol} \\ \times \ 6.022 \times 10^{23} \frac{\text{molecules}}{\text{mol}} \end{array} \right)$$
$$= 3.74 \times 10^{13} \text{ molecules}$$

Each alveolus contains an estimated 3.74×10^{13} molecules of oxygen.

6. A

The relationship of pressure, volume, temperature, and moles of a gas is given by the ideal gas law, $n = \dfrac{PV}{RT}$, in which n is the number of moles, P is the pressure in kilopascals, V is the volume in litres, R is the universal gas constant, and T is the temperature in kelvins.

The maximum volume of air in the diver's lungs is determined by the total capacity of her alveoli, which is the same at 10 m as it is at the surface. Since V, R, and T are constant, doubling the number of moles (n) will double the pressure (P), according to the ideal gas law equation.

Let the amount and pressure of oxygen at sea level be n_0 and P_0, respectively, and let the amount and pressure of oxygen at the 10 m depth be n_{10} and P_{10}, respectively.
$$n_0 = \frac{P_0 V}{RT}$$
$$n_{10} = \frac{P_{10} V}{RT}$$

Since $P_{10} = 2P_0$, substitute $n_{10} = \dfrac{2P_0 V}{RT}$.

$$n_0 = \dfrac{P_0 V}{RT} \therefore P_0 = \dfrac{n_0 RT}{V}$$

$$n_{10} = \dfrac{2P_0 V}{RT}$$

$$n_{10} = 2\left(\dfrac{n_0 RT}{V}\right)\dfrac{V}{RT}$$

$$n_{10} = 2n_0$$

There is twice as much gas present at twice the gas pressure.

Therefore, the amount of oxygen in the diver's alveoli at 10 m is twice as much as it would be at the surface.

7. a) D

A quantitative analysis measuring the amount, or quantity, of a substance. Measuring the concentration of CFC in the atmosphere is an example of a quantitative analysis as it measures the quantity of CFC per unit of volume.

A qualitative analysis detects the presence of a chemical entity but does not measure it. An example of a qualitative analysis would be a starch test for iodine.

b) B

Intermolecular bonding describes the weak forces of interaction between molecules in the liquid and solid states. Intramolecular bonding describes the covalent bonds that bind atoms together within molecules. The atoms in molecules of CH_2FCF_3 are held together by covalent bonds. The electrons that form a covalent bond between two atoms are shared between, that is, are mutually attracted to, the bound nuclei by the overlap of partially filled valence atomic orbitals.

c) D

CH_2FCF_3 is a molecular compound held together by strong C–H, C–F, and C–C intramolecular bonds. It will not dissociate into aqueous ions in water. Any substance that dissociates into ions and conducts electricity is called an electrolyte. If the substance does not dissociate into ions, it will not conduct electricity and is called a non-electrolyte.

Therefore, CH_2FCF_3 will become a non-electrolyte when dissolved in water.

8. A

$CaCl_{2(s)}$ is an ionic compound held together by ionic bonds resulting from the attraction between two oppositely charged ions. Ionic compounds form lattice structures, which gives the compound its high melting point.

9. a) 15.0

$$m_{salt} = 3.00\% \times 500 \text{ g}$$
$$= \dfrac{3.00}{100} \times 500 \text{ g}$$
$$= 15.0 \text{ g}$$

There are 15.0 g of salt in a 500 g kimchi portion.

b) 1921

For dilution purposes, use the formula $c_1 V_1 = c_2 V_2$.

Step 1
Define the variables for the equation.

c_1 = initial concentration
  = 0.400 mol/L
V_1 = initial volume
  = 48.0 mL
c_2 = final concentration
  = ?
V_2 = final volume
  = 100 mL

Step 2
Substitute the known values into the equation, and rearrange the equation to solve for the final concentration.

$$c_2 = \dfrac{c_1 V_1}{V_2}$$
$$= \dfrac{0.400 \text{ mol/L} \times 48.0 \text{ ml}}{100 \text{ ml}}$$
$$= 0.192 \text{ mol/L or } 1.92 \times 10^{-1} \text{ mol/L}$$

The values for a, b, c and d are 1, 9, 2, and 1.

10. 1.64

Substitute the known values into the equation $PV = nRT$, which can be rewritten as $n = \dfrac{PV}{RT}$.

$$n_{He} = \dfrac{(101.325 \text{ kPa})(10.0 \text{ L})}{(8.314 \text{ KPa·L / mol· k})(298.15 \text{ k})}$$
$$= 0.409 \text{ mol}$$
$$mass_{He} = 0.409 \text{ mol} \times 4.00 \text{ g/mol}$$
$$= 1.64 \text{ g}$$

11. A

In all solutions in which a saturated aqueous solution and undissolved solid solute occupy the same vessel, the following dynamic solubility equilibrium occurs:

solute$_{(s)}$ $\rightleftharpoons$ solute$_{(aq)}$

Equilibria like this occur when the rate of the forward process, solute$_{(s)}$ $\rightarrow$ solute$_{(aq)}$ (dissolution), is equal to the rate of the reverse process, solute$_{(s)}$ $\leftarrow$ solute$_{(aq)}$ (crystallization).

For the solubility equilibrium

$AgBr_{(s)} \rightleftharpoons Ag^+_{(aq)} + Br^-_{(aq)}$, the solute dissociates when it dissolves as all ionic compounds do.

12. 5

pH is a function of $\left[H^+_{(aq)}\right]$ defined as

pH $= -\log\left[H^+_{(aq)}\right]$, where $\left[H^+_{(aq)}\right]$ is the molar concentration of the hydrogen ions.

In this example, the pH can be calculated as follows:

$$pH = -\log\left[10^{-5}\right]$$
$$= 5$$

13. C

Step 1

It is stated that all of the hydrogen (H) in $NH_4ClO_{4(s)}$ is released as water vapour, so begin the equation by showing $NH_4ClO_{4(s)}$ producing water vapour ($H_2O_{(g)}$). The coefficient 2 is added to $H_2O_{(g)}$ to balance the four H atoms in $NH_4ClO_{4(s)}$.

$NH_4ClO_{4(s)} \rightarrow 2H_2O_{(g)}$

Step 2

As stated, the remaining products are pure elements. Add the symbols for nitrogen (N) and chlorine (Cl) to the equation.

$NH_4ClO_{4(s)} \rightarrow 2H_2O_{(g)} + N + Cl$

Step 3

There are not enough oxygen (O) atoms in the two $H_2O_{(g)}$ molecules to account for the four O atoms in $NH_4ClO_{4(s)}$, so add O to the product side as well.

$NH_4ClO_{4(s)} \rightarrow 2H_2O_{(g)} + N + Cl + O$

Step 4

N, Cl, and O are all diatomic elements in their elemental form. They consist of molecules containing two atoms each. Add a subscript of 2 to each of these three elements in the equation.

$NH_4ClO_{4(s)} \rightarrow 2H_2O_{(g)} + N_2 + Cl_2 + O_2$

Step 5

Because N, Cl, and O are diatomic, two atoms of N and Cl are needed on the reactant side of the equation. The equation is balanced by doubling the number of $NH_4ClO_{4(s)}$ molecules from one molecule to two.

Add the coefficient 2 in front of $NH_4ClO_{4(s)}$.

$2NH_4ClO_{4(s)}$
$\rightarrow 2H_2O_{(g)} + N_2 + Cl_2 + O_2$

Step 6

Since there are now twice as many H atoms, the number of $H_2O_{(g)}$ molecules must be doubled as well. Likewise, there are now twice as many O atoms. Since four of the eight O atoms are represented in the four $H_2O_{(g)}$ molecules, the number of O_2 molecules must be doubled to account for the remaining four O atoms.

Change the coefficient in front of $H_2O_{(g)}$ to 4, and add the coefficient 2 in front of O_2.

$2NH_4ClO_{4(s)}$
$\rightarrow 4H_2O_{(g)} + N_2 + Cl_2 + 2O_2$

Step 7

Since N, Cl, and O are all gaseous at 200°C, add subscripts indicating that these products are gases.

$2NH_4ClO_{4(s)}$
$\rightarrow 4H_2O_{(g)} + N_{2(g)} + Cl_{2(g)} + 2O_{2(g)}$

The correct balanced equation for the decomposition of ammonium perchlorate at 200°C is

$2NH_4ClO_{4(s)}$
$\rightarrow 4H_2O_{(g)} + N_{2(g)} + Cl_{2(g)} + 2O_{2(g)}$

14. C

When solid aluminum ($Al_{(s)}$) reacts with elemental oxygen (O_2), it produces the ionic compound aluminum oxide. Aluminum oxide consists of Al^{3+} and O^{2-} ions, which combine to form the molecule Al_2O_3. The equation for the formation of aluminum oxide from its elements is

$4Al_{(s)} + 3O_{2(g)} \rightarrow 2Al_2O_{3(s)}$.

When solid aluminum ($Al_{(s)}$) reacts with elemental chlorine (Cl_2), it produces the ionic compound aluminum chloride. Aluminum chloride consists of Al^{3+} and Cl^- ions, which combine to form the molecule $AlCl_3$. The equation for the formation of aluminum chloride from its elements is

$2Al_{(s)} + 3Cl_{2(g)} \rightarrow 2AlCl_{3(s)}$.

Therefore, two substances formed from the decomposition products of ammonium perchlorate and solid aluminum are aluminum oxide (Al_2O_3) and aluminum chloride $(AlCl_{3(s)})$.

15. a) C

Spectator ions will survive unchanged in a chemical reaction. They are removed when a net reaction is written.

Step 1
Write the non-ionic equation.
$$K_2CrO_{4(aq)} + Pb(CH_3COO)_{2(aq)}$$
$$\rightarrow PbCrO_{4(aq)} + 2CH_3COOK_{(aq)}$$

Step 2
Write the total ionic equation.
$$2K^+_{(aq)} + CrO^{2-}_{4(aq)} + Pb^{2+}_{(aq)} + 2CH_3COO^-_{(aq)}$$
$$\rightarrow PbCrO_{4(s)} + 2K^+_{(aq)} + 2CH_3COO^-_{(aq)}$$

Step 3
Write the net ionic equation.
$$CrO^{2-}_{4(aq)} + Pb^{2+}_{(aq)} \rightarrow PbCrO_{4(s)}$$
Since they remain unaltered on both sides of the total ionic equation, $K^+_{(aq)}$ and $CH_3COO^-_{(aq)}$ are the spectator ions.

b) 6191

Since the mass of $PbCrO_{4(s)}$ is given and the concentration of $K_2CrO_{4(aq)}$ is unknown, use this plan:
$$M_{PbCrO_4} \rightarrow n_{PbCrO_4} \rightarrow n_{K_2CrO_4} \rightarrow c_{K_2CrO_4}$$

Step 1
Calculate the molar mass of $PbCrO_4$ using the atomic masses of Pb, Cr, and O.
$$M_{PbCrO_4} = 207.2 \text{ g/mol} + 52.00 \text{ g/mol}$$
$$+ 4(16.00 \text{ g/mol})$$
$$= 323.2 \text{ g/mol}$$

Step 2
Convert the given mass of $PbCrO_4$ to moles.
$$n_{PbCrO_4} = \frac{m_{PbCrO_4}}{M_{PbCrO_4}}$$
$$= \frac{2.00 \times 10^2 \text{ kg} \times \frac{10^3 \text{ g}}{1 \text{ kg}}}{323.2 \text{ g/mol}}$$
$$= 6.19 \times 10^2 \text{ mol}$$

Step 3
Use the coefficient ratio of K_2CrO_4 to $PbCrO_4$ in the balanced equation to determine the moles of K_2CrO_4 used.
$$\frac{n_{K_2CrO_4}}{n_{PbCrO_4}} = \frac{1}{1}$$
$$n_{K_2CrO_4} = \frac{1}{1} \times n_{PbCrO_4}$$
$$= \frac{1}{1}(6.19 \times 10^2 \text{ mol})$$
$$= 6.19 \times 10^2 \text{ mol}$$

Step 4
Calculate the molar concentration of $K_2CrO_{4(aq)}$.
$$c_{K_2CrO_4} = \frac{n_{K_2CrO_4}}{V_{K_2CrO_4}}$$
$$= \frac{6.19 \times 10^2 \text{ mol}}{1.00 \times 10^3 \text{ L}}$$
$$= 0.619 \text{ mol/L}$$
The molar concentration of $K_2CrO_{4(aq)}$ is 0.619 mol/L or 6.19×10^{-1} mol/L.

16. 71.5

Use an excess limiting stoichiometric method.

Step 1
Calculate the moles of $H_{2(g)}$ present.
$$n_{H_2} = \frac{m_{H_2}}{M_{H_2}}$$
$$= \frac{9.00 \text{ kg}}{2.02 \text{ g/mol}}$$
$$= \frac{9\,000 \text{ g}}{2.02 \text{ g/mol}}$$
$$= 4.46 \times 10^3 \text{ mol}$$

Step 2
Calculate the moles of $CO_{(g)}$ needed to react with the $H_{2(g)}$.
$$n_{CO} = \frac{1}{2}n_H$$
$$= \frac{1}{2}(4.46 \times 10^3 \text{ mol})$$
$$= 2.23 \times 10^3 \text{ mol}$$

Step 3

Calculate the moles of $CO_{(g)}$ present.

$$n_{CO} = \frac{m}{M}$$

$$= \frac{70.0 \text{ kg}}{28.01 \text{ g/mol}}$$

$$= \frac{70\,000 \text{ g}}{28.01 \text{ g/mol}}$$

$$= 2.50 \times 10^3 \text{ mol}$$

Since there is more $CO_{(g)}$ present than is needed, $H_{2(g)}$ is the limiting reagent in the reaction.

Step 4

Calculate the moles of CH_3OH produced.

$$n_{CH_3OH} = \frac{1}{2}n_{H_2}$$

$$= \frac{1}{2}\left(4.46 \times 10^3 \text{ mol}\right)$$

$$= 2.23 \times 10^3 \text{ mol}$$

Step 5

Calculate the mass of CH_3OH produced.

$$m_{CH_3OH} = nM$$

$$= \left(2.23 \times 10^3 \text{ mol}\right)(32.05 \text{ g/mol})$$

$$= 71\,471.5 \text{ g}$$

$$= 71.5 \text{ kg}$$

In this reaction, 71.5 kg of methanol is predicted.

17. **a) 1.75**

Use a stoichiometric calculation.

$$CaC_{2(s)} + 2H_2O_{(l)} \rightarrow C_2H_{2(g)} + Ca(OH)_{2(s)}$$

Step 1

Calculate the moles of calcium carbide consumed.

$$n_{CaC_2} = 4.30 \times 10^3 \text{ g} \times \frac{\text{mol}}{64.10 \text{ g}}$$

$$= 67.1 \text{ mol}$$

Step 2

Calculate the moles of acetylene produced.

From the balanced equation, the moles of calcium carbide consumed equal the moles of acetylene produced.

$$n_{C_2H_2} = \frac{1}{1}n_{CaC_2}$$

$$= \frac{1}{1} \times 67.1 \text{ mol}$$

$$= 67.1 \text{ mol}$$

Step 3

Calculate the mass of acetylene.

$$m_{C_2H_2} = 67.1 \text{ mol} \times \frac{26.04 \text{ g}}{\text{mol}}$$

$$= 1\,747 \text{ g}$$

$$= 1.75 \text{ kg}$$

The mass of acetylene produced is 1.75 kg.

b) 4.97

Since the mass of calcium carbide is given and the mass of calcium hydroxide must be found, a useful plan to solve this problem can be summarized as

$$m_{CaC_2} \rightarrow n_{CaC_2} \rightarrow n_{Ca(OH)_2} \rightarrow m_{Ca(OH)_2}$$

Step 1

Convert the mass of CaC_2 to moles.

$$n_{CaC_2} = \frac{m_{CaC_2}}{M_{CaC_2}}$$

$$= \frac{4.30 \text{ kg} \times \dfrac{10^3 \text{ g}}{1 \text{ kg}}}{64.10 \text{ g/mol}}$$

$$= 67.1 \text{ mol}$$

Step 2

Use the coefficient ratio of $Ca(OH)_2$ to CaC_2 in the balanced equation to determine the moles of $Ca(OH)_2$ formed.

$$\frac{n_{Ca(OH)_2}}{n_{CaC_2}} = \frac{1}{1}$$

$$n_{Ca(OH)_2} = \frac{1}{1} \times n_{CaC_2}$$

$$= \frac{1}{1}(67.1 \text{ mol})$$

$$= 67.1 \text{ mol}$$

Step 3

Calculate the molar mass of $Ca(OH)_2$ using the atomic masses of Ca, O, and H.

$$M_{Ca(OH)_2} = 40.08 \text{ g/mol}$$
$$+2(16.00 \text{ g/mol})$$
$$+2(1.01 \text{ g/mol})$$
$$= 74.10 \text{ g/mol}$$

Step 4

Convert the moles of $Ca(OH)_2$ to mass, and express the mass in kilograms.

$$m_{Ca(OH)_2} = n_{Ca(OH)_2} \times M_{Ca(OH)_2}$$

$$= 67.1 \text{ mol} \times 74.10 \text{ g/mol}$$

$$= 4.97 \times 10^3 \text{ g} \times \frac{1 \text{ kg}}{10^3 \text{ g}}$$

$$= 4.97 \text{ kg}$$

The mass of $Ca(OH)_{2(s)}$ produced by 4.30 kg of $CaC_{2(s)}$ is 4.97 kg.

c) 2502

Calculate the molar solubility of calcium hydroxide at 0°C from the given data.

$$\left[Ca(OH)_{2(aq)}\right] = \frac{\left(0.185 \text{ g} \times \dfrac{\text{mol}}{74.10 \text{ g}}\right)}{0.100 \text{ L}}$$

$$= 2.50 \times 10^{-2} \text{ mol/L}$$

The molar solubility of $Ca(OH)_{2(aq)}$ is 2.50×10^{-2} mol/L at 0°C. The values for a, b, c and d are 2, 5, 0, and 2.

18. B

Generally speaking, molecular acids are weak electrolytes because of the covalent bonds that hold their atoms together. Molecular acids, particularly organic ones, produce very few ions in a solution and predominantly remain as molecules.

The concentration of molecules of weak acids and bases is greater than the ions produced in solution, so both weak acids and bases are poor conductors of electricity. Without exception, all strong acids dissociate virtually completely and are therefore strong electrolytes—they conduct electricity well.

19. B

In a solution with a hydrogen ion concentration $\left(H^+_{(aq)}\right)$ of 10^{-x} mol/L, x represents the pH value. By definition, $\left[H^+_{(aq)}\right] = 10^{-pH}$.

Therefore, at pH = 5, $\left[H^+_{(aq)}\right] = 10^{-5}$ mol/L, and at pH = 8, $\left[H^+_{(aq)}\right] = 10^{-8}$ mol/L.

20. WR

The easiest method for balancing combustion equations involving hydrocarbons is to balance the carbon atoms first, the hydrogen atoms second, and the oxygen atoms last. If the coefficient of $O_{2(g)}$ is a fraction to balance the oxygen atoms, multiply all of the coefficients by the denominator of the fraction. All the coefficients will then be whole numbers.

The unbalanced equation for the combustion reaction of ethyne is as follows:
$$C_2H_{2(g)} + O_{2(g)} \rightarrow CO_{2(g)} + H_2O_{(g)}$$

Step 1
Balance the carbon atoms on both sides of the equation.
Place the coefficient 2 in front of the $CO_{2(g)}$ on the right side of the equation. There are 2 carbon atoms on both sides.
$$C_2H_{2(g)} + O_{2(g)} \rightarrow 2CO_{2(g)} + H_2O_{(g)}$$

Step 2
Balance the hydrogen atoms on both sides of the equation.
There are 2 hydrogen atoms on both sides of the equation, so the hydrogen atoms are already balanced.

Step 3
Balance the oxygen atoms on both sides of the equation.
At this stage, there are 5 oxygen atoms on the right side of the reaction and 2 oxygen atoms on the left side. In order to balance the oxygen atoms, the $O_{2(g)}$ on the left side of the equation needs a coefficient of $\frac{5}{2}$ to balance the 5 atoms on the right side.
$$C_2H_{2(g)} + \frac{5}{2}O_{2(g)} \rightarrow 2CO_{2(g)} + H_2O_{(g)}$$

Step 4
Multiply the coefficients by the denominator of the fraction so all the coefficients are whole numbers. Multiply each coefficient by 2.
$$2C_2H_{2(g)} + 5O_{2(g)} \rightarrow 4CO_{2(g)} + 2H_2O_{(g)}$$
There are 4 C atoms, 4 H atoms, and 10 O atoms on both sides of the equation. The balanced equation for the combustion of ethyne is as follows:
$$2C_2H_{2(g)} + 5O_{2(g)} \rightarrow 4CO_{2(g)} + 2H_2O_{(g)}$$

21. C

Bromocresol green is yellow when the pH < 3.8. Cresol red is yellow when the pH is between 1.0 and 7.0. Orange IV is yellow when the pH is > 2.8. Therefore the solution has a pH > 2.8 and < 3.8. An approximate pH for this solution is 3.0.

22. 5066

Step 1
Calculate the molar mass of $COCl_{2(g)}$.

C	12.01
O	16.00
Cl_2	+2(35.45)
$COCl_2$	98.91 g/mol

Step 2
Calculate the molar concentration using the molar mass and the given concentration value.
$$\left[COCl_{2(g)}\right] = \frac{0.000\ 500\ g \times \frac{mol}{98.91\ g}}{L}$$
$$= 5.06 \times 10^{-6}\ mol/L$$
The molar concentration of $COCl_{2(g)}$ is 5.06×10^{-6} mol/L. The values of $abcd$ are 5 066.

23. 73.6

The stoichiometric method can be used to answer this question.

Step 1

Write the balanced equation for the neutralization reaction.

$$2HCl_{(aq)} + Mg(OH)_{2(s)} \rightarrow MgCl_{2(aq)} + 2H_2O_{(l)}$$

Step 2

Determine the molar mass of $Mg(OH)_2$ using the atomic masses of Mg, O, and H.

$$M_{Mg(OH)_2}$$
$$= \left(\begin{array}{c} 24.31 \ g/mol \\ + \ 2(16.00 \ g/mol + 2(1.01 \ g/mol)) \end{array} \right)$$
$$= 58.33 \ g/mol$$

Step 3

Calculate the number of moles of $Mg(OH)_2$ using the given mass and the molar mass.

$$n_{Mg(OH)_2} = \frac{m_{Mg(OH)_2}}{M_{Mg(OH)_2}}$$
$$= \frac{0.236 \ g}{58.33 \ g/mol}$$
$$= 0.004 \ 05 \ mol$$

Step 4

Determine the number of moles of HCl in the solution using the ratio of coefficients of HCl and $Mg(OH)_2$ in the balanced equation.

$$\frac{n_{HCl}}{n_{Mg(OH)_2}} = \frac{2}{1}$$
$$n_{HCl} = \frac{2}{1}\left(n_{Mg(OH)_2}\right)$$
$$= \frac{2}{1}(0.004 \ 05 \ mol)$$
$$= 0.008 \ 10 \ mol$$

Step 5

Calculate the volume of the HCl solution using the number of moles and the concentration of HCl.

$$V_{HCl} = \frac{n_{HCl}}{c_{HCl}}$$
$$= \frac{0.008 \ 10 \ mol}{0.110 \ mol/L}$$
$$= 0.0736 \ L$$
$$= 73.6 \ mL$$

The volume of 0.110 mol/L $HCl_{(aq)}$ needed to neutralize 0.236 g of $Mg(OH)_{2(s)}$ is 73.6 mL.

24. D

$NO_{(g)}$ is a molecular species, a form of chemical whose atoms are bound together by covalent bonds. Covalent bonds result from the sharing of electrons, whereas ionic bonds result from the attraction of oppositely charged ions.

25. a) WR

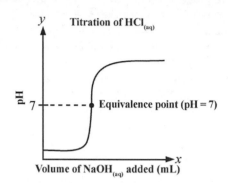

b) WR

Bromothymol blue turns from yellow to blue in the pH range of 6.0 to 7.6. The colour of the solution at the end-point should be green. The colour of the indicator bromothymol blue will change near the equivalence point, a pH of 7, so it is a good choice of indicator for this titration.

26. WR

The first step in the procedure should be the removal of $Ag^+_{(aq)}$ as $AgCH_3COO_{(s)}$ by adding $NaCH_3COO_{(aq)}$.

Next, precipitate the $Pb^{2+}_{(aq)}$ by adding one of $NaCl_{(aq)}$, $NaBr_{(aq)}$, $NaI_{(aq)}$, $Na_2SO_{4(aq)}$, $NaOH_{(aq)}$, or another suitable reagent.

Obtain the mass of the filter paper used to remove the precipitate containing the lead. Allow the filter paper and the lead precipitate to dry thoroughly. Obtain the mass of the dry filter paper and lead precipitate.

27. C

Arrhenius acids are acids that contain H^+ ions.

Arrhenius bases are bases that contain OH^- ions. When these acids and bases react, they do so according to the generic equation
acid + base → salt + water.

Following normal balancing rules, which fulfill the law of conservation of mass, equate the moles of reactants with those of the products. The balanced reaction is

$$2HCl_{(aq)} + Mg(OH)_{2(s)} \rightarrow 2H_2O_{(l)} + MgCl_{2(aq)}.$$

ANSWERS AND SOLUTIONS — PRACTICE TEST 2

1. 873	9. a) A	15. A	22. D	29. a) C
2. D	b) 1.99	16. B	23. D	b) D
3. C	10. 8371	17. a) C	24. B	30. A
4. 26.1	11. C	b) D	25. C	31. C
5. A	12. D	18. D	26. a) WR	32. A
6. A	13. a) 0.017	19. C	b) WR	
7. A	b) 884	20. A	27. A	
8. 202	14. WR	21. D	28. 2.11	

1. 873

Add 273.15 to the Celsius temperature (°C) in order to convert it into a Kelvin temperature (K).

$T = (600 + 273.15)$ K
$= 873.15$ K
$= 873$ K

Rounded to three digits, the absolute temperature of 600°C is 873 K.

2. D

Decomposition reactions split one molecule into multiple molecules or atoms, and a formation (synthesis) reaction takes two or more molecules or atoms and combines them into a single molecule.

3. C

When a solid is first added, there are no ions in solution yet. The rate of dissolving is high, and the rate of precipitation is zero. As the amount of aqueous ions increases, the rate of precipitation increases and the rate of dissolving decreases. At equilibrium, they become equal.

4. 26.1

Apply the ideal gas law.
$R = 8.314$ kPa·L / mol·K
$T = 10°C = 283.15$ K
$V = \dfrac{nRT}{P}$

$= \dfrac{1 \text{ mol} \times 8.314 \dfrac{\text{kPa·L}}{\text{mol·K}} \times 283.15 \text{ K}}{90.0 \text{ kPa}}$

$= 26.1$ L

The volume occupied by 1.00 mol of oxygen will be 26.1 L.

5. A

Concentrations in excess of about 1.0 mol/L are commonly referred to as concentrated. In water, the acids $HClO_4$, HI, HBr, HCl, HNO_3, and H_2SO_4 are referred to as strong acids because they dissociate completely.

$pH = -\log\left[H^+_{(aq)}\right]$
$\left[H^+_{(aq)}\right] = \left[H_2SO_{4(aq)}\right]$
$pH = -\log(10.0 \text{ mol/L})$
$= -1.000$

6. A

Hydrocarbons and their derivatives, which contain C, H, and possibly O, can be assumed to produce carbon dioxide (CO_2) and water when they undergo complete combustion. When balancing the combustion reactions of hydrocarbons and their derivatives, it is best to balance C atoms first, then H atoms, and lastly, O atoms.

Step 1
Write an unbalanced equation showing the reactants and products.
O_2 is added as a reactant, and CO_2 and H_2O are added as products to the equation.
$C_2H_5OH + O_2 \rightarrow CO_2 + H_2O$

Step 2
Balance the carbon atoms.
There are two carbon atoms on the left side, so place the coefficient 2 in front of CO_2 on the right side.
$C_2H_5OH + O_2 \rightarrow 2CO_2 + H_2O$

Step 3
Balance the hydrogen atoms.
There is a total of 6 hydrogen atoms on the left side. These are balanced by adding the coefficient 3 in front of H_2O on the right side.
$C_2H_5OH + O_2 \rightarrow 2CO_2 + 3H_2O$

Step 4

Balance the oxygen atoms.

There is a total of 7 oxygen atoms on the right side of the equation, so the left side would have to contain 7 oxygen atoms in order for it to be balanced. There is 1 oxygen atom already present in C_2H_5OH, so in order to get 7 oxygen atoms on the left side, 6 more are needed. The 6 oxygen atoms are supplied by adding the coefficient 3 to O_2 on the left side.

$$C_2H_5OH + 3O_2 \rightarrow 2CO_2 + 3H_2O$$

The balanced equation has 2 C atoms, 6 H atoms, and 7 O atoms on both sides.

7. A

The reaction is $2AgNO_{3(aq)} + K_2CO_{3(aq)}$

$\rightarrow Ag_2CO_{3(s)} + 2KNO_{3(aq)}$.

Only Ag_2CO_3 is expected to precipitate, as indicated by the (s) subscript. The $K^+_{(aq)}$ and $CO_3^{2-}_{(aq)}$ ions are spectator ions in the reaction.

8. 202

Step 1

A stoichiometric calculation incorporating $PV = nRT$ is needed to find the solution.

$$2NaN_{3(s)} \rightarrow 2Na_{(s)} + 3N_{2(g)}$$

Convert –60 °C into kelvins.

$T_{kelvin} = -60°C + 273.15\ K$

$\qquad = 213\ K$

Step 2

Calculate the moles of nitrogen gas ($N_{2(g)}$) using the ideal gas law equation, where $P = 1.0$ atm (or 101.325 kPa) and $V = 80$ L.

$$n_{N_2} = \frac{PV}{RT}$$

$$= \frac{1.0\ atm \times 80\ L}{0.08206\dfrac{L \times atm}{mol \times K} \times 213\ K}$$

$$= 4.6\ mol$$

Step 3

Calculate the moles of $NaN_{3(s)}$ using the coefficient ratio from the balanced chemical equation.

$$n_{NaN_3} = \frac{2}{3}n_{N_2}$$

$$= \frac{2}{3} \times 4.6\ mol$$

$$= 3.1\ mol$$

Step 4

Calculate the mass of $NaN_{3(s)}$ where $M = 65.02$ g/mol.

$$m_{NaN_3} = 3.1\ mol \times 65.02\ g/mol$$

$$= 2.0 \times 10^2\ g$$

The mass of $NaN_{3(s)}$ that must decompose to produce 80 L of gas for air bag deployment is 2.0×10^2 g. The values of *abc* and 202.

9. a) A

Step 1

Calculate the initial moles of nicotine present. To calculate the initial moles of nicotine present, convert the milligrams into grams.

$$m_{nicotine} = 60.0\ mg \times \frac{1\ g}{1\ 000\ mg}$$

$$= 0.0600\ g$$

$$n_{nicotine} = \frac{m_{nicotine}}{M_{nicotine}}$$

$$= \frac{0.060\ g}{162.26\ g/mol}$$

$$= 3.70 \times 10^{-4}\ mol$$

Step 2

Calculate the initial moles of HCl present.

$$n_{HCl} = c_{HCl} \times V_{HCl}$$

$$= 1.00 \times 10^{-3}\ mol/L \times 0.0100\ L$$

$$= 1.00 \times 10^{-5}\ mol$$

Step 3

Use the coefficient ratio of HCl to nicotine in the balanced equation to determine the moles of HCl required to completely react with the nicotine present.

Nicotine   Nicotine Salt

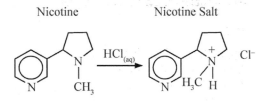

The diagram shows that 1 mol of nicotine reacts with 1 mol of HCl to produce the given salt.

$$\frac{n_{HCl}}{n_{nicotine}} = \frac{1}{1}$$

$$n_{HCl} = \frac{1}{1}(n_{nicotine})$$

$$n_{HCl} = \frac{1}{1}(3.70 \times 10^{-4}\ mol)$$

$$= 3.70 \times 10^{-4}\ mol$$

For a complete reaction with the given amount of nicotine, 3.70×10^{-4} mol of HCl is required.

Step 4

Compare the moles of HCl present with the moles of HCl required to determine the limiting reagent in the reaction.

There are 1.00×10^{-5} mol of HCl present, but 3.70×10^{-4} mol are required to react completely with the 3.70×10^{-4} mol of nicotine present. Since there is less HCl present than required, HCl is the limiting reagent in this reaction.

Hydrochloric acid, $HCl_{(aq)}$, is the limiting reagent in this reaction.

b) 1.99

Step 1

Convert milligrams into grams.

$$m_{nicotine} = 60.0 \text{ mg} \times \frac{1 \text{ g}}{1\,000 \text{ mg}}$$
$$= 0.0600 \text{ g}$$

Step 2

Calculate the initial moles of nicotine present in the reaction.

$$n_{nicotine} = \frac{m_{nicotine}}{M_{nicotine}}$$
$$= \frac{0.0600 \text{ g}}{162.26 \text{ g/mol}}$$
$$= 3.70 \times 10^{-4} \text{ mol}$$

Step 3

Calculate the initial moles of HCl present in the reaction.

$$n_{HCl} = c_{HCl} \times V_{HCl}$$
$$= 1.00 \times 10^{-3} \text{ mol/L} \times 0.0100 \text{ L}$$
$$= 1.00 \times 10^{-5} \text{ mol}$$

Step 4

Use the coefficient ratio of HCl to nicotine in the balanced equation to determine the moles of HCl required to completely react with all the nicotine present.

$$\frac{n_{HCl}}{n_{nicotine}} = \frac{1}{1}$$
$$n_{HCl} = \frac{1}{1}(n_{nicotine})$$
$$n_{HCl} = \frac{1}{1}(3.70 \times 10^{-4} \text{ mol})$$
$$= 3.70 \times 10^{-4} \text{ mol}$$

The diagram shows that 1 mol of nicotine reacts with 1 mol of HCl to produce the given salt.

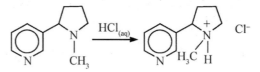

For a complete reaction with the given nicotine, 3.70×10^{-4} mol of HCl is required.

Step 5

Compare the moles of HCl present with the moles of HCl required to determine the limiting reagent in the reaction.

- If $n_{HCl\ (present)} > n_{HCl\ (required)}$, then there is excess HCl, and nicotine is the limiting reagent in the reaction.
- If $n_{HCl\ (present)} < n_{HCl\ (required)}$, then HCl is the limiting reagent.

$n_{HCl\ (present)}$
$= 1.00 \times 10^{-5} \text{ mol} < 3.70 \times 10^{-4} \text{ mol}$
$= n_{HCl\ (required)}$

A complete reaction with nicotine requires 3.70×10^{-4} mol of HCl, but only 1.00×10^{-5} mol of HCl are present. Since there is less HCl present than required, HCl is the limiting reagent in this reaction.

Hydrochloric acid $(HCl_{(aq)})$ is the limiting reagent in this reaction.

Step 6

Calculate the predicted product yield as a result of the amount of limiting reagent present.

$$n_{salt} = \frac{1}{1} n_{HCl}$$
$$= \frac{1}{1} \times \left(1 \times 10^{-5}\ mol\right)$$
$$= \left(1 \times 10^{-5}\ mol\right)$$
$$m_{salt} = n_{salt} M_{salt}$$
$$= \left(1 \times 10^{-5}\ mol\right)(198.72\ g/mol)$$
$$= 1.99 \times 10^{-3}\ g = 1.99\ mg$$

The predicted yield of nicotine hydrochloride salt is 1.99 mg.

10. 8371

Write the chemical equation for the reaction taking place.

According to the given information, solid zinc from the galvanized nails reacts with $HCl_{(aq)}$ to form $H_{2(g)}$. Completing and balancing the reaction, the chemical equation is

$$Zn_{(s)} + 2HCl_{(aq)} \rightarrow H_{2(g)} + ZnCl_{2(aq)}.$$

In order to calculate the mass of zinc consumed, determine the moles of zinc consumed. In order to calculate the moles of zinc consumed, determine the moles of $H_{2(g)}$ produced. The moles of $H_{2(g)}$ produced can be calculated using the ideal gas law:

$$P_{H_2} V = n_{H_2} RT$$

The following data for the $H_{2(g)}$ produced is given.
$V = 0.325\ L$
$T = (20.0 + 273)K = 293.0\ K$

$$P_{H_2} = 720\ torr \times \frac{101.325\ kPa}{760\ torr} = 96.0\ kPa$$

Rearrange the formula for the ideal gas law.

$$n_{H_2} = \frac{PV}{RT} = \frac{96.0\ kPa \times 0.325\ L}{8.314 \frac{kPa \cdot L}{mol \cdot K} \times 293\ K}$$
$$= 0.0128\ mol$$

Calculate the mass of zinc that reacts with $HCl_{(aq)}$.

$$n_{Zn} = \frac{1}{1} n_{H_2} = \frac{1}{1} \times 0.0128\ mol$$
$$= 0.0128\ mol$$
$$m_{Zn} = 0.0128\ mol \times \frac{65.41g}{mol}$$
$$= 0.837\ g\ or\ 8.37 \times 10^{-1}\ g$$

11. C

First, calculate the moles of each reactant.

$$n_{Cu} = (50.0\ g)\left(\frac{1\ mol\ Cu}{63.55\ g\ Cu}\right)$$
$$= 0.787\ moles\ Cu$$
$$n_{O_2} = (80.0\ g)\left(\frac{1\ mol\ O_2}{32.00\ g\ O_2}\right)$$
$$= 2.50\ moles\ O_2$$

Next, choose one of the two reagents. In this case, calculate how many moles of O_2 are required to react all 0.787 moles of Cu.

$$n_{O_2\ needed} = (0.787\ mol\ Cu)\left(\frac{1\ mol\ O_2}{2\ mol\ Cu}\right)$$
$$= 0.393\ moles\ O_2$$

Since consuming all copper would require less than the provided amount of oxygen $\left(n_{O_2\ needed} < n_{O_2}\right)$, copper is the limiting reagent. Therefore, oxygen is the excess reagent. The excess mass of oxygen is determined as follows:

$$m_{O_2\ excess} = \left([2.50 - 0.393]\ mol\ O_2\right)\left(\frac{32.00\ g\ O_2}{1\ mol\ O_2}\right)$$
$$= 67.4\ g\ O_2$$

12. D

Acetic acid is a weak acid, which means it dissociates partially in aqueous solution at normal concentrations. Weak acids are weak electrolytes, so acetic acid would not conduct an electric current efficiently. Empirical evidence shows that pure water, such as distilled water, is a very weak conductor of electric current because it does not contain any dissolved salts. Water is a good electrical conductor only when there is an impurity or an electrolyte (commonly salts) dissolved in it.

13. a) 0.017

Calculate the percentage weight per volume.

$$\% \text{ caffeine} = \frac{\text{mass of caffeine (g)}}{\text{solution volume (mL)}} \times 100\%$$
$$= \frac{0.0400\ g}{235\ mL} \times 100\%$$
$$= 0.017\%$$

The percentage of caffeine (w/v) present in a cup of tea is 0.017%.

b) 884

$$[\text{caffeine}] = \frac{n_{\text{caffeine}}}{V_{\text{tea}}}$$

$$= \frac{0.040 \text{ g} \times \dfrac{\text{mol}}{194.19 \text{ g}}}{0.235 \text{ L}}$$

$$= 8.8 \times 10^{-4} \text{ mol/L}$$

The caffeine concentration is 8.8×10^{-4} mol/L.

14. **WR**

Step 1

Calculate the percentage mass of water in the light margarine.

The light margarine contained 6.00 g of water in the 14.0 g sample.

$$\% \text{ mass} = \frac{6.00 \text{ g}}{14.0 \text{ g}} \times 100\% = 42.9\%$$

Step 2

Calculate the percentage mass of water in the light margarine.

The regular margarine contained 3.00 g of water in the 14.0 g sample.

$$\% \text{ mass} = \frac{3.00 \text{ g}}{14.0 \text{ g}} \times 100\% = 21.4\%$$

Step 3

Calculate the difference in the percentage masses.
$$\% \text{ mass difference} = 42.9\% - 21.4\%$$
$$= 21.5\%$$

15. **A**

Palmitic $\left(C_{16}H_{32}O_2\right)$ acid has a molar mass of 256.48 g/mol.

$$\%C = \frac{(16 \times 12.01) \text{ g}}{256.48 \text{ g}} \times 100\%$$
$$= 74.92 (75\%)$$

$$\% \text{ H} = \frac{(32 \times 1.01) \text{ g}}{256.48 \text{ g}} \times 100\%$$
$$= 12.60 (13\%)$$

$$\%O = \frac{(2 \times 16.00) \text{ g}}{256.48 \text{ g}} \times 100\%$$
$$= 12.48\% (12\%)$$

The approximate mass percentage of each element in palmitic acid is 75% carbon, 13% hydrogen, and 12% oxygen.

16. **B**

Step 1

Calculate the number of moles of $Na_2CO_{3(aq)}$ using the given volume and concentration.

$$n_{Na_2CO_3} = 0.100 \text{ L} \times 0.100 \text{ mol/L}$$
$$= 0.0100 \text{ mol}$$

Step 2

Calculate the mass of $Na_2CO_{3(aq)}$ needed using the number of moles and the molar mass.

$$m = 0.0100 \text{ mol} \times 105.99 \text{ g/mol}$$
$$= 1.06 \text{ g}$$

To prepare a 100 mL solution with a concentration of 0.100 mol/L, 1.06 g of $Na_2CO_{3(s)}$ are required.

17. **a) C**

Acids such as lactic acid and acetic acid partially dissociate in aqueous solution, making them poor conductors of electricity. In contrast, strong acids such as HCl completely dissociate in aqueous solution, so they are good conductors. Because the ions in a solution are responsible for conductivity, fewer ions result in poorer conductivity.

b) D

Like acetic acid, lactic acid is a carboxylic acid. The structure of lactic acid can be written as $H_3C - CH(OH) - COOH$. Such carboxylic acids partially dissociate in aqueous solution following the reaction $H_3C - CH(OH) - COOH_{(aq)} + H_2O_{(l)}$

$$\rightleftharpoons H_3C - CH(OH) - COO^-_{(aq)} + H_3O^+_{(aq)}.$$

This partial dissociation produces fewer ions in solution, and as a result an aqueous solution of lactic acid will conduct electricity less effectively than a strong acid such as HCl, which completely dissociates in solution to produce more ions.
The dissociation of lactic acid produces hydronium ions (H_3O^+), making the solution slightly acidic.

A lactic acid solution would have a pH lower than 7, but not the very low pH of a strongly acidic solution.

18. **D**

When comparing two containers that have the same volume of the same gas at the same temperature, the one that contains the higher pressure contains more of
that gas. (Twice the pressure = twice the amount of gas, so 20% higher pressure = 20% more gas.)

It is possible to perform a simple $PV = nRT$ comparison. Assume that V, R and T are the same per both partial pressures, P_1 and P_2.

$$P_1V = n_1RT$$
$$P_2V = n_2RT$$

$$n_1 = \frac{P_1V}{RT} \quad n_2 = \frac{P_2V}{RT}.$$

$$n_1 = \frac{1(V)}{RT} \quad n_2 = \frac{1.20(V)}{RT}$$

Since V, R, and T are the same in both equations, they can be ignored. This means $n_1 = 1$ and $n_2 = 1.20$.

At a 20% increase in partial pressure (120 kPa compared to 100 kPa), there are 20% more moles of a given gas (1.20 mol compared to 1.00 mol). At 120 kPa, there are 20% more moles of air (oxygen) available in the same volume.

19. C

In the equation $2H_2O_{(l)} \rightarrow 2H_{2(g)} + O_{2(g)}$, water is split. In the equation $H_2O_{(l)} \rightarrow H_2O_{(g)}$, water is only vapourised. When a molecular compound is vapourised, only weak intermolecular bonds are broken. However, if a molecular compound is chemically transformed, strong intramolecular (covalent in this case) bonds must be broken. A process that breaks stronger bonds requires more energy.

20. A

Polar solvents, such as water, readily accommodate polar solutes (like dissolves like). A non-polar solute, such as *beta*-carotene, is likely to have a low solubility in water.

21. D

The energy change in all chemical reactions has two components. A chemical reaction involves the formation of new bonds in the products after bonds have been broken in the reactants. Breaking bonds requires energy, and making bonds releases energy. In an endothermic, or heat-absorbing, reaction, more energy is necessary to break the bonds in the reactants than is released in forming the bonds in the products. Conversely, in an exothermic reaction, more energy is released in making bonds in the products than is absorbed to break bonds in the reactants.

This can be represented in simpler terms:

- E_{in} represents the energy needed to break reactant bonds.
- E_{out} represents the energy released in making product bonds.
- If $E_{out} > E_{in}$, the reaction releases energy, and is exothermic.

22. D

Chlorine is a molecular element that is held together by a single covalent bond. Since each bonded atom has the same electronegativity, the electrons are shared equally.

23. D

Fluorine has a greater electronegativity (4.0) than oxygen (3.4). This will produce a stronger ionic bond with the silicon ions. Fluorine will out-compete oxygen for the silicon electrons.

The fact that fluorine is a halogen does not explain the effect that hydrofluoric acid has on glass. Solutions of HCl, HBr, and HI do not react similarly with glass. The Si-F bond is ionic and very polar. Finally, an examination of the Lewis dot diagrams of F and O will show that fluorine has more lone pairs of outer electrons than oxygen.

24. B

NaCl is an ionic compound. The large difference in electronegativity between sodium and chlorine means that the outer electron from the sodium atom is transferred to the chlorine to form two ions, Na^+ and Cl^-. The bonding in NaCl is then the attraction between these two ions.

NaK is a compound of two metals, sodium and potassium. The valence electrons of these two metals are free to move about between the atoms of sodium and potassium. A typical picture is that of positive metal ions in a "sea" of electrons. Cl_2 represents a molecule of chlorine gas.

Because the two atoms are identical, they have equal sharing of the electrons that form the covalent bond between them.

HCl– the correct answer is made up of 2 atoms where the difference in electronegativity is such that there is more sharing of the bonding electrons, although the electrons will remain closer to the more electronegative chlorine atom. This would create a polar-covalent bond in this molecule.

25. C

Water molecules are called polar molecules because they have one end that is more negatively charged and another end that is more positively charged. The oxygen and hydrogen atoms of water share electrons. The oxygen end is more negative because the shared electrons are held quite close to the oxygen. The hydrogens are more positively charged because the electrons are further from them.

26. a) WR

Compound	Bonding Electrons	Polarity	Intermolecular Bonds
$CH_3CH_2CH_3$	20	Non-polar	London dispersion forces
CH_3CH_2F	14	Polar	London dispersion forces and dipole bond
$CH_3CH_2NH_2$	18	Polar	London dispersion forces, dipole bonds, and hydrogen bonds
CH_3CH_2OH	16	Polar	London dispersion forces, dipole bonds, and hydrogen bonds

b) WR

Since propane is the compound with the fewest intermolecular bonds, it will have the lowest boiling point. Fluoroethane has only two types of intermolecular bonds, so it has the second lowest boiling point. The boiling point of ethanol is higher than the boiling point of ethylamine because –OH functional groups tend to be more strongly hydrogen-bonded than –NH functional groups. In other words, the –OH bond is more polar. Both ethanol and ethylamine will have boiling points higher than the boiling point of fluoroethane.

27. A

Step 1

Calculate the hydrogen ion concentration from the given pH.

$$\left[H_3O^+_{(aq)}\right] = 10^{-pH} = 10^{-8} \text{ mol/L}$$

Therefore, a pH of 8 corresponds to a hydrogen ion concentration of 10^{-8} mol/L.

Step 2

Calculate the hydroxide ion concentration by using the K_w expression.

$$\left[H_3O^+_{(aq)}\right]\left[OH^-_{(aq)}\right] = K_w = 1.0 \times 10^{-14}$$

$$\left[H_3O^+_{(aq)}\right] = 10^{-pH} = 10^{-8} \text{ mol/L}$$

$$\left[OH^-_{(aq)}\right] = \frac{K_w}{\left[H_3O^+_{(aq)}\right]}$$

$$\left[OH^-_{(aq)}\right] = \frac{1.0 \times 10^{-14}}{1.0 \times 10^{-8}\text{mol/L}}$$

$$\left[OH^-_{(aq)}\right] = 1.0 \times 10^{-6}\text{mol/L}$$

The hydroxide ion concentration of the solution is 10^{-6} mol/L.

28. 2.11

The combined gas law can be used to determine the final pressure of the gas.

$P_1 = 3.00$ atm

$V_1 = 2.00$ L

$T_1 = (273.15 + 10.0°C) = 283$ K

$P_2 = ?$

$V_2 = 3.00$ L

$T_2 = (273.15 + 25.0°C) = 298$ K

$$\frac{P_1V_1}{T_1} = \frac{P_2V_2}{T_2}$$

$$P_2 = \frac{P_1V_1T_2}{T_1V_2}$$

$$P_2 = \frac{(298 \text{ K})(3.00 \text{ atm})(2.00 \text{ L})}{(283 \text{ K})(3.00 \text{ L})}$$

$$= 2.11 \text{ atm}$$

The final pressure of the helium gas is 2.11 atm.

29. a) C

The equivalence point of a titration is represented by the midpoint on the steep section of the titration curve. In this titration, the equivalence point occurs at point III, where the pH = 7.

b) D

The initial pH of the titration is approximately 11, this indicates a basic solution. As the titrant is added the pH decreases until reaching a pH of approximately 3. A decrease in pH indicates the addition of an acidic solution. This titration represents the titration of a strong base with a strong acid. A suitable indicator for this titration would be phenolphthalein because it changes from pink to colourless at a pH = 8.2, which is near the mid-point of the steep section on the titration curve. Indigo carmine would remain blue throughout the entire titration.

30. A

Strong electrolytes dissociate, or ionize, completely in aqueous solution and conduct an electric current efficiently. Weak electrolytes dissociate, or ionize, partially in aqueous solution and conduct an electric current less efficiently than the solutions of strong electrolytes. Therefore, strong acids such as $HClO_{4(aq)}$, $HI_{(aq)}$, $HBr_{(aq)}$, $HCl_{(aq)}$, $HNO_{3(aq)}$, and $H_2SO_{4(aq)}$ are strong electrolytes.

Sulfuric acid ($H_2SO_{4(aq)}$) is a strong acid that dissociates completely to form a strong electrolyte.

$$H_2SO_{4(aq)} \rightarrow H^+_{(aq)} + HSO^-_{4(aq)}$$

This means that one reason sulfuric acid is used in industry because it is a good conductor of electricity.

31. C

A test that only detects the presence of a minimum amount of a chemical entity versus the actual amount is essentially a qualitative analysis.

32. A

$Fe_3O_{4(g)}$ is an ionic compound in which bonding results from the simultaneous attractions of oppositely charged ions. Metals tend to lose electrons and form positive ions, while non-metals tend to gain electrons and form negative ions during chemical reactions. In this case, the iron lost electrons (e^-), and the oxygen gained electrons (e^-).

NOTES

Appendices

| 1 | 2 | 3 | 4 | 5 | 6 | 7 | 8 | 9 |

1 1.01 1+,1−
2.2
H
hydrogen

Table of Common Polyatomic Ions

acetate (ethanoate)	CH_3COO^-	chromate	CrO_4^{2-}	phosphate	PO_4^{3-}
ammonium	NH_4^+	dichromate	$Cr_2O_7^{2-}$	hydrogen phosphate	HPO_4^{2-}
benzoate	$C_6H_5COO^-$	cyanide	CN^-	dihydrogen phosphate	$H_2PO_4^-$
borate	BO_3^{3-}	hydroxide	OH^-	silicate	SiO_3^{2-}
carbide	C_2^{2-}	iodate	IO_3^-	sulfate	SO_4^{2-}
carbonate	CO_3^{2-}	nitrate	NO_3^-	hydrogen sulfate	HSO_4^-
hydrogen carbonate	HCO_3^-	nitrite	NO_2^-	sulfite	SO_3^{2-}
perchlorate	ClO_4^-	oxalate	$OOCCOO^{2-}$	hydrogen sulfite	HSO_3^-
chlorate	ClO_3^-	hydrogen oxalate	$HOOCCOO^-$	hydrogen sulfide	HS^-
chlorite	ClO_2^-	permanganate	MnO_4^-	thiocyanate	SCN^-
hypochlorite	OCl^- or ClO^-	peroxide	O_2^{2-}	thiosulfate	$S_2O_3^{2-}$
		persulfide	S_2^{2-}		

3 6.94 1+ / 1.0 / **Li** lithium   **4** 9.01 2+ / 1.6 / **Be** beryllium

11 22.99 1+ / 0.9 / **Na** sodium   **12** 24.31 2+ / 1.3 / **Mg** magnesium

19 39.10 1+ / 0.8 / **K** potassium   **20** 40.08 2+ / 1.0 / **Ca** calcium   **21** 44.96 3+ / 1.4 / **Sc** scandium   **22** 47.87 4+, 3+ / 1.5 / **Ti** titanium   **23** 50.94 5+, 4+ / 1.6 / **V** vanadium   **24** 52.00 3+, 2+ / 1.7 / **Cr** chromium   **25** 54.94 2+, 4+ / 1.6 / **Mn** manganese   **26** 55.85 3+, 2+ / 1.8 / **Fe** iron   **27** 58.93 2+, 3+ / 1.9 / **Co** cobalt

37 85.47 1+ / 0.8 / **Rb** rubidium   **38** 87.62 2+ / 1.0 / **Sr** strontium   **39** 88.91 3+ / 1.2 / **Y** yttrium   **40** 91.22 4+ / 1.3 / **Zr** zirconium   **41** 92.91 5+, 3+ / 1.6 / **Nb** niobium   **42** 95.94 6+ / 2.2 / **Mo** molybdenum   **43** (98) 7+ / 2.2 / **Tc** technetium   **44** 101.07 3+ / 2.2 / **Ru** ruthenium   **45** 102.91 3+ / 2.3 / **Rh** rhodium

55 132.91 1+ / 0.8 / **Cs** cesium   **56** 137.33 2+ / 0.9 / **Ba** barium   **57** 138.91 3+ / 1.1 / **La** lanthanum   **72** 178.49 4+ / 1.3 / **Hf** hafnium   **73** 180.95 5+ / 1.5 / **Ta** tantalum   **74** 183.84 6+ / 1.7 / **W** tungsten   **75** 186.21 7+ / 1.9 / **Re** rhenium   **76** 190.23 4+ / 2.2 / **Os** osmium   **77** 192.22 4+ / 2.2 / **Ir** iridium

87 (223) 1+ / 0.7 / **Fr** francium   **88** (226) 2+ / 0.9 / **Ra** radium   **89** (227) 3+ / 1.1 / **Ac** actinium   **104** (261) 4+ / **Rf** rutherfordium   **105** (262) / **Db** dubnium   **106** (266) / **Sg** seaborgium   **107** (264) / **Bh** bohrium   **108** (277) / **Hs** hassium   **109** (268) / **Mt** meitnerium

└─ lanthanide and actinide series begin

58 140.12 3+ / 1.1 / **Ce** cerium   **59** 140.91 3+ / 1.1 / **Pr** praseodymium   **60** 144.24 3+ / 1.1 / **Nd** neodymium   **61** (145) 3+ / — / **Pm** promethium   **62** 150.36 3+, 2+ / 1.2 / **Sm** samarium

90 232.04 4+ / 1.3 / **Th** thorium   **91** 231.04 5+, 4+ / 1.5 / **Pa** protactinium   **92** 238.03 6+, 4+ / 1.7 / **U** uranium   **93** (237) 5+ / 1.3 / **Np** neptunium   **94** (244) 4+, 6+ / 1.3 / **Pu** plutonium

References

Lide, D.R. 2005. *CRC Handbook of Chemistry and Physics*. 86th ed. Boca Raton: CRC Press.

Speight, James G. 2005. *Lange's Handbook of Chemistry*. 16th ed. New York: McGraw-Hill, Inc.

IUPAC *commission on atomic weights and isotopic abundances*. 2002. http://www.chem.qmw.ac.uk/iupac/AtWt/index.html.

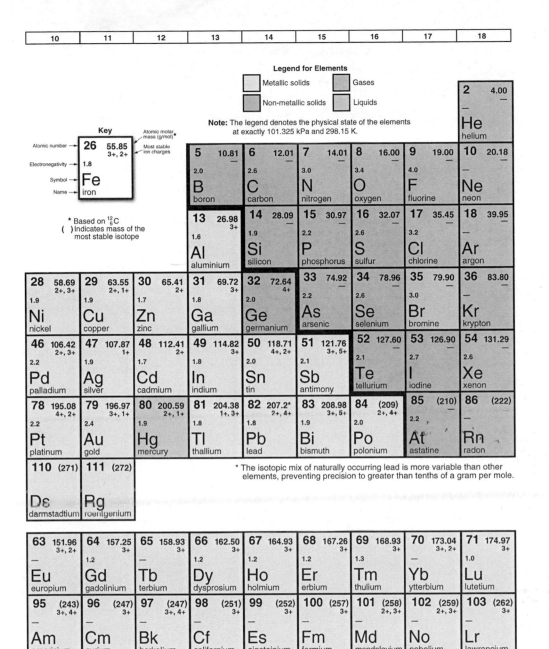

10	11	12	13	14	15	16	17	18

Legend for Elements

Metallic solids   Gases

Non-metallic solids   Liquids

Note: The legend denotes the physical state of the elements at exactly 101.325 kPa and 298.15 K.

Key

Atomic number → 26   55.85   ← Atomic molar mass (g/mol)*
                      3+, 2+   ← Most stable ion charges
Electronegativity → 1.8
Symbol → Fe
Name → iron

* Based on $^{12}_{6}C$
( ) Indicates mass of the most stable isotope

2	4.00
He	helium

5	10.81
2.0 B	boron

6	12.01
2.6 C	carbon

7	14.01
3.0 N	nitrogen

8	16.00
3.4 O	oxygen

9	19.00
4.0 F	fluorine

10	20.18
Ne	neon

13	26.98 3+
1.6 Al	aluminium

14	28.09
1.9 Si	silicon

15	30.97
2.2 P	phosphorus

16	32.07
2.6 S	sulfur

17	35.45
3.2 Cl	chlorine

18	39.95
Ar	argon

28	58.69 2+, 3+
1.9 Ni	nickel

29	63.55 2+, 1+
1.9 Cu	copper

30	65.41 2+
1.7 Zn	zinc

31	69.72 3+
1.8 Ga	gallium

32	72.64 4+
2.0 Ge	germanium

33	74.92
2.2 As	arsenic

34	78.96
2.6 Se	selenium

35	79.90
3.0 Br	bromine

36	83.80
Kr	krypton

46	106.42 2+, 3+
2.2 Pd	palladium

47	107.87 1+
1.9 Ag	silver

48	112.41 2+
1.7 Cd	cadmium

49	114.82 3+
1.8 In	indium

50	118.71 4+, 2+
2.0 Sn	tin

51	121.76 3+, 5+
2.1 Sb	antimony

52	127.60
2.1 Te	tellurium

53	126.90
2.7 I	iodine

54	131.29
2.6 Xe	xenon

78	195.08 4+, 2+
2.2 Pt	platinum

79	196.97 3+, 1+
2.4 Au	gold

80	200.59 2+, 1+
1.9 Hg	mercury

81	204.38 1+, 3+
1.8 Tl	thallium

82	207.2* 2+, 4+
1.8 Pb	lead

83	208.98 3+, 5+
1.9 Bi	bismuth

84	(209) 2+, 4+
2.0 Po	polonium

85	(210)
2.2 At	astatine

86	(222)
Rn	radon

110	(271)
Ds	darmstadtium

111	(272)
Rg	roentgenium

* The isotopic mix of naturally occurring lead is more variable than other elements, preventing precision to greater than tenths of a gram per mole.

63	151.96 3+, 2+
— Eu	europium

64	157.25 3+
1.2 Gd	gadolinium

65	158.93 3+
— Tb	terbium

66	162.50 3+
1.2 Dy	dysprosium

67	164.93 3+
1.2 Ho	holmium

68	167.26 3+
1.2 Er	erbium

69	168.93 3+
1.3 Tm	thulium

70	173.04 3+, 2+
— Yb	ytterbium

71	174.97 3+
1.0 Lu	lutetium

95	(243) 3+, 4+
— Am	americium

96	(247) 3+
— Cm	curium

97	(247) 3+, 4+
— Bk	berkelium

98	(251) 3+
— Cf	californium

99	(252) 3+
— Es	einsteinium

100	(257) 3+
— Fm	fermium

101	(258) 2+, 3+
— Md	mendelevium

102	(259) 2+, 3+
— No	nobelium

103	(262) 3+
— Lr	lawrencium

Chemistry Notation

Symbol	Term	Unit(s)
c	specific heat capacity	$J/(g \cdot °C)$ or $J/(g \cdot K)$
$E°$	standard electrical potential	V or J/C
E_k	kinetic energy	kJ
E_p	potential energy	kJ
ΔH	enthalpy (heat)	kJ
$\Delta_f H°$	standard molar enthalpy of formation	kJ/mol
I	current	A or C/s
K_c	equilibrium constant	—
K_a	acid ionization (dissociation) constant	—
K_b	base ionization (dissociation) constant	—
M	molar mass	g/mol
m	mass	g
n	amount of substance	mol
P	pressure	kPa
Q	charge	C
T	temperature (absolute)	K
t	temperature (Celsius)	°C
t	time	s
V	volume	L
c	amount concentration	mol/L

Symbol	Term
Δ	delta (change in)
°	standard
[ ]	amount concentration

25.00 °C is equivalent to 298.15 K

Specific Heat Capacities at 298.15 K and 100.000 kPa

$$c_{air} = 1.01 \text{ J/(g·°C)}$$

$$c_{polystyrene foam cup} = 1.01 \text{ J/(g·°C)}$$

$$c_{copper} = 0.385 \text{ J/(g·°C)}$$

$$c_{aluminium} = 0.897 \text{ J/(g·°C)}$$

$$c_{iron} = 0.449 \text{ J/(g·°C)}$$

$$c_{tin} = 0.227 \text{ J/(g·°C)}$$

$$c_{water} = 4.19 \text{ J/(g·°C)}$$

Water Autoionization Constant (Dissociation Constant)

$K_w = 1.0 \times 10^{-14}$ at 298.15 K (for ion concentrations in mol/L)

Faraday Constant

$$F = 9.65 \times 10^4 \text{ C/mol e}^-$$

Quadratic Formula

$$x = \frac{-b \pm \sqrt{b^2 - 4ac}}{2a}$$

Selected SI Prefixes

Prefix	Exponential Symbol	Value
tera	T	10^{12}
giga	G	10^{9}
mega	M	10^{6}
kilo	k	10^{3}
milli	m	10^{-3}
micro	μ	10^{-6}
nano	n	10^{-9}
pico	p	10^{-12}

Name	Formula	$\Delta_f H°$ (kJ/mol)
aluminium oxide	$Al_2O_3(s)$	$-1\ 675.7$
ammonia	$NH_3(g)$	-45.9
ammonium chloride	$NH_4Cl(s)$	-314.4
ammonium nitrate	$NH_4NO_3(s)$	-365.6
barium carbonate	$BaCO_3(s)$	$-1\ 213.0$
barium chloride	$BaCl_2(s)$	-855.0
barium hydroxide	$Ba(OH)_2(s)$	-944.7
barium oxide	$BaO(s)$	-548.0
barium sulfate	$BaSO_4(s)$	$-1\ 473.2$
benzene	$C_6H_6(l)$	$+49.1$
butane	$C_4H_{10}(g)$	-125.7
calcium carbonate	$CaCO_3(s)$	$-1\ 207.6$
calcium chloride	$CaCl_2(s)$	-795.4
calcium hydroxide	$Ca(OH)_2(s)$	-985.2
calcium oxide	$CaO(s)$	-634.9
calcium sulfate	$CaSO_4(s)$	$-1\ 434.5$
carbon dioxide	$CO_2(g)$	-393.5
carbon monoxide	$CO(g)$	-110.5
chromium(III) oxide	$Cr_2O_3(s)$	$-1\ 139.7$
copper(I) oxide	$Cu_2O(s)$	-168.6
copper(II) oxide	$CuO(s)$	-157.3
copper(II) sulfate	$CuSO_4(s)$	-771.4
copper(I) sulfide	$Cu_2S(s)$	-79.5
copper(II) sulfide	$CuS(s)$	-53.1
dinitrogen tetroxide	$N_2O_4(g)$	$+11.1$
ethane	$C_2H_6(g)$	-84.0
ethanoic acid (acetic acid)	$CH_3COOH(l)$	-484.3
ethanol	$C_2H_5OH(l)$	-277.6
ethene (ethylene)	$C_2H_4(g)$	$+52.4$
ethyne (acetylene)	$C_2H_2(g)$	$+227.4$
glucose	$C_6H_{12}O_6(s)$	$-1\ 273.3$
hydrogen bromide	$HBr(g)$	-36.3
hydrogen chloride	$HCl(g)$	-92.3
hydrogen fluoride	$HF(g)$	-273.3
hydrogen iodide	$HI(g)$	$+26.5$
hydrogen perchlorate	$HClO_4(l)$	-40.6
hydrogen peroxide	$H_2O_2(l)$	-187.8
hydrogen sulfide	$H_2S(g)$	-20.6
iron(II) oxide	$FeO(s)$	-272.0
iron(III) oxide	$Fe_2O_3(s)$	-824.2
iron(II,III) oxide (magnetite)	$Fe_3O_4(s)$	$-1\ 118.4$
lead(II) bromide	$PbBr_2(s)$	-278.7
lead(II) chloride	$PbCl_2(s)$	-359.4
lead(II) oxide (red)	$PbO(s)$	-219.0
lead(IV) oxide	$PbO_2(s)$	-277.4
magnesium carbonate	$MgCO_3(s)$	$-1\ 095.8$
magnesium chloride	$MgCl_2(s)$	-641.3

Name	Formula	$\Delta_f H°$ (kJ/mol)
magnesium hydroxide	$Mg(OH)_2(s)$	− 924.5
magnesium oxide	$MgO(s)$	− 601.6
magnesium sulfate	$MgSO_4(s)$	− 1 284.9
manganese(II) oxide	$MnO(s)$	− 385.2
manganese(IV) oxide	$MnO_2(s)$	− 520.0
mercury(II) oxide (red)	$HgO(s)$	− 90.8
mercury(II) sulfide (red)	$HgS(s)$	− 58.2
methanal (formaldehyde)	$CH_2O(g)$	− 108.6
methane	$CH_4(g)$	− 74.6
methanoic acid (formic acid)	$HCOOH(l)$	− 425.0
methanol	$CH_3OH(l)$	− 239.2
nickel(II) oxide	$NiO(s)$	− 240.6
nitric acid	$HNO_3(l)$	− 174.1
nitrogen dioxide	$NO_2(g)$	+ 33.2
nitrogen monoxide	$NO(g)$	+ 91.3
octane	$C_8H_{18}(l)$	− 250.1
pentane	$C_5H_{12}(l)$	− 173.5
phosphorus pentachloride	$PCl_5(s)$	− 443.5
phosphorus trichloride (liquid)	$PCl_3(l)$	− 319.7
phosphorus trichloride (vapour)	$PCl_3(g)$	− 287.0
potassium bromide	$KBr(s)$	− 393.8
potassium chlorate	$KClO_3(s)$	− 397.7
potassium chloride	$KCl(s)$	− 436.5
potassium hydroxide	$KOH(s)$	− 424.6
propane	$C_3H_8(g)$	− 103.8
silicon dioxide (α-quartz)	$SiO_2(s)$	− 910.7
silver bromide	$AgBr(s)$	− 100.4
silver chloride	$AgCl(s)$	− 127.0
silver iodide	$AgI(s)$	− 61.8
sodium bromide	$NaBr(s)$	− 361.1
sodium chloride	$NaCl(s)$	− 411.2
sodium hydroxide	$NaOH(s)$	− 425.8
sodium iodide	$NaI(s)$	− 287.8
sucrose	$C_{12}H_{22}O_{11}(s)$	− 2 226.1
sulfur dioxide	$SO_2(g)$	− 296.8
sulfuric acid	$H_2SO_4(l)$	− 814.0
sulfur trioxide (liquid)	$SO_3(l)$	− 441.0
sulfur trioxide (vapour)	$SO_3(g)$	− 395.7
tin(II) chloride	$SnCl_2(s)$	− 325.1
tin(IV) chloride	$SnCl_4(l)$	− 511.3
tin(II) oxide	$SnO(s)$	− 280.7
tin(IV) oxide	$SnO_2(s)$	− 577.6
water (liquid)	$H_2O(l)$	− 285.8
water (vapour)	$H_2O(g)$	− 241.8
zinc oxide	$ZnO(s)$	− 350.5
zinc sulfide (sphalerite)	$ZnS(s)$	− 206.0

Solubility of Some Common Ionic Compounds in Water at 298.15 K

Ion	Group 1 ions NH_4^+ NO_3^- ClO_3^- ClO_4^- CH_3COO^-	F^-	Cl^- Br^- I^-	SO_4^{2-}	CO_3^{2-} PO_4^{3-} SO_3^{2-}	IO_3^- $OOCCOO^{2-}$	OH^-
Solubility greater than or equal to 0.1 mol/L (very soluble)	most	most	most	most	Group 1 ions NH_4^+	Group 1 ions NH_4^+ $Co(IO_3)_2$ $Fe_2(OOCCOO)_3$	Group 1 ions NH_4^+
Solubility less than 0.1 mol/L (slightly soluble)	$RbClO_4$ $CsClO_4$ $AgCH_3COO$ $Hg_2(CH_3COO)_2$	Li^+ Mg^{2+} Ca^{2+} Sr^{2+} Ba^{2+} Fe^{2+} Hg_2^{2+} Pb^{2+}	Cu^+ Ag^+ Hg_2^{2+} Pb^{2+} Tl^+	Ca^{2+} Sr^{2+} Ba^{2+} Ag^+ Hg_2^{2+} Pb^{2+} Ra^{2+}	most	most	most

Note: This solubility table is only a guideline that is established using the K_{sp} values. A concentration of 0.1 mol/L corresponds to approximately 10 g/L to 30 g/L depending on molar mass. Hg_2^{2+} is a polyatomic ion of mercury.

Flame Colour of Elements

Element	Symbol	Colour
lithium	Li	red
sodium	Na	yellow
potassium	K	violet
rubidium	Rb	violet
cesium	Cs	violet
calcium	Ca	yellowish red
strontium	Sr	scarlet red
barium	Ba	yellowish green
copper	Cu	blue to green
boron	B	yellowish green
lead	Pb	blue-white

Note: The flame test can be used to determine the identity of a metal or a metal ion. Blue to green indicates a range of colours that might appear.

Table of Selected Standard Electrode Potentials*

Reduction Half-Reaction	Electrical Potential $E°$ (V)
$F_2(g) + 2e^- \rightleftharpoons 2F^-(aq)$	+2.87
$PbO_2(s) + SO_4^{2-}(aq) + 4H^+(aq) + 2e^- \rightleftharpoons PbSO_4(s) + 2H_2O(l)$	+1.69
$MnO_4^-(aq) + 8H^+(aq) + 5e^- \rightleftharpoons Mn^{2+}(aq) + 4H_2O(l)$	+1.51
$Au^{3+}(aq) + 3e^- \rightleftharpoons Au(s)$	+1.50
$ClO_4^-(aq) + 8H^+(aq) + 8e^- \rightleftharpoons Cl^-(aq) + 4H_2O(l)$	+1.39
$Cl_2(g) + 2e^- \rightleftharpoons 2Cl^-(aq)$	+1.36
$2HNO_2(aq) + 4H^+(aq) + 4e^- \rightleftharpoons N_2O(g) + 3H_2O(l)$	+1.30
$Cr_2O_7^{2-}(aq) + 14H^+(aq) + 6e^- \rightleftharpoons 2Cr^{3+}(aq) + 7H_2O(l)$	+1.23
$O_2(g) + 4H^+(aq) + 4e^- \rightleftharpoons 2H_2O(l)$	+1.23
$MnO_2(s) + 4H^+(aq) + 2e^- \rightleftharpoons Mn^{2+}(aq) + 2H_2O(l)$	+1.22
$Br_2(l) + 2e^- \rightleftharpoons 2Br^-(aq)$	+1.07
$Hg^{2+}(aq) + 2e^- \rightleftharpoons Hg(l)$	+0.85
$OCl^-(aq) + H_2O(l) + 2e^- \rightleftharpoons Cl^-(aq) + 2OH^-(aq)$	+0.84
$2NO_3^-(aq) + 4H^+(aq) + 2e^- \rightleftharpoons N_2O_4(g) + 2H_2O(l)$	+0.80
$Ag^+(aq) + e^- \rightleftharpoons Ag(s)$	+0.80
$Fe^{3+}(aq) + e^- \rightleftharpoons Fe^{2+}(aq)$	+0.77
$O_2(g) + 2H^+(aq) + 2e^- \rightleftharpoons H_2O_2(l)$	+0.70
$I_2(s) + 2e^- \rightleftharpoons 2I^-(aq)$	+0.54
$O_2(g) + 2H_2O(l) + 4e^- \rightleftharpoons 4OH^-(aq)$	+0.40
$Cu^{2+}(aq) + 2e^- \rightleftharpoons Cu(s)$	+0.34
$SO_4^{2-}(aq) + 4H^+(aq) + 2e^- \rightleftharpoons H_2SO_3(aq) + H_2O(l)$	+0.17
$Sn^{4+}(aq) + 2e^- \rightleftharpoons Sn^{2+}(aq)$	+0.15
$S(s) + 2H^+(aq) + 2e^- \rightleftharpoons H_2S(aq)$	+0.14
$AgBr(s) + e^- \rightleftharpoons Ag(s) + Br^-(aq)$	+0.07
$2H^+(aq) + 2e^- \rightleftharpoons H_2(g)$	0.00
$Pb^{2+}(aq) + 2e^- \rightleftharpoons Pb(s)$	−0.13
$Sn^{2+}(aq) + 2e^- \rightleftharpoons Sn(s)$	−0.14
$AgI(s) + e^- \rightleftharpoons Ag(s) + I^-(aq)$	−0.15
$Ni^{2+}(aq) + 2e^- \rightleftharpoons Ni(s)$	−0.26
$Co^{2+}(aq) + 2e^- \rightleftharpoons Co(s)$	−0.28
$PbSO_4(s) + 2e^- \rightleftharpoons Pb(s) + SO_4^{2-}(aq)$	−0.36
$Se(s) + 2H^+(aq) + 2e^- \rightleftharpoons H_2Se(aq)$	−0.40
$Cd^{2+}(aq) + 2e^- \rightleftharpoons Cd(s)$	−0.40
$Cr^{3+}(aq) + e^- \rightleftharpoons Cr^{2+}(aq)$	−0.41
$Fe^{2+}(aq) + 2e^- \rightleftharpoons Fe(s)$	−0.45
$NO_2^-(aq) + H_2O(l) + e^- \rightleftharpoons NO(g) + 2OH^-(aq)$	−0.46
$Ag_2S(s) + 2e^- \rightleftharpoons 2Ag(s) + S^{2-}(aq)$	−0.69
$Zn^{2+}(aq) + 2e^- \rightleftharpoons Zn(s)$	−0.76
$2H_2O(l) + 2e^- \rightleftharpoons H_2(g) + 2OH^-(aq)$	−0.83
$Cr^{2+}(aq) + 2e^- \rightleftharpoons Cr(s)$	−0.91
$Se(s) + 2e^- \rightleftharpoons Se^{2-}(aq)$	−0.92
$SO_4^{2-}(aq) + H_2O(l) + 2e^- \rightleftharpoons SO_3^{2-}(aq) + 2OH^-(aq)$	−0.93
$Al^{3+}(aq) + 3e^- \rightleftharpoons Al(s)$	−1.66
$Mg^{2+}(aq) + 2e^- \rightleftharpoons Mg(s)$	−2.37
$Na^+(aq) + e^- \rightleftharpoons Na(s)$	−2.71
$Ca^{2+}(aq) + 2e^- \rightleftharpoons Ca(s)$	−2.87
$Ba^{2+}(aq) + 2e^- \rightleftharpoons Ba(s)$	−2.91
$K^+(aq) + e^- \rightleftharpoons K(s)$	−2.93
$Li^+(aq) + e^- \rightleftharpoons Li(s)$	−3.04

*For 1.0 mol/L solutions at 298.15 K (25.00 °C) and a pressure of 101.325 kPa

Relative Strengths of Acids and Bases at 298.15 K

Common Name / IUPAC / Systematic Name	Acid Formula	Conjugate Base Formula	K_a
perchloric acid / aqueous hydrogen perchlorate	$HClO_4(aq)$	$ClO_4^-(aq)$	very large
hydroiodic acid / aqueous hydrogen iodide	$HI(aq)$	$I^-(aq)$	very large
hydrobromic acid / aqueous hydrogen bromide	$HBr(aq)$	$Br^-(aq)$	very large
hydrochloric acid / aqueous hydrogen chloride	$HCl(aq)$	$Cl^-(aq)$	very large
sulfuric acid / aqueous hydrogen sulfate	$H_2SO_4(aq)$	$HSO_4^-(aq)$	very large
nitric acid / aqueous hydrogen nitrate	$HNO_3(aq)$	$NO_3^-(aq)$	very large
hydronium ion	$H_3O^+(aq)$	$H_2O(l)$	1
oxalic acid	$HOOCCOOH(aq)$	$HOOCCOO^-(aq)$	5.6×10^{-2}
sulfurous acid / aqueous hydrogen sulfite	$H_2SO_3(aq)$	$HSO_3^-(aq)$	1.4×10^{-2}
hydrogen sulfate ion	$HSO_4^-(aq)$	$SO_4^{2-}(aq)$	1.0×10^{-2}
phosphoric acid / aqueous hydrogen phosphate	$H_3PO_4(aq)$	$H_2PO_4^-(aq)$	6.9×10^{-3}
citric acid / 2-hydroxy-1,2,3-propanetricarboxylic acid	$C_3H_5O(COOH)_3(aq)$	$C_3H_5O(COOH)_2COO^-(aq)$	7.4×10^{-4}
hydrofluoric acid / aqueous hydrogen fluoride	$HF(aq)$	$F^-(aq)$	6.3×10^{-4}
nitrous acid / aqueous hydrogen nitrite	$HNO_2(aq)$	$NO_2^-(aq)$	5.6×10^{-4}
formic acid / methanoic acid	$HCOOH(aq)$	$HCOO^-(aq)$	1.8×10^{-4}
hydrogen oxalate ion	$HOOCCOO^-(aq)$	$OOCCOO^{2-}(aq)$	1.5×10^{-4}
lactic acid / 2-hydroxypropanoic acid	$C_2H_5OCOOH(aq)$	$C_2H_5OCOO^-(aq)$	1.4×10^{-4}
ascorbic acid / 2(1,2-dihydroxyethyl)-4,5-dihydroxy-furan-3-one	$H_2C_6H_6O_6(aq)$	$HC_6H_6O_6^-(aq)$	9.1×10^{-5}

Name	Acid	Conjugate Base	K_a
benzoic acid / benzenecarboxylic acid	$C_6H_5COOH(aq)$	$C_6H_5COO^-(aq)$	6.3×10^{-5}
acetic acid / ethanoic acid	$CH_3COOH(aq)$	$CH_3COO^-(aq)$	1.8×10^{-5}
dihydrogen citrate ion	$C_3H_5O(COOH)_2COO^-(aq)$	$C_3H_5OCOOH(COO)_2{}^{2-}(aq)$	1.7×10^{-5}
butanoic acid	$C_3H_7COOH(aq)$	$C_3H_7COO^-(aq)$	1.5×10^{-5}
propanoic acid	$C_2H_5COOH(aq)$	$C_2H_5COO^-(aq)$	1.3×10^{-5}
carbonic acid ($CO_2 + H_2O$) / aqueous hydrogen carbonate	$H_2CO_3(aq)$	$HCO_3^-(aq)$	4.5×10^{-7}
hydrogen citrate ion	$C_3H_5OCOOH(COO)_2{}^{2-}(aq)$	$C_3H_5O(COO)_3{}^{3-}(aq)$	4.0×10^{-7}
hydrosulfuric acid / aqueous hydrogen sulfide	$H_2S(aq)$	$HS^-(aq)$	8.9×10^{-8}
hydrogen sulfite ion	$HSO_3^-(aq)$	$SO_3{}^{2-}(aq)$	6.3×10^{-8}
dihydrogen phosphate ion	$H_2PO_4^-(aq)$	$HPO_4{}^{2-}(aq)$	6.2×10^{-8}
hypochlorous acid / aqueous hydrogen hypochlorite	$HOCl(aq)$	$OCl^-(aq)$	4.0×10^{-8}
hydrocyanic acid / aqueous hydrogen cyanide	$HCN(aq)$	$CN^-(aq)$	6.2×10^{-10}
ammonium ion	$NH_4^+(aq)$	$NH_3(aq)$	5.6×10^{-10}
hydrogen carbonate ion	$HCO_3^-(aq)$	$CO_3{}^{2-}(aq)$	4.7×10^{-11}
hydrogen ascorbate ion	$HC_6H_6O_6^-(aq)$	$C_6H_6O_6{}^{2-}(aq)$	2.0×10^{-12}
hydrogen phosphate ion	$HPO_4{}^{2-}(aq)$	$PO_4{}^{3-}(aq)$	4.8×10^{-13}
water	$H_2O(l)$	$OH^-(aq)$	1.0×10^{-14}

Note: An approximation may be used instead of the quadratic formula when the concentration of H_3O^+ produced is less than 5% of the original acid concentration (or the concentration of the acid is 1 000 times greater than the K_a). An approximation can also be used for weak bases. The formulas of the carboxylic acids have been written so that the COOH group can be easily recognized. Either the common or IUPAC name is acceptable.

Acid–Base Indicators at 298.15 K

Indicator	Suggested Abbreviations	pH Range	Colour Change as pH Increases	K_a
methyl violet	HMv(aq) / Mv⁻(aq)	0.0 – 1.6	yellow to blue	$\sim2 \times 10^{-1}$
cresol red	H_2Cr(aq) / HCr⁻(aq) HCr⁻(aq) / Cr²⁻(aq)	0.0 – 1.0 7.0 – 8.8	red to yellow yellow to red	$\sim3 \times 10^{-1}$ 3.5×10^{-9}
thymol blue	H_2Tb(aq) / HTb⁻(aq) HTb⁻(aq) / Tb²⁻(aq)	1.2 – 2.8 8.0 – 9.6	red to yellow yellow to blue	2.2×10^{-2} 6.3×10^{-10}
orange IV	HOr(aq) / Or⁻(aq)	1.4 – 2.8	red to yellow	$\sim1 \times 10^{-2}$
methyl orange	HMo(aq) / Mo⁻(aq)	3.2 – 4.4	red to yellow	3.5×10^{-4}
bromocresol green	HBg(aq) / Bg⁻(aq)	3.8 – 5.4	yellow to blue	1.3×10^{-5}
methyl red	HMr(aq) / Mr⁻(aq)	4.8 – 6.0	red to yellow	1.0×10^{-5}
chlorophenol red	HCh(aq) / Ch⁻(aq)	5.2 – 6.8	yellow to red	5.6×10^{-7}
bromothymol blue	HBb(aq) / Bb⁻(aq)	6.0 – 7.6	yellow to blue	5.0×10^{-8}
phenol red	HPr(aq) / Pr⁻(aq)	6.6 – 8.0	yellow to red	1.0×10^{-8}
phenolphthalein	HPh(aq) / Ph⁻(aq)	8.2 – 10.0	colourless to pink	3.2×10^{-10}
thymolphthalein	HTh(aq) / Th⁻(aq)	9.4 – 10.6	colourless to blue	1.0×10^{-10}
alizarin yellow R	HAy(aq) / Ay⁻(aq)	10.1 – 12.0	yellow to red	6.9×10^{-12}
indigo carmine	HIc(aq) / Ic⁻(aq)	11.4 – 13.0	blue to yellow	$\sim6 \times 10^{-12}$
1,3,5–trinitrobenzene	HNb(aq) / Nb⁻(aq)	12.0 – 14.0	colourless to orange	$\sim1 \times 10^{-13}$

Colours of Common Aqueous Ions

Ionic Species	Solution Concentration	
	1.0 mol/L	0.010 mol/L
chromate	yellow	pale yellow
chromium(III)	blue-green	green
chromium(II)	dark blue	pale blue
cobalt(II)	red	pink
copper(I)	blue-green	pale blue-green
copper(II)	blue	pale blue
dichromate	orange	pale orange
iron(II)	lime green	colourless
iron(III)	orange-yellow	pale yellow
manganese(II)	pale pink	colourless
nickel(II)	blue-green	pale blue-green
permanganate	deep purple	purple-pink

CREDITS

Every effort has been made to provide proper acknowledgement of the original source and to comply with copyright law. However, some attempts to establish original copyright ownership may have been unsuccessful. If copyright ownership can be identified, please notify Castle Rock Research Corp so that appropriate corrective action can be taken.

Some images in this document are from www.clipart.com, copyright © 2013 Clipart.com, a division of Getty Images.

The data tables have been reproduced from http://education.alberta.ca/admin/testing/diplomaexams.aspx

NOTES

NOTES

NOTES

NOTES

NOTES

NOTES

ORDERING INFORMATION

SCHOOL ORDERS

Schools and school jurisdictions are eligible for our educational discount rate. Contact Castle Rock Research for more information.

THE KEY **Study Guides** are specifically designed to assist students in preparing for unit tests, final exams, and provincial examinations.

THE KEY **Study Guides**—$29.95 each plus G.S.T.

SENIOR HIGH		JUNIOR HIGH	ELEMENTARY
Biology 30	Biology 20	English Language Arts 9	English Language Arts 6
Chemistry 30	Chemistry 20	Mathematics 9	Mathematics 6
English 30-1	English 20-1	Science 9	Science 6
English 30-2	Mathematics 20-1	Social Studies 9	Social Studies 6
Mathematics 30-1	Physics 20	Mathematics 8	Mathematics 4
Mathematics 30-2	Social Studies 20-1	Mathematics 7	English Language Arts 3
Physics 30	English 10-1		Mathematics 3
Social Studies 30-1	Mathematics 10 Combined		
Social Studies 30-2	Science 10		
	Social Studies 10-1		

Student Notes and Problems (SNAP) Workbooks contain complete explanations of curriculum concepts, examples, and exercise questions.

SNAP Workbooks—$29.95 each plus G.S.T.

SENIOR HIGH		JUNIOR HIGH	ELEMENTARY
Biology 30	Biology 20	Mathematics 9	Mathematics 6
Chemistry 30	Chemistry 20	Science 9	Mathematics 5
Mathematics 30-1	Mathematics 20-1	Mathematics 8	Mathematics 4
Mathematics 30-2	Physics 20	Science 8	Mathematics 3
Mathematics 31	Mathematics 10 Combined	Mathematics 7	
Physics 30	Science 10	Science 7	

Class Notes and Problem Solved—$19.95 each plus G.S.T.

SENIOR HIGH		JUNIOR HIGH
Biology 30	Biology 20	Mathematics 9
Chemistry 30	Chemistry 20	Science 9
Mathematics 30-1	Mathematics 20-1	Mathematics 8
Mathematics 30-2	Physics 20	Science 8
Mathematics 31	Mathematics 10 Combined	Mathematics 7
Physics 30		Science 7

Visit our website for a tour of resource content and features or order resources online at
www.castlerockresearch.com/store/

#2410, 10180 – 101 Street NW
Edmonton, AB Canada T5J 3S4
e-mail: learn@castlerockresearch.com

Phone: 780.448.9619
Toll-free: 1.800.840.6224
Fax: 780.426.3917

CASTLE ROCK
RESEARCH CORP

ORDER FORM

THE KEY	QUANTITY	Student Notes and Problems Workbooks	QUANTITY		Problem Solved and Class Notes	QUANTITY	
			SNAP Workbooks	Solution Manuals		Class Notes	Problem Solved
Biology 30		Mathematics 31			Mathematics 31		
Chemistry 30		Biology 30			Biology 30		
English 30-1		Chemistry 30			Chemistry 30		
English 30-2		Mathematics 30-1			Mathematics 30-1		
Mathematics 30-1		Mathematics 30-2			Mathematics 30-2		
Mathematics 30-2		Physics 30			Physics 30		
Physics 30		Biology 20			Biology 20		
Social Studies 30-1		Chemistry 20			Chemistry 20		
Social Studies 30-2		Mathematics 20-1			Mathematics 20-1		
Biology 20		Physics 20			Physics 20		
Chemistry 20		Mathematics 10 Combined			Mathematics 10 Combined		
English 20-1		Science 10			Mathematics 9		
Mathematics 20-1		Mathematics 9			Science 9		
Physics 20		Science 9			Mathematics 8		
Social Studies 20-1		Mathematics 8			Science 8		
English 10-1		Science 8			Mathematics 7		
Math 10 Combined		Mathematics 7			Science 7		
Science 10		Science 7					
Social Studies 10-1		Mathematics 6					
Social Studies 9		Mathematics 5					
English Language Arts 9		Mathematics 4					
Mathematics 9		Mathematics 3					
Science 9							
Mathematics 8							
Mathematics 7							
English Language Arts 6							
Mathematics 6							
Science 6							
Social Studies 6							
Mathematics 4							
Mathematics 3							
English Language Arts 3							

Total Cost

Subtotal 1	
Subtotal 2	
Subtotal 3	
Cost Subtotal	
Shipping and Handling*	
G.S.T	
Order Total	

*(Please call for current rates)

PAYMENT AND SHIPPING INFORMATION

Name: _____

School _____

Telephone: _____

SHIP TO

School: _____

Address: _____

City: _____ Postal Code: _____

PAYMENT

☐ By credit card   VISA/MC

Number: _____

Expiry Date: _____

Name on card: _____

☐ Enclosed cheque

☐ Invoice school   P.O. number: _____

CASTLE ROCK RESEARCH CORP

#2410, 10180 – 101 Street NW, Edmonton, AB T5J 3S4   **Phone:** 780.448.9619   **Fax:** 780.426.3917

Email: learn@castlerockresearch.com   **Toll-free:** 1.800.840.6224

www.castlerockresearch.com